NCHEC
National Commission
for Health Education Credentialing

The Health Education Specialist:
A Companion Guide for Professional Excellence

Eighth Edition

National Commission for
Health Education Credentialing, Inc.

Copyright 2020 National Commission for Health Education Credentialing, Inc.
Copyright 2015 National Commission for Health Education Credentialing, Inc.
Copyright 2010 National Commission for Health Education Credentialing, Inc.
Copyright 2007 National Commission for Health Education Credentialing, Inc.
Copyright 2000 National Commission for Health Education Credentialing, Inc.
Copyright 1998 National Commission for Health Education Credentialing, Inc.
Copyright 1996 National Commission for Health Education Credentialing, Inc.
Copyright 1992 Loose Cannon Publication

Published by: National Commission for Health Education Credentialing, Inc.
                1541 Alta Drive, Suite 303
                Whitehall, PA 18052-5642
                Local phone: (484) 223-0770
                Phone: (888) NCHEC-4-U, (888) 624-3248
                Fax: (800) 813-0727
                www.nchec.org

Second Printing - March 2022

ISBN 978-1-7345537-1-0

Acknowledgements

In 1992, Sigred G. Deeds, DrPH, CHES®, authored the original edition of *The Health Education Specialist: A Self-Study Guide for Professional Competence*. Her work was based on 25 years' experience in a variety of health education settings. In 1995, Dr. Deeds donated her book to the National Commission for Health Education Credentialing, Inc.

This edition marks the eighth revision to Dr. Deeds' original work. The seventh edition was revised by Martha Alexander, MPH, MCHES®; Chris Arthur, PhD, MCHES®; Michelle Carvalho, MPH, CHES®; Cam Escoffery, PhD, MPH, CHES® (author/editor); Linda E. Forys, EdM, MCHES®; Patricia A. Frye, DrPH, MPA, MCHES®; Melissa Grim, PhD, MCHES®, (author/editor); Adam P. Knowlden, MBA, PhD CHES®; Maurice "Bud" Martin, PhD, CHES®; C. Suzette McClellan, MPH, MCHES®; Angela D. Mickalide, PhD, MCHES®; Stacy Robison, MPH, MCHES®; Leah Roman, MPH, MCHES®; Christopher N. Thomas, MS, CHES®; and Amy Thompson, PhD, CHES®.

The difference in this companion guide is that it is based on the results of the Health Education Specialist Practice Analysis II 2020 (HESPA II 2020). The resultant revised Areas of Responsibility, Competencies, and Sub-competencies identified in that project have been incorporated into this companion guide, and additional material on the new and revised Responsibilities and Competencies have been included.The publication includes both entry- and advanced-level Competencies and Sub-competencies. In addition, the sample questions have been reviewed and revised; and questions have been added to reflect the new material.

The eighth edition of *The Health Education Specialist: A Companion Guide for Professional Excellence* was compiled with efforts of health education specialists with expertise and experience in the now Eight Areas of Responsibility identified in this companion guide. The authors refined and added to previous editions. Much gratitude to the co-editors, Melissa Grim, PhD, MCHES® and Cam Escoffery, PhD, CHES® for their tireless work to meet deadlines and juggle work during the COVID-19 pandemic in order to release this publication in a timely manner.

Sincere appreciation and recognition is extended to Carol Cox, PhD, MCHES®, and Betty Jung, PhD, MCHES® for reviewing and assisting in polishing practice examination questions.

Co-Editors:
Melissa Grim, PhD, MCHES®
Cam Escoffrey, PhD, MPH, CHES®

Contributing Authors:

Chapter I: Assessment of Needs and Capacity
C. Suzette McClellan, MPH, MCHES®
Linda E. Forys, EdM, MCHES®

Chapter II: Planning
Angela Mickalide, PhD, MCHES®

Chapter III: Implementation
Anna Armstrong, PhD, MPH, MCHES®, CPH
Phyllis Stoll, MPH, MCHES®

Chapter IV: Evaluation and Research
Cynthia Karlsson, MS, MPH, CHES®
Ty Oehrtman, MS, MCHES®

Chapter V: Advocacy
Alexis Blavos, PhD, MCHES®
Carol Cox, PhD, MCHES®

Chapter VI: Communication
Beth Chaney, PhD, MCHES®
Mike Stellefson, PhD, MCHES®
Samantha Paige, PhD, CHES®

Chapter VII: Leadership and Management
William Potts-Datema, DrPH, MS, MCHES®

Chapter VIII: Ethics and Professionalism
Cam Escoffery, PhD, MPH, CHES®
Michelle Carvalho, MPH, , MCHES®

Study Companion - Practice Question Reviewers:
Carol Cox, PhD, MCHES®
Betty Jung, PhD, MCHES®

Study Companion Reviewer:
Melissa Opp, MPH, MCHES®

Copy Editor:
Dixie Dennis, PhD, MCHES®

Table of Contents

Introduction

The purpose of this book is to guide health education specialists in advancing their knowledge and skills in the field of health education and promotion, at both the entry- and advanced-levels of practice. The title of the eighth edition, *The Health Education Specialist: A Companion Guide for Professional Excellence*, incorporates the concept of "companion guide" to reflect the broad intention of the publication. This companion guide can assist individuals in preparation for the national examination for either the Certified Health Education Specialist (CHES®) or Master Certified Health Education Specialist (MCHES®) credential. It can also be used as a professional development tool and as the basis for professional preparation programs. *The Health Education Specialist: A Companion Guide for Professional Excellence, Eighth Edition* can be used to help assess health education knowledge and direct continuing education studies. Employers can encourage their personnel to use this book as a tool to determine whether additional professional development in specific areas may be needed. Instructors in professional preparation programs may find the format and organization of this book to be useful as a supplement to textbooks and classroom lectures. Students enrolled in health education professional preparation programs can utilize this guide as an excellent reference source for their studies. It should be understood that relying on this book as the only resource for studying for the CHES® or MCHES® exams is strongly discouraged.

The Health Education Specialist: A Companion Guide for Professional Excellence, Eighth Edition is organized to follow the Eight Areas of Responsibility, their related Competencies and Sub-competencies at both entry- and advanced- levels as delineated in *A Competency Based Framework for Health Education Specialists - 2020* (National Commission for Health Education Credentialing, Inc. [NCHEC] and Society for Public Health Education [SOPHE], 2020). That framework is based on the Health Education Specialist Practice Analysis II-2020 (HESPA II 2020) (NCHEC et al., 2020), a 22-month project to update, refine and validate the model of health education practice. The updated model comprises 193 Sub-competencies, organized into 35 Competencies within Eight major Areas of Responsibility. Of the Sub-competencies, 79 were validated as advanced-level only. The HESPA II- 2020 study expanded upon the three previous studies: HESPA I (McKenzie, et al. 2016), HEJA 2010 (Doyle et al., 2012) and the Competency Update Project (CUP) (Gilmore, et al., 2005), which also utilized a model of three levels of practice (entry-, advanced 1-, and advanced 2-) with each subsequent level building upon the previous level(s).

Extensive research involving health education specialists across the nation has verified the existence of both entry- and advanced- levels of health education practice. NCHEC has been credentialing the advanced-level (or Master's level) of certification since 2011. This proves to be an exciting time for the profession as we continue to recognize the varying and evolving levels of practice of the health education specialist.

Much like earlier versions of practice analyses, the HESPA II 2020 model includes Responsibilities, Competencies and Sub-competencies that are considered generic and independent of the setting in which the health education specialist works (NCHEC et al., 2015). However, HESPA II 2020 differs from the previous practice analysis, since Eight Areas of Responsibility were identified in this study. Most significantly, Area VIII was identified as Ethics and Professionalism, creating one unified place for Competencies and Sub-competencies that were previously interspersed among other Areas of Responsibility. The CHES® examination addresses only those Competencies and Sub-competencies that were identified in the HESPA II-2020 as entry-level. The MCHES® examination addresses all of the Competencies and Sub-competencies, including entry-level, advanced 1-level, and advanced 2-level. Additional details regarding the role and history of credentialing can be found in Chapter VIII of *The Health Education Specialist: A Companion Guide for Professional Excellence, Eighth Edition*.

How to Use this Book

This book can be used to identify areas of practice that may require further study using nationally recognized scholarly references. Whether for purposes of exam preparation, part of academic preparation or for professional development activities, learning should not be limited to this one resource, as it is a summary of many important topics that will require in depth exploration and study through use of supplementary resources. Those preparing for the CHES® or MCHES® exam are reminded that these exams are national competency-based tests that measure the possession, application and interpretation of knowledge related to the Eight Areas of Responsibility. Further, the information included in this companion guide should not be considered exhaustive by the reader. Additional optional readings that may also assist in supporting study are listed on the NCHEC website, http://www.nchec.org. Textbooks from one's professional preparation programs in health education and promotion also are helpful resources to review.

Many CHES® and MCHES® who utilized previous NCHEC study companion guides reported that incorporating the publication as a basic resource for a study group was very helpful. Using a discussion format to work through the practice questions was reported as a useful way to prepare not only for the exam but also for professional development activities.

As a starting point to assist in identifying potential gaps in a student or professional's formal preparation for health education practice, a *Self-Assessment for Health Education Specialists: Perceived Competence* tool is included in the companion guide and follows this Introduction. After completing this self-assessment tool, it may be helpful to review each chapter and note any other apparent weaknesses. Each chapter follows a logical organization: Area of Responsibility, followed by the role of a health education specialist relative to the Responsibility, examples of each role in the practice setting, key terms, and information germane to each of the corresponding Competencies and Sub-

competencies. It is important to note that while key terms may appear in more than one chapter, users are advised that definitions within chapters may vary given the context in which it is being used.

Throughout the *Health Education Specialist: A Companion Guide for Professional Excellence Eighth Edition*, there is a graphic differentiation between entry-level and advanced-level Sub-competencies. After reviewing the material, it may be beneficial to complete the practice questions. Practice questions for entry- and advanced-levels are located in Appendix C and Appendix D respectively.

The content of this publication reflects consensus about a common core of professional preparation leading to entry- and advanced-level practice as a health education specialist. This publication should be considered a supplemental tool, and not a primary source, for identifying areas of practice that may require further study using nationally recognized scholarly references. In addition, study and preparation for the CHES® and MCHES® certification exams should not be limited to *Health Education Specialist: A Companion Guide for Professional Excellence*, but should include the resources acquired during an individual's academic preparation program.

> **KEY:**
> No symbol - entry level
> ▲ advanced 1
> ■ advanced 2

Self-Assessment for Health Education Specialists: Perceived Competence

The competency statement in this assessment describes the broadly defined skills that a qualified entry-level, generic health education specialist is expected to be able to demonstrate at least at minimum levels. To assess individual skill level for each competency statement, rate each competency from 1 to 4, with 1 indicating not competent and 4 indicating very competent.

Area of Responsibility I: Assessment of Needs and Capacity
The health education specialist can:

COMPETENCY 1.1: Plan assessment.	Not Competent		Very Competent	
1.1.1	Define the purpose and scope of the assessment.	1	2	3	4
1.1.2	Identify priority population(s).	1	2	3	4
1.1.3	Identify existing and available resources, policies, programs, practices and interventions.	1	2	3	4
1.1.4	Examine the factors and determinants that influence the assessment process.	1	2	3	4
1.1.5	Recruit and/or engage priority population(s), partners, and stakeholders to participate throughout all steps in the assessment, planning, implementation, and evaluation processes.	1	2	3	4

COMPETENCY 1.2: Obtain primary data, secondary data, and other evidence-informed sources.	Not Competent		Very Competent	
1.2.1	Identify primary data, secondary data, and evidence-informed resources.	1	2	3	4
1.2.2▲	Establish collaborative relationships and agreements that facilitate access to data.	1	2	3	4
1.2.3	Conduct a literature review.	1	2	3	4
1.2.4	Procure secondary data.	1	2	3	4
1.2.5	Determine the validity and reliability of the secondary data.	1	2	3	4
1.2.6	Identify data gaps.	1	2	3	4
1.2.7	Determine primary data collection needs, instruments, methods, and procedures.	1	2	3	4
1.2.8	Adhere to established procedures to collect data.	1	2	3	4
1.2.9▲	Develop a data analysis plan.	1	2	3	4

KEY: No symbol - entry level; ▲ - advanced 1; ■ - advanced 2

COMPETENCY 1.3: Analyze the data to determine the health of the priority population(s) and the factors that influence health.			Not Competent		Very Competent	
1.3.1	Determine the health status of the priority population(s).		1	2	3	4
1.3.2	Determine the knowledge, attitudes, beliefs, skills, and behaviors that impact the health and health literacy of the priority population(s).		1	2	3	4
1.3.3	Identify the social, cultural, economic, political, and environmental factors that impact the health and/or learning processes of the priority population(s).		1	2	3	4
1.3.4	Assess existing and available resources, policies, programs, practices, and interventions.		1	2	3	4
1.3.5	Determine the capacity (available resources, policies, programs, practices, and interventions) to improve and/or maintain health.		1	2	3	4
1.3.6	List the needs of the priority population(s).		1	2	3	4

COMPETENCY 1.4: Synthesize assessment findings to inform the planning process.			Not Competent		Very Competent	
1.4.1▲	Compare findings to norms, existing data, and other information.		1	2	3	4
1.4.2	Prioritize health education and promotion needs.		1	2	3	4
1.4.3	Summarize the capacity of priority population(s) to meet the needs of the priority population(s).		1	2	3	4
1.4.4	Develop recommendations based on findings.		1	2	3	4
1.4.5	Report assessment findings.		1	2	3	4

Area of Responsibility II: Planning

COMPETENCY 2.1: Engage priority populations, partners, and stakeholders for participation in the planning process.			Not Competent		Very Competent	
2.1.1	Convene priority populations, partners, and stakeholders.		1	2	3	4
2.1.2	Facilitate collaborative efforts among priority populations, partners and stakeholders.		1	2	3	4
2.1.3	Establish the rationale for the intervention.		1	2	3	4

COMPETENCY 2.2: Define desired outcomes.			Not Competent		Very Competent	
2.2.1	Identify desired outcomes using the needs and capacity assessment.		1	2	3	4
2.2.2	Elicit input from priority populations, partners, and stakeholders regarding desired outcomes.		1	2	3	4
2.2.3	Develop vision, mission, and goal statements for the intervention(s).		1	2	3	4
2.2.4	Develop specific, measurable, achievable, realistic, and time-bound (SMART) objectives.		1	2	3	4

Self-Assessment for Health Education Specialists: Perceived Competence

COMPETENCY 2.3: Determine health education and promotion interventions.		Not Competent		Very Competent	
2.3.1	Select planning model(s) for health education and promotion.	1	2	3	4
2.3.2 ▲	Create a logic model.	1	2	3	4
2.3.3 ▲	Assess the effectiveness and alignment of existing interventions to desired outcomes.	1	2	3	4
2.3.4	Adopt, adapt, and/or develop tailored intervention(s) for priority population(s) to achieve desired outcomes.	1	2	3	4
2.3.5 ▲	Plan for acquisition of required tools and resources.	1	2	3	4
2.3.6 ▲	Conduct a pilot test of intervention(s).	1	2	3	4
2.3.7 ▲	Revise intervention(s) based on pilot feedback.	1	2	3	4

COMPETENCY 2.4: Develop plans and materials for implementation and evaluations.		Not Competent		Very Competent	
2.4.1 ▲	Develop an implementation plan inclusive of logic model, work plan, responsible parties, timeline, marketing, and communication.	1	2	3	4
2.4.2	Develop materials needed for implementation.	1	2	3	4
2.4.3	Address factors that influence implementation.	1	2	3	4
2.4.4 ▲	Plan for evaluation and dissemination of results.	1	2	3	4
2.4.5 ▲	Plan for sustainability.	1	2	3	4

Area of Responsibility III: Implementation

COMPETENCY 3.1: Coordinate the delivery of intervention(s) consistent with the implementation plan.		Not Competent		Very Competent	
3.1.1	Secure implementation resources.	1	2	3	4
3.1.2	Arrange for implementation services.	1	2	3	4
3.1.3	Comply with contractual obligations.	1	2	3	4
3.1.4 ▲	Establish training protocol.	1	2	3	4
3.1.5	Train staff and volunteers to ensure fidelity.	1	2	3	4

KEY: No symbol - entry level; ▲ - advanced 1; ■ - advanced 2

COMPETENCY 3.2: Deliver health education and promotion interventions.		Not Competent		Very Competent	
3.2.1	Create an environment conducive to learning.	1	2	3	4
3.2.2	Collect baseline data.	1	2	3	4
3.2.3	Implement a marketing plan.	1	2	3	4
3.2.4	Deliver health education and promotion as designed.	1	2	3	4
3.2.5	Employ an appropriate variety of instructional methodologies.	1	2	3	4

COMPETENCY 3.3: Monitor implementation.		Not Competent		Very Competent	
3.3.1	Monitor progress in accordance with the timeline.	1	2	3	4
3.3.2	Assess progress in achieving objectives.	1	2	3	4
3.3.3	Modify interventions as needed to meet individual needs.	1	2	3	4
3.3.4	Ensure plan is implemented with fidelity.	1	2	3	4
3.3.5	Monitor use of resources.	1	2	3	4
3.3.6	Evaluate the sustainability of implementation.	1	2	3	4

Area of Responsibility IV: Evaluation and Research

COMPETENCY 4.1: Design process, impact, and outcome evaluation of the intervention.		Not Competent		Very Competent	
4.1.1 ▲	Align the evaluation plan with the intervention goals and objectives.	1	2	3	4
4.1.2	Comply with institutional requirements for evaluation.	1	2	3	4
4.1.3 ▲	Use a logic model and/or theory for evaluations.	1	2	3	4
4.1.4 ▲	Assess capacity to conduct evaluation.	1	2	3	4
4.1.5 ▲	Select an evaluation design model and the types of data to be collected.	1	2	3	4
4.1.6 ▲	Develop a sampling plan and procedures for data collection, management, and security.	1	2	3	4
4.1.7 ▲	Select quantitative and qualitative tools consistent with assumptions and data requirements.	1	2	3	4
4.1.8	Adopt or modify existing instruments for collecting data.	1	2	3	4

4.1.9 ▲	Develop instruments for collecting data.	1	2	3	4
4.1.10 ▲	Implement a pilot test to refine data collection instruments and procedures.	1	2	3	4

COMPETENCY 4.2: Design research studies.		Not Competent		Very Competent	
4.2.1 ■	Determine purpose, hypothesis, and questions.	1	2	3	4
4.2.2 ▲	Comply with institutional and/or IRB requirements for research.	1	2	3	4
4.2.3 ▲	Use a logic model and/or theory for research.	1	2	3	4
4.2.4 ■	Assess capacity to conduct research.	1	2	3	4
4.2.5 ▲	Select a research design model and the types of data to be collected.	1	2	3	4
4.2.6 ▲	Develop a sampling plan and procedures for data collection, management, and security.	1	2	3	4
4.2.7 ▲	Select a quantitative and qualitative tools consistent with assumptions and data requirements.	1	2	3	4
4.2.8 ■	Adopt, adapt, and/or develop instruments for collecting data.	1	2	3	4
4.2.9 ■	Implement a pilot test to refine and validate data collection instruments and procedures.	1	2	3	4

COMPETENCY 4.3: Manage the collection and analysis of evaluation and/or research data using appropriate technology.		Not Competent		Very Competent	
4.3.1 ■	Train data collectors.	1	2	3	4
4.3.2	Implement data collection procedures.	1	2	3	4
4.3.3	Use appropriate modalities to collect and manage data.	1	2	3	4
4.3.4 ■	Monitor data collection procedures.	1	2	3	4
4.3.5	Prepare data for analysis.	1	2	3	4
4.3.6 ■	Analyze data.	1	2	3	4

COMPETENCY 4.4: Interpret data.		Not Competent		Very Competent	
4.4.1 ■	Explain how findings address the questions and/or hypotheses.	1	2	3	4
4.4.2 ▲	Compare findings to other evaluations or studies.	1	2	3	4

KEY: No symbol - entry level; ▲ - advanced 1; ■ - advanced 2

4.4.3	Identify limitations and delimitations of findings.	1	2	3	4
4.4.4 ■	Draw conclusions based on findings.	1	2	3	4
4.4.5 ■	Identify implications for practice.	1	2	3	4
4.4.6 ■	Synthesize findings.	1	2	3	4
4.4.7 ■	Develop recommendations based on findings.	1	2	3	4
4.4.8 ■	Evaluate feasibility of implementing recommendations.	1	2	3	4

COMPETENCY 4.5: Use findings.		Not Competent		Very Competent	
4.5.1 ▲	Communicate findings by preparing reports, and presentations, and by other means.	1	2	3	4
4.5.2 ■	Disseminate findings.	1	2	3	4
4.5.3 ■	Identify recommendations for quality improvement.	1	2	3	4
4.5.4 ▲	Translate findings into practice and interventions.	1	2	3	4

Area of Responsibility V: Advocacy

COMPETENCY 5.1: Identify a current or emerging health issue requiring policy, systems, or environmental change.		Not Competent		Very Competent	
5.1.1	Examine the determinants of health and their underlying causes (e.g., poverty, trauma, and population-based discrimination) related to identified health issues.	1	2	3	4
5.1.2	Examine evidence-informed findings related to identified health issues and desired changes.	1	2	3	4
5.1.3	Identify factors that facilitate and/or hinder advocacy efforts (e.g., amount of evidence to prove the issue, potential for partnerships, political readiness, organizational experience or risk, and feasibility of success.	1	2	3	4
5.1.4	Write specific, measurable, achievable, realistic, and time-bound (SMART) advocacy objective(s).	1	2	3	4
5.1.5	Identify existing coalition(s) or stakeholders that can be engaged in advocacy efforts.	1	2	3	4

COMPETENCY 5.2: Engage coalitions and stakeholders in addressing the health issue and planning advocacy efforts.		Not Competent		Very Competent	
5.2.1	Identify existing coalitions and stakeholders that favor and oppose the proposed policy, system, or environmental change and their reasons.	1	2	3	4
5.2.2	Identify factors that influence decision-makers (e.g., societal and cultural norms, financial considerations, upcoming elections, and voting record).	1	2	3	4

5.2.3 ▲	Create formal and/or informal alliances, task forces, and coalitions to address the proposed change.	1	2	3	4
5.2.4	Educate stakeholders on the health issue and the proposed policy, system, or environmental change.	1	2	3	4
5.2.5	Identify available resources and gaps (e.g., financial, personnel, information and data).	1	2	3	4
5.2.6	Identify organizational policies and procedures and federal, state, and local laws that pertain to the advocacy efforts.	1	2	3	4
5.2.7	Develop persuasive messages and materials (e.g., briefs, resolutions, and fact sheets) to communicate the policy, system, or environmental change.	1	2	3	4
5.2.8	Specify strategies, a timeline, and roles and responsibilities to address the proposed policy, system, or environmental change (e.g., develop ongoing relationships with decision makers and stakeholders, use social media, register others to vote, and seek political appointment).	1	2	3	4

COMPETENCY 5.3: Engage in advocacy.		Not Competent		Very Competent	
5.3.1	Use media to conduct advocacy (e.g., social media, press releases, public service announcements, and op-eds).	1	2	3	4
5.3.2	Use traditional, social, and emerging technologies and methods to mobilize support for policy, system, or environmental change.	1	2	3	4
5.3.3 ▲	Sustain coalitions and stakeholder relationships to achieve and maintain policy, system, or environmental change.	1	2	3	4

COMPETENCY 5.4: Evaluate advocacy.		Not Competent		Very Competent	
5.4.1	Conduct process, impact, and outcome evaluation of advocacy efforts.	1	2	3	4
5.4.2	Use the results of the evaluation to inform next steps.	1	2	3	4

Area of Responsibility VI: Communications

COMPETENCY 6.1: Determine factors that affect communication with the identified audience(s).		Not Competent		Very Competent	
6.1.1	Segment the audience(s) to be addressed, as needed.	1	2	3	4
6.1.2	Identify the assets, needs, and characteristics of the audience(s) that affect communication and message design (e.g., literacy levels, language, culture, and cognitive and perceptual abilities).	1	2	3	4
6.1.3	Identify communication channels (e.g., social media and mass media) available to and used by the audience(s).	1	2	3	4
6.1.4	Identify environmental and other factors that affect communication (e.g., resources and the availability of Internet access).	1	2	3	4

KEY: No symbol - entry level; ▲ - advanced 1; ■ - advanced 2

COMPETENCY 6.2: Determine communication objective(s) for audience(s).	Not Competent		Very Competent	
6.2.1	Describe the intended outcome of the communication (e.g., raise awareness, advocacy, behavioral change, and risk communication).	1	2	3	4
6.2.2	Write specific, measurable, achievable, realistic, and time-bound (SMART) communication objective(s).	1	2	3	4
6.2.3	Identify factors that facilitate and/or hinder the intended outcome of the communication.	1	2	3	4

COMPETENCY 6.3: Develop message(s) using communication theories and/or models.	Not Competent		Very Competent	
6.3.1	Use communications theory to develop or select communication message(s).	1	2	3	4
6.3.2	Develop persuasive communications (e.g., storytelling and program rationale).	1	2	3	4
6.3.3	Tailor message(s) for the audience(s).	1	2	3	4
6.3.4	Employ media literacy skills (e.g., identifying credible sources and balancing multiple viewpoints).	1	2	3	4

COMPETENCY 6.4: Select methods and technologies used to deliver message(s).	Not Competent		Very Competent	
6.4.1	Differentiate the strengths and weaknesses of various communication channels and technologies (e.g., mass media, community mobilization, counseling, peer communication, information/digital technology, and apps).	1	2	3	4
6.4.2	Select communication channels and current and emerging technologies that are most appropriate for the audience(s) and message(s).	1	2	3	4
6.4.3	Develop communication aids, materials, or tools using appropriate multimedia (e.g., infographics, presentation software, brochures, and posters).	1	2	3	4
6.4.4	Assess the suitability of new and/or existing communication aids, materials, or tools for audience(s) (e.g., the CDC Clear Communication Index and the Suitability Assessment Materials (SAM)).	1	2	3	4
6.4.5	Pilot test message(s) and communication aids, materials, or tools.	1	2	3	4
6.4.6	Revise communication aids, materials, or tools based on pilot results.	1	2	3	4

COMPETENCY 6.5: Deliver the message(s) effectively using the identified media and strategies.	Not Competent		Very Competent	
6.5.1	Deliver presentation(s) tailored to the audience(s).	1	2	3	4
6.5.2	Use public speaking skills.	1	2	3	4
6.5.3	Use facilitation skills with large and/or small groups.	1	2	3	4
6.5.4	Use current and emerging communication tools and trends (e.g., social media).	1	2	3	4

| 6.5.5 | Deliver oral and written communication that aligns with professional standards of grammar, punctuation, and style. | 1 | 2 | 3 | 4 |
| 6.5.6 | Use digital media to engage audience(s) (e.g., social media management tools and platforms). | 1 | 2 | 3 | 4 |

COMPETENCY 6.6: Evaluate communication.	Not Competent		Very Competent	
6.6.1	Conduct process and impact evaluations of communications.	1	2	3	4
6.6.2 ■	Conduct outcome evaluations of communications.	1	2	3	4
6.6.3 ▲	Assess reach and dose of communication using tools (e.g., data mining software, social media analytics and website analytics).	1	2	3	4

Area of Responsibility VII: Leadership and Management

COMPETENCY 7.1: Coordinate relationships with partners and stakeholders (e.g. individuals, teams, coalitions, and committees).	Not Competent		Very Competent	
7.1.1	Identify potential partners and stakeholders.	1	2	3	4
7.1.2	Assess the capacity of potential partners and stakeholders.	1	2	3	4
7.1.3	Involve partners and stakeholders throughout the health education and promotion process in meaningful and sustainable ways.	1	2	3	4
7.1.4 ▲	Execute formal and informal agreements with partners and stakeholders.	1	2	3	4
7.1.5	Evaluate relationships with partners and stakeholders on an ongoing basis to make appropriate modifications.	1	2	3	4

COMPETENCY 7.2: Prepare others to provide health education and promotion.	Not Competent		Very Competent	
7.2.1	Develop culturally responsive content.	1	2	3	4
7.2.2	Recruit individuals needed in implementation.	1	2	3	4
7.2.3 ▲	Assess training needs.	1	2	3	4
7.2.4 ▲	Plan training, including technical assistance and support.	1	2	3	4
7.2.5 ▲	Implement training.	1	2	3	4
7.2.6 ▲	Evaluate training as appropriate throughout the process.	1	2	3	4

KEY: No symbol - entry level; ▲ - advanced 1; ■ - advanced 2

COMPETENCY 7.3: Manage human resources.		Not Competent		Very Competent	
7.3.1 ▲	Facilitate understanding and sensitivity for various cultures, values, and traditions.	1	2	3	4
7.3.2 ▲	Facilitate positive organizational culture and climate.	1	2	3	4
7.3.3 ▲	Develop job descriptions to meet staffing needs.	1	2	3	4
7.3.4 ▲	Recruit qualified staff (including paraprofessionals) and volunteers.	1	2	3	4
7.3.5 ▲	Evaluate performance of staff and volunteers formally and informally.	1	2	3	4
7.3.6 ▲	Provide professional development and training for staff volunteers.	1	2	3	4
7.3.7 ▲	Facilitate the engagement and retention of staff and volunteers.	1	2	3	4
7.3.8 ▲	Apply team building and conflict resolution techniques as appropriate.	1	2	3	4

COMPETENCY 7.4: Manage fiduciary and material resources.		Not Competent		Very Competent	
7.4.1 ▲	Evaluate internal and external financial needs and funding sources.	1	2	3	4
7.4.2 ▲	Develop financial budgets and plans.	1	2	3	4
7.4.3 ▲	Monitor budget performance.	1	2	3	4
7.4.4 ■	Justify value of health education and promotion using economic (e.g., cost-benefit, re-turn-on-investment, and value-on-investment) and/or other analyses.	1	2	3	4
7.4.5 ▲	Write grants and funding proposals.	1	2	3	4
7.4.6 ■	Conduct reviews of funding and grant proposals.	1	2	3	4
7.4.7 ▲	Monitor performance and/or compliance of funding recipients.	1	2	3	4
7.4.8 ▲	Maintain up-to-date technology infrastructure.	1	2	3	4
7.4.9 ▲	Manage current and future facilities and resources (e.g., space and equipment).	1	2	3	4

COMPETENCY 7.5: Conduct strategic planning with appropriate stakeholders.		Not Competent		Very Competent	
7.5.1 ▲	Facilitate the development of strategic and/or improvement plans using systems thinking to promote the mission, vision, and goal statements for health education and promotion.	1	2	3	4
7.5.2 ▲	Gain organizational acceptance for strategic and/or improvement plans.	1	2	3	4
7.5.3 ▲	Implement the strategic plan, incorporating status updates and making refinements as appro-priate.	1	2	3	4

Area of Responsibility VIII: Ethics and Professionalism

COMPETENCY 8.1: Practice in accordance with established ethical principles.		Not Competent		Very Competent	
8.1.1	Apply professional codes of ethics and ethical principles throughout assessment, planning, implementation, evaluation and research, communication, consulting and advocacy processes.	1	2	3	4
8.1.2 ▲	Demonstrate ethical leadership, management, and behavior.	1	2	3	4
8.1.3	Comply with legal standards and regulatory guidelines in assessment, planning, implementation, evaluation and research, advocacy, management, communication, and reporting processes.	1	2	3	4
8.1.4	Promote health equity.	1	2	3	4
8.1.5	Use evidence-informed theories, models, and strategies.	1	2	3	4
8.1.6	Apply principles of cultural humility, inclusion, and diversity in all aspects of practice (e.g., Culturally and Linguistically Appropriate Services (CLAS) standards and culturally responsive pedagogy).	1	2	3	4

COMPETENCY 8.2: Serve as an authoritative resource on health education and promotion.		Not Competent		Very Competent	
8.2.1 ▲	Evaluate personal and organizational capacity to provide consultation.	1	2	3	4
8.2.2 ▲	Provide expert consultation, assistance, and guidance to individuals, groups, and organizations.	1	2	3	4
8.2.3 ■	Conduct peer reviews (e.g., manuscripts, abstracts, proposals, and tenure folios).	1	2	3	4

COMPETENCY 8.3: Engage in professional development to maintain and/or enhance proficiency.		Not Competent		Very Competent	
8.3.1	Participate in professional associations, coalitions, and networks (e.g., serving on committees, attending conferences, and providing leadership.)	1	2	3	4
8.3.2	Participate in continuing education opportunities to maintain or enhance continuing competence.	1	2	3	4
8.3.3	Develop a career advancement plan.	1	2	3	4
8.3.4	Build relationships with other professionals within and outside the profession.	1	2	3	4
8.3.5 ■	Serve as a mentor.	1	2	3	4

COMPETENCY 8.4: Promote the health education profession to stakeholders, the public, and others.		Not Competent		Very Competent	
8.4.1	Explain the major responsibilities, contributions, and value of the health education specialist.	1	2	3	4
8.4.2	Explain the role of professional organizations and the benefits of participating in them.	1	2	3	4

8.4.3	Advocate for professional development for health education specialists.	1	2	3	4
8.4.4	Educate others about the history of the profession, its current status, and its implications for professional practice.	1	2	3	4
8.4.5	Explain the role and benefits of credentialing (e.g., individual and program).	1	2	3	4
8.4.6 ▲	Develop presentations and publications that contribute to the profession.	1	2	3	4
8.4.7 ▲	Engage in service to advance the profession.	1	2	3	4

Chapter 1
Area of Responsibility I: Assessment of Needs and Capacity
KEY: No symbol - entry level; ▲ - advanced 1; ■ - advanced 2

1.1. Plan assessment.
   1.1.1   Define the purpose and scope of the assessment.
   1.1.2   Identify priority population(s).
   1.1.3   Identify existing and available resources, policies, programs, practices, and interventions.
   1.1.4   Examine the factors and determinants that influence the assessment process.
   1.1.5   Recruit and/or engage priority population(s), partners, and stakeholders to participate throughout all steps in the assessment, planning, implementation, and evaluation processes.

1.2. Obtain primary data, secondary data, and other evidence-informed sources.
   1.2.1   Identify primary data, secondary data, and evidence-informed resources.
   1.2.2 ▲ Establish collaborative relationships and agreements that facilitate access to data.
   1.2.3   Conduct a literature review.
   1.2.4   Procure secondary data.
   1.2.5   Determine the validity and reliability of the secondary data.
   1.2.6   Identify data gaps.
   1.2.7   Determine primary data collection needs, instruments, methods, and procedures.
   1.2.8   Adhere to established procedures to collect data.
   1.2.9 ▲ Develop a data analysis plan.

1.3. Analyze the data to determine the health of the priority population(s) and the factors that influence health.
   1.3.1   Determine the health status of the priority population(s).
   1.3.2   Determine the knowledge, attitudes, beliefs, skills, and behaviors that impact the health and health literacy of the priority population(s).
   1.3.3   Identify the social, cultural, economic, political, and environmental factors that impact the health and/or learning processes of the priority population(s).
   1.3.4   Assess existing and available resources, policies, programs, practices, and interventions.
   1.3.5   Determine the capacity (available resources, policies, programs, practices, and interventions) to improve and/or maintain health.
   1.3.6   List the needs of the priority population(s).

1.4. Synthesize assessment findings to inform the planning process.
   1.4.1 ▲ Compare findings to norms, existing data, and other information.
   1.4.2   Prioritize health education and promotion needs.
   1.4.3   Summarize the capacity of priority population(s) to meet the needs of the priority population(s).
   1.4.4   Develop recommendations based on findings.
   1.4.5   Report assessment findings.

The Role. The first step in developing a health education program in any given setting is to gather data and information to assess the needs of the priority population. This needs assessment then becomes the foundation of the entire planning process. The needs assessment is used to determine priority programs and will assist in identifying the most appropriate interventions. Failure to conduct a thorough and comprehensive needs assessment can result in wasted time and resources. To successfully conduct a needs assessment, health education specialists collect and analyze both primary and secondary data. To assess capacity, the health education specialist must determine the resources that are present and available for use in developing programs to meet the needs of priority populations as identified via the needs assessment. Gaps in existing resources must be identified and addressed prior to initiating programs. No program should be initiated until there is sufficient capacity to be reasonably sure of success. As McKenzie, et al. (2017) have noted, "Conducting a needs assessment may be the most critical step in the planning process…" (p.90) (NCHEC, 2020).

Setting: The following text is presented to describe how assessment is used in different practice settings (NCHEC, 2020).

Community Setting: In a community setting, health education specialists rely on many sources of primary and secondary data to determine the needs of those in the priority population. Such data can come from external sources including health planning agencies, public health departments, census reports, data sets (e.g., Behavioral Risk Factor Surveillance System and Youth Risk Behavior Surveillance System), and literature reviews. Integration of public health datasets with GIS software provides a link between a priority community and health characteristics. Critical data is also collected internally from the proposed setting and the priority population including focus groups, town hall meetings, and interviews with community leaders and members, especially when assessing capacity. Health education specialists will assess capacity considering resources such as organizational infrastructure, staff, previous and current programming efforts, readiness, and budget when available. Data provide information about both real and perceived health needs and capacity. Depending on the types of needs identified, a well-planned health education program could address these needs if the capacity exists to do so. For example, if specific behaviors or health practices are causally linked to the incidence of major health problems, then a health education program can be planned to motivate and facilitate voluntary, desirable changes in those behaviors (e.g., develop an educational campaign for communities with high numbers of immunization avoidant parents [perceived risk/misinformation] and the outcome of a recent disease outbreak [known risks/complications], such as the measles). The needs assessment may also point to needed policy or environmental changes that the health education specialist may advocate for and support as appropriate.

School (K-12) Setting: Health education specialists in a K-12 setting rely primarily on local data to determine the needs of the youth population, although state and national data may indicate trends which can be helpful in local planning. Ideally schools will utilize the Whole School, Whole Community, Whole Child (WSCC) model, which is an expansion and update of the Coordinated School Health (CSH) approach. The WSCC model focuses its attention on the child, emphasizes a school-wide approach, and acknowledges learning, health, and the school as an important part of the local community. Data should be gathered directly from students to assess their health knowledge, attitudes, skills, and practices. The data will be used to guide instruction, school policies, and modifications in the school environment. Data should also be gathered from parents and administrators to determine potential gaps and/or barriers to health education in the school setting. Further, a community assessment should be completed to determine assets in the community that may be utilized and possible gaps in the community that should be addressed.

Health Care Setting: In the health care setting, health education specialists may be utilized to assess and review existing and/or new reports and data collected from different sources to improve health care delivery. The sources of data could include the Electronic Health Record (EHR), Electronic Medical Record (EMR), safety data such as incident reports, The Hospital Consumer Assessment of Healthcare Providers and Systems (HCAHPS), and other patient satisfaction assessment tools such as the Press-Ganey Survey. Health education specialists must be able to conduct online research and literature reviews using various medical and scientific databases including MedlinePlus, PubMed, online journals, and other core databases. For a practical example, suppose clinical staff become concerned about patients' compliance in taking their prescribed medicine and its impact on the growing number of emergency room visits. The health education specialist is given the responsibility to examine this concern and begins by conducting a needs/capacity assessment. The health education specialist may utilize gap analysis techniques to identify existing process, existing outcome(s), desired outcome(s), and document the need(s). In addition, a capacity assessment should be completed to assess and identify the stakeholders, availability of staff, aides, volunteers, funding, and other resources needed to address prescription medicine compliance and ultimately improve patient outcomes and patient experience. In another example, health education specialists may work directly with patients and/or staff to improve their health behaviors and health status. In this situation the health education specialist may use a needs assessment survey, direct individual interviewing, focus group, and/or review the medical records of the priority population to determine health needs, and determine interest in learning opportunities, educational programs, and classes offered in a health care setting. When assessing health education needs in a clinical setting, health education specialists may assess the priority populations' knowledge, perceptions, attitudes, motivations, health literacy, health numeracy, linguistic preferences, and cultural and religious beliefs regarding their current health status. This information is specifically useful to address any potential changes that the patients and/or staff members may be considering in order to improve and/or maintain their health.

College/University Setting: In the college or university setting, health education specialists often serve as faculty and are involved in assessing student academic performance via formative and summative assessments to meet state and national certification/licensure standards, as well as to meet program accreditation requirements. For example, a review of curriculum to assess alignment with the expected roles and responsibilities of a health education specialist could identify gaps in professional preparation. To revise curricula and meet accreditation standards, health education specialists also track students' progress in meeting the standards, assess the learning environment, and analyze any links between the two.

Worksite/Business Setting: Health education specialists may develop their own data collection strategies or work with healthcare professionals, specialty health and wellbeing vendors, and/or health insurance carriers to obtain and analyze aggregate data that can be used to identify the health needs of employees. For example, these analyses might include data from health risk assessments (HRAs), needs and interest surveys, health insurance claims, pharmacy data, predictive modeling tools (future risk projections), disease prevalence, disability claims, and absenteeism. Analyses of these data and other data sets would indicate priority needs for worksite programs.

College/University Health Promotion Services Setting: Health education specialists in this setting work closely with clinical practitioners and staff in health, counseling, student life, human resources, and fitness/wellness centers. They determine the individual and community health needs of students, faculty, and staff through the use of multiple strategies including, for example, focus groups, surveys, and interviews. In the assessment process, health education specialists develop avenues for obtaining information on the priority populations' knowledge, skills, perceptions, attitudes, beliefs, behaviors, learning preferences, and perceived needs in addition to health problems. In addition, available resources must be identified and needed resources must be obtained. Once data are collected, health education specialists analyze them to determine need and identify capacity, including factors that may impact the effectiveness of health education and promotion programs and interventions. These assessments form the basis for establishing priorities and recommendations for programs and interventions within the campus health promotion services setting.

Key Terms

Advisory Committee – usually consists of individuals who are in a position to periodically report on their actual experiences related to some common issue. In doing so, members of this committee may offer their advice to a key individual who is bringing them together or to another group of people who will be making programmatic decisions (Gilmore, 2012).

Capacity assessment – a measure of actual and potential individual, group, and community resources that can be inherent, and/or brought, to bear for health maintenance and enhancement. The process of mapping community assets is included in the capacity assessment (Gilmore, 2012).

Coalition – a group of diverse organizations and constituencies working together toward a common goal (Butterfoss, 2013).

Needs assessment – the process of identifying, analyzing, and prioritizing the needs of a priority population (McKenzie, Neiger & Thackeray, 2017).

Qualitative data – data in narrative form, which is collected to better understand motivation, thoughts, feelings, and behaviors (McKenzie et al., 2017).

Quantitative data – data collected in numerical form (e.g., mortality rates or number of cigarettes smoked) or easily translated to numerical form (e.g., patient satisfaction using a 5 point scale from dissatisfied to satisfied) (McKenzie et al., 2017).

Planning Committee – advisory committee members, experts, and agency staff. The lifespan of this committee may be episodic (with limited duration) or continuing (on-going) (Gilmore, 2012).

Primary data – data that a health education specialist collects directly (via a survey, a focus group, in-depth interview, etc.), which are used to answer unique questions related to the specific needs assessment (McKenzie et al., 2017).

Secondary data – data that already have been collected by others that may or may not be directly gathered from the individual or population being assessed. Examples include existing research published in peer-reviewed journals and/or datasets, such as the United States Census, Vital Records, and Disease Registries (Gilmore, 2012).

Stakeholders – individuals or agencies with a vested interest in the health education program (Bartholomew Eldredge, Markham, Ruiter, Fernandez, Kok, & Parcel, 2016).

Social determinants of health – conditions in which people are born, live, work, play, as well as age, that affect their health risks, health, daily functioning, and quality of life (Centers for Disease Control and Prevention [CDC], 2018a).

Competency 1.1 Plan Assessment.

One of the first steps in planning a health promotion program is conducting a needs assessment and capacity assessment. A **needs assessment** is the process of identifying, analyzing, and prioritizing the needs of a priority population (McKenzie et al., 2017). The **needs assessment** provides the essential foundation that is used to guide the direction in the development and support of an intervention while the **capacity (asset-based) assessment** is directed toward actual and potential influential resources in the community (e.g., stakeholders) and the support (e.g., individual protective factors, significant others, settings) at an individual level to address needs (Gilmore, 2012).

The assessment plan that is used to direct the appropriate use of limited resources, provides a focus on priority populations (equity and social justice), informs planners of the capacity of community to address needs, ensures the priority population needs are the focal point in developing the intervention and can be a baseline for future assessments and/ or evaluations (McKenzie et al., 2017). To conduct a thorough assessment, health education specialists must carefully plan for the process, including: defining the purpose and scope; identifying and engaging the community in all phases of the assessment process; assessing current resources, policies, programs, and interventions; and identifying factors that may impact the assessment process.

1.1.1 Define the purpose and scope of the assessment.

Defining the purpose of the assessment will provide the direction necessary to develop the scope and details of the assessment effort. McKenzie et al. (2017) outlined the questions that the planning committee should ask and address at this stage of the assessment process. The questions include the following:
- What is the goal of the needs assessment?
- What does the planning committee hope to gain from the needs assessment?
- How extensive will the needs assessment be?
- What types of resources will be available to conduct the needs assessment?
- What type of needs assessment is appropriate? (e.g., comprehensive, focused)

Fertman and Allensworth (2016) recommend that planning committees critically consider who should be involved and what decisions will be based on needs assessment. The assessment process might involve recruiting members of the priority population to participate throughout all steps in the assessment, planning, implementation, and evaluation process. Please refer to Sub-competency 1.1.5 Recruit and engage priority population(s), partners and stakeholders for more information on recruiting the priority population.

Developing a needs assessment plan will allow health education specialists to establish a roadmap that provides an overview of the process, resources needed, activities, and results that support the goals and objectives of the assessment. This roadmap provides a clear direction to ensure that all aspects of the process are completed.

1.1.2 Identify priority population(s).

The foundation of any needs assessment process is to clearly identify the priority population to be assessed. The priority population consists of the entire population if an intervention is being implemented for the total community. Priority populations can be identified by the demographic qualities of the population such as age, sex, ethnicity, and income that will impact the information gathered for the needs assessment. In addition to demographics, using a community perspective allows health education specialists to use specific criteria including geography (i.e., state, county, zip code), sector (i.e., school, worksite, faith-based), environmental conditions, culture and social aspects, size of population, and shared characteristics within the community to further and more comprehensively define the population for the needs assessment. Health education specialists also should understand that the priority population may change as needs assessment data are processed (Issel & Wells, 2018).

1.1.3 Identify existing and available resources, policies, programs, practices, and interventions.

Health education specialists must identify resources, policies, programs, practices, and interventions that already exist or are available for the priority population, health topic(s) of focus, and assessment process. This information will add value to ensure a more comprehensive analysis of the community/priority population needs and enhance effectiveness of program planning efforts.

To assist in the identification of potential factors that relate to the purpose and scope of the assessment, health education specialists should consider the following five factors.
Resources such as:
- human resources (e.g., staff, data collectors), supplies, incentives for participation, and travel funds that are available to conduct assessment.
- individuals, organizations and institutions, buildings, landscapes, equipment that may be a potential asset for development of the program/intervention.
- assessments that have been conducted in the targeted community to avoid duplication of efforts. (Doyle, et al., 2019).

Policies: (e.g., laws, regulations, both formal/informal) at the sector/organizational, local, state and/or federal level that may influence the actions or behaviors of the priority population (McKenzie et al., 2017)

Programs: available for the priority population to assess usage, effectiveness, accessibility and if priority population needs are being met to avoid duplication (McKenzie et al., 2017)

Practices: evidence-based, or best practices, that can have the potential to impact assessment process/findings and program planning efforts in multiple settings and populations (Doyle et al., 2019)

Interventions: designed to change environmental or behavioral factors related to health (Bartholomew Eldredge et al., 2016)

Many of the resources listed are considered community assets or strengths. Doyle et al. (2010) listed six types of community assets: individual, institutional, organizational, governmental, physical and land, and cultural. Refer to Sub-competency 1.3.4 for more information regarding assessing existing and available resources, policies, programs, practices and interventions.

1.1.4 Examine the factors and determinants that influence the assessment process.

Framing the Assessment Factors and Determinants

Given the complexity of health education and promotion practice, multi-level comprehensive interventions are needed to develop effective programs. Health education specialists need to consider many levels of influence, such as investigating the role of each level of the socioecological model – individual, family, relational, community/peers and societal/cultural (DiClemente et al., 2019). Theories and models can provide a framework for the assessment.

The breadth and depth of information collected in needs assessment can vary depending on the needs assessment model used. Issel and Wells (2018) identified 5 models for conducting a needs assessment: epidemiological, public health, social, asset, and rapid.

The epidemiological model is focused on epidemiological data (death rates, prevalence rates, birth rates, etc.) Similarly, the public health model in which epidemiological data often are used to quantify health problems. This model, however, can be more focused on a specific population and can take use of limitations of resources. The social model is useful to investigate social or political issues that influence health. The asset model is focused on the strength of a community, organization, or population. The rapid model is used when time and money are lacking for a needs assessment. This model offers some basic information but is lacking in detail.

These assessment models are not independent, meaning that health education specialists might use several at once. Some program planning models include one or more steps involved in collecting data for a needs assessment. Some models include PRECEDE-PROCEDE, Mobilizing for Action through Planning and Partnership (MAPP) and Intervention Mapping Approach. Refer to Sub-competency 2.3.1 Select planning model(s) for health education programs.

In addition to assessment and planning models, it is necessary to review behavior change models to understand the diverse influences on health and behaviors to be considered in the needs assessment process. Refer to Sub-competency 2.4.3 Address factors that influence implementation.

Because health and health behaviors are influenced by many factors, it is important to collect data not only on what is happening but why it is happening. Health education specialists also must consider health equity and social-ecological influences in their assessment process to fully understand the needs of their community. Health education specialists should identify both a planning model and implementation model in this stage, which will help to identify the types of data that need to be collected to fully understand the complex influences on health (Doyle et al., 2019).

Priority Population Perspective

Expressed, actual, perceived, and relative needs should all be addressed in the needs assessment, because community concerns may not always reflect empirical evidence (Doyle et al., 2019; Issel & Wells, 2018). Expressed needs can be observed through individuals' use of services, such as an exercise class taken by older adults at a senior center. Actual needs may be inferred through the discrepancy of services provided to one community group as compared to another, such as bicycling and walking lanes. Perceived needs refer to what individuals in a community state that they want, such as more healthy food choices in a school vending machine. Relative needs describe a discrepancy between an individual's or group's current status and that of others, such as smoke free environment in restaurants among different cities.

1.1.5 Recruit and/or engage priority population(s), partners, and stakeholders to participate throughout all steps in the assessment, planning, implementation, and evaluation processes.

Involving those who will be impacted by the health promotion program/intervention at the very beginning of the planning process is critical. In so doing, it will ensure that the goals and objectives of the assessment, planning, implementation, and evaluation phases will be effectively completed.

Stakeholders and partners serve different purposes and make separate contributions. Partners are either individuals or organizations that bring knowledge, skills, or resources to the table and are willing to share risks, responsibilities, and rewards. Stakeholders are those who affect, and are affected by, change and those who have an interest in the results and/or what would be done with the results. Increasing the involvement of the priority population, partners, and stakeholders in the assessment process as well as other program planning, implementation and evaluation can not only result in an improved assessment but also increase the value of the results. Sometimes health education specialists or researchers might develop assessment plans using theories and their experience collecting these data. Stakeholders can provide useful information or other ways of gathering information that might be relevant in that situation. A strong planning team needs to be led by trusted and effective leadership and include members that are motivated achievers and have the power or capacity to affect change.

Benefits of Partnerships
McKenzie et al. (2017) identified 8 reasons why partnering is beneficial. These include the following:
- Meeting the needs of a priority population, which could not be met by the capacities of an individual partner.
- Sharing of financial resources.
- Solving a problem or achieving a goal that is a priority to several partners.
- Bringing more stakeholders to the "table."
- Bringing more credibility to the program.
- Seeing and solving a problem from multiple perspectives.
- Creating a greater response to a need because there is strength in numbers.

Roles and Partnering Efforts
When forming a team, the health education specialist should determine what knowledge, skills, resources, and experiences are needed that stakeholders, partners, and priority populations can bring to the planning activities. Developing relationships with stakeholders, partners, and priority populations will help create an effective planning team to conduct a needs assessment, as well as to help with the development, implementation, and evaluation of programs. McKenzie et al. (2017) suggested including the following constituents in a planning committee:
- Members of the priority population
- Both doers and influencers
- Members of the agency
- Other important stakeholders

McKenzie et al. (2017) also emphasized the need for good leaders to provide the greatest chance of success.

Health education specialists must consider carefully what type and level of engagement is needed with the priority populations, partners, and stakeholders to participate throughout all steps of the assessment, planning, implementation, and evaluation process. Gilmore (2012) discussed two types of partnering efforts, advisory committees and planning committees, which are both tasks orientated and critical throughout the process.

Another level of partnering, coalitions, should be considered for larger community-wide initiatives that require more intense, complex, and detailed efforts. Butterfoss (2013) indicated that for coalitions to be successful, they need to use principles of collective impact conditions that include:

- a common agenda,
- shared measurement,
- mutually reinforcing activities,
- continuous communications, and
- a backbone organization.

Health education specialists can look at elements of facilitating participatory action and partnerships to measure and ensure effective community based participatory efforts. These elements include the following:

- Recognize a partner community as a unit of identity.
- Build on community strengths.
- Facilitate collaborative, equitable decision making.
- Foster co-learning among partners.
- Balance knowledge generation with community benefit.
- Focus on ecological perspectives, local problems, and multiple determinants of health.
- Develop systems using an iterative process.
- Disseminate information, results, and benefits to all partners.
- Develop a commitment and long-term process.
  Bartholomew Eldredge et al., (2016).

Recruiting Members for Planning Teams

Health education specialists must develop planned strategies to recruit members for their planning teams. The strategies for how members are chosen will be dependent on the size of the team, the type (stakeholder, partner, priority population), and skills, experience, and knowledge needed for the team (McKenzie et. al, 2017). As an example, members from the priority population could be considered volunteers; therefore, their motivating factor to participate may be different from a paid staff person (Issel & Wells, 2018). In comparison, recruiting a partner organization may be determined by establishing common goals and objectives. In addition, the diversity on the planning committee should reflect the priority populations of the health problem. McKenzie et al. (2017) outlined 5 strategies to select team members. They include the following:

- Asking for volunteers (word of mouth, a newsletter, a needs assessment widely distributed publication),
- holding an election (throughout the community or subdivision of community),
- inviting/recruiting people to serve,
- having members formally appointed, and
- having an application process and then selecting specific to most desirable characteristics.

Competency 1.2 Obtain primary data, secondary data, and other evidence-informed sources.

An assessment is a critical part of program planning. The assessment allows health education specialists to determine what health problems exist in a particular setting or with a particular group of people as well as the level of capacity in the community to address the results of the assessment. To obtain health-related data, multiple methods should be used. First, primary data include information health education specialists collect firsthand to answer unique questions about the specific purpose of the project. Additionally, secondary data have been collected previously for some other purpose and are available for use by others (McKenzie et al., 2017). Not all collection methods and sources, however, are appropriate in all practice settings.

Secondary data is important in defining the needs of the population. Collecting primary data, however, allows the health education specialist to obtain accurate data about problems, influences, and potential solutions to health issues specific to the community. Engaging community members in the assessment process helps to establish important relationships, which help in interpretation of the findings and support implementation of intervention (Doyle et al., 2019).

When planning a program, health education specialists must use evidence to make decisions. Types of evidence-informed sources can range from objective (systematic reviews) to subjective (personal experience and observations) data (McKenzie et al., 2017).

1.2.1 Identify primary data, secondary data, and evidence-informed resources.

Health education specialists must locate and obtain valid and reliable data pertaining to a specific population. Most health education specialists identify needs of the priority population through a review of the current literature. Literature databases are available in libraries (specific computer databases) and through the Internet. Refer to Sub-competency 1.2.3 Conduct a literature review for additional information on the literature review process. Health education specialists need to be sure to gather data on a specific population that have characteristics similar to those of the priority population (McKenzie et al., 2017).

Primary Data Resources
A variety of methods can be used to collect primary data. Samples of primary data sources include individual- and group-level sources. Individual-level sources may include surveys, interviews, and self-assessment. Group-level primary sources are Delphi technique, community forums, focus groups, nominal group process, and observations (McKenzie et al., 2017). Refer to Sub-competency 1.2.7 Determine primary data collection needs, instruments, methods and procedures for additional information on these techniques.

Secondary Resources
Health education specialists can use secondary data sources to gain important insight on community capacity, assets, and needs. Collecting secondary data often involves gathering epidemiological data, such as health status, risk factors, incidence and/or prevalence rates, death rates, birth rates, and more.

Sample of Secondary Data Sources (McKenzie et al., 2017):

- Government Agencies
  - ⊙ Centers for Disease Control and Prevention (CDC)
    - Morbidity/Mortality Weekly Report (MMWR)
    - CDC Wonder
    - Behavioral Risk Factor Surveillance System (BRFSS) data
    - Youth Risk Behavior Surveillance System (YRBSS) data
  - ⊙ National Center for Health Statistics (NCHS)
    - Vital records
  - ⊙ United States Bureau of Census
    - Population, employment, income, family size, education, housing, and other social indicators
    - The Statistical Abstract of the United States, which provides summary statistics of populations by metropolitan area, state, and the country as a whole, as well as information on health expenditures and health coverage (including Medicare and Medicaid), injuries, disability status, nutritional intakes, and food consumption
- State and local Agencies
  - ⊙ County, city, and state health departments or related agencies
    - Vital records, disease registries, police records, morbidity/mortality records, epidemiological studies, incident reports, safety surveys
  - ⊙ Service, social, and religious organizations (e.g., Rotary Club, United Way)
- Nongovernment Agencies and Organizations
  - ⊙ Health care system
    - Hospital discharge data, emergency room visit data, injury/hospitalization records
  - ⊙ Voluntary health agencies (e.g., American Heart Association, American Cancer Society)
  - ⊙ Business, Civic, and Commerce Groups (e.g., United Way)
  - ⊙ County Health Rankings
    - Henry J. Kaiser Family Foundation
- Existing records
  - ⊙ Health data that are collected as a by-product of services, such as clinical records, data from immunization programs, data from water pollution control programs, clinical indicators, data from physicians' offices, data on absenteeism, and data from insurance claims
- Literature
  - ⊙ Peer-reviewed journals
  - ⊙ Published scientific studies and reports

Health education specialists need to be able to assess and identify credible sources of data needed for the assessment. Refer to Sub-competency 1.2.5 for more information on determining credibility of secondary data.

1.2.2 ▲ Establish collaborative relationships and agreements that facilitate access to data.

Through collaborative relationships and formal/informal agreements with stakeholders and agencies, health education specialists have been able to facilitate access to data. The collaborative relationship requires effort to identify common goals by which the organizations or groups could work together (Butterfoss, 20013). Refer to Sub-competency 7.1.2 for more information about assessing capacity of potential partners and stakeholders.

The level of the collaborative relationship could be identified as networking, cooperating, coordinating, or collaborating. Establishing an agreement with the organization or group outlining the intended outcome, audience, the purposes for which the data will be used, the ownership of data, confidentiality aspects, and conditions of the release of data can be an effective method to obtain or exchange needed data and practice data ethics. Data-sharing agreement guides and templates are accessible online for health education specialists to integrate into their needs assessment process. Refer to Sub-competency 7.1.4 for more information on formal and informal partner and stakeholder agreements.

1.2.3 Conduct a literature review.

A literature review is a highly systematic method of locating, synthesizing, and interpreting a collection of work by researchers and practitioners (Fink, 2013). An effective literature review is conducted in a systematic manner to uncover what is already known about a topic resulting in a summary and synthesis of the review.

Preparing
Conducting a literature review during the needs assessment phase helps health education specialists understand the existing body of knowledge on the topic and populations, as well as identify information gaps to be included in the needs assessment. The topics for the literature review should be related to the key questions from the planning team. The basic components of the literature review process include the following:
- What questions do you want to answer?
- What evidence will address the question?
- What are the inclusion and exclusion criteria for the evidence?
- How will you find the evidence you want? What is the search strategy?
- What evidence from the search process meets your criteria?
- How will you document answers to your question?
- What metric will you use to judge strength of the evidence? How will you summarize the findings and draw conclusions based on the data and the limitations?

(Bartholomew Eldredge et al., 2016)

Conducting literature searches involves identifying a search strategy. Search strategies typically require health education specialists to identify:
- key search terms,
- search sources (e.g., online and bibliographic databases such as MEDLINE),
- a period of time to conduct the search (e.g., 2010 to 2019),
- characteristics of the priority population (e.g., age, race, gender, geographic location) or intervention, and
- health conditions (e.g., diabetes, obesity, asthma, teenage pregnancy) of interest.

In many cases, the topics being searched by health education specialists already have been evaluated or researched with a plethora of published results in the literature.

Sources

Given that systematic reviews, meta-analyses, and pooled analyses are not always available, it is sometimes useful to find other publications in the literature. In this instance, publications on the topic of interest generated in the most recent reviews may serve as useful resources. Information can be found in indices, abstracts, government documents, and computerized databases. Methods for researching the literature are constantly evolving. Computer databases are widely used because they compile large amounts of information and are easily searched (Cottrell et al., 2018). Databases available today not only have catalogue resources, but, in many cases, they also provide full text copies of the latest research and evaluation findings.

The Internet makes available a wide array of interactive information and data that can be used by health education specialists; however, not all information found on the Internet should be considered valid and/or reliable (McKenzie et al., 2017). When using the Internet to access information, health education specialists must ensure the information provided by the resource is valid and reliable. Examples of credible databases include BIOETHICSLINE, ERIC, HAPI, MEDLINE, National Library of Medicine, and TOXNET. In addition, databased services for high-level evidence-based information include Cochrane Library, PubMed, and SUMSearch. Other government documents can be retrieved via CDC for the National Center for Health Statistics (NCHS) and other secondary sources. (Neutens & Rubinson 2014). Health education specialists also can work with health science librarians to locate sources of data.

Accuracy of Published Information

As a literature review is conducted, it is important to understand and evaluate published information for accuracy (Cottrell et al., 2018). The eight questions that can be asked when evaluating research in the literature include:

- Was the purpose of the study stated?
- Was the research question or hypothesis stated?
- Were the subjects in the study described? Did the literature describe participant recruitment?
- Was the design and location of the study described?
- Were the data collection instruments described?
- Did the presented results reflect the research question or hypothesis?
- Were the conclusions reflective of the research design and data analysis?
- Were the implications meaningful to the priority population?

Analyze and Synthesize Information

Research findings and results of assessments and program evaluations, including current trends and issues, are made available in published literature. Health education specialists strive to provide evidence of effective approaches to health education problems through a synthesis of professional literature. Health education specialists refer to peer-reviewed journals in which published papers are reviewed by experts in the field or in a specific content area (Cottrell et al., 2018).

The strategy established during the planning phase of the literature review process provides the bases for the analysis and synthesis of the information gathered. The systematic method of organizing identified constructs into subheadings provides the basis to analyze, synthesize, and write the review (Neutens & Rubinson, 2014).

1.2.4 Procure secondary data.

To obtain meaningful secondary data that is related to the purpose and scope of the assessment, health education specialists must have a thorough understanding of the strengths and weakness of the source of the dataset/ information. Before using secondary data, health education specialists must consider the following qualities of the secondary data:

- Reliability data – Who collected the data? Source of data? Methods used to collect the data?
- Accessibility to data – Is the database available? What are costs? Is there a need for informal/formal agreements?
- Timeliness of data – Is the information too old to be relevant?
- Applicable to priority population – Do results only apply to a broader population? (Issel & Wells, 2018)

Computerized reference databases are accessible at most universities and public libraries. Many reference databases are accessible to the public, such as the American FactFinder - United States Census Bureau, the BRFSS, the National Library of Medicine's PubMed, Google Scholar, and the Education Resources Information Center (ERIC). Refer to Sub-competency 1.2.1 Identify primary data, secondary data and evidence informed resources or examples of secondary data resources for a list of databases.

Health education specialists need to consider the organization of the secondary data collection process and analysis prior to obtaining data. Refer to Sub-competency 1.2.8 and 1.2.9 for general concepts related to creating a plan to analyze secondary data.

1.2.5 Determine the validity and reliability of the secondary data.

Valid and reliable data are necessary components in a thorough needs assessment. If data are valid, they are representative of what is intended to be measured. Reliable data are consistent across multiple assessments of a specific measure (McKenzie et al., 2017). For example, if secondary data sources are to be used, health education specialists must be able to locate valid and reliable health and environmental data from a variety of sources. If valid and reliable instruments are used, then more meaningful comparisons of data can be made. These meaningful comparisons allow health education specialists to draw conclusions about needs for health programs.

Information is commonly obtained from the Internet, computerized reference databases, books, and peer-reviewed journals. The technology field is constantly producing new innovations, and the role of health education specialists is to make sound decisions about the appropriateness, credibility, and compatibility of the data. With knowledge from health behavior theories or models, health education specialists can make realistic decisions to meet the needs of the priority population.

There is an increasing demand for health information, and health education specialists may find a variety of sources. The roles of health education specialists include being a resource person and communicating information about the needs, concerns, and resources of the community. Health education specialists also must have the skills to evaluate sources of information and must become a skeptical, critical consumer of health information (McKenzie et al., 2017).

1.2.6 Identify data gaps.

As data are analyzed, health education specialists might note where there are little data that inform the key questions of the needs assessment that include certain health problems, health behaviors, attitudes, beliefs, or other theoretical constructs related to health behaviors. This observation might lead to further data collection to gather the information or it might lead to the prioritization of health issues among a population based upon these gaps in data. Theories and models are useful for program planning, intervention, and evaluation. In the needs assessment stage, health education specialists can apply explanatory theories and models to identify gaps in data, to help understand why a health problem exists, or to guide the search for modifiable factors (Glanz et al., 2015).

1.2.7 Determine primary data collection needs, instruments, methods and procedures.

Health education specialists should identify existing instruments that may be applicable to the health education specialist's assessment efforts and priority population. Using or adapting a valid and reliable data collection instrument may provide details on methods used for development, collection, implementation, and analysis.

Primary Collection Needs:

The planning team identifies the primary data to be collected to support the purpose and scope of the assessment. While collection of primary data can directly be used to obtain needs identified by the priority population(s), they can be costly and require a great deal of time (McKenzie et al., 2017). The health education specialists should consider prioritizing the collection of primary data based on gaps identified through secondary sources and literature review.

Instruments

Primary data can be collected through a variety of sources and strategies at the individual, group, and community level. Health education specialists should become familiar with the various strategies to provide the framework to select and prioritize the best method for data collection. Refer to Sub-competency 1.2.1 Identify primary data, secondary data, and evidence informed resources for types of strategies.

Individual:

Surveys are used to determine the knowledge, attitudes, beliefs, behaviors, skills, and health status of a priority population. Surveys should be well-constructed and have been tested for validity and reliability, have a high response rate, and have been administered to a valid sample. Interviews are similar to pencil-and-paper surveys in that they can be conducted in a variety of ways. They can be completed by telephone, face-to-face, electronically, or in groups.

- Key informant interviews are conducted with individuals whom have knowledge of, and the ability to report on, the needs of a corporation, hospital, or organization. To conduct interviews requires trained interviewers to ensure consistency and accuracy in an unbiased manner.
- Telephone interviews offer a relatively easy method of collecting data at moderate cost. They allow the interviewer to clarify questions, but they do not have the advantage of visual cues that the face-to-face method offers.
- Electronic (or Web-based) interviews are growing as a viable means of collecting data from a large number of individuals quickly and at low cost. The disadvantages (such as access to a limited population [only those with Internet access], lack of anonymity, and the fact that e-mails easily can be ignored) are difficult to overcome (McKenzie et al., 2017).

Self-assessment instruments can allow people to answer questions about their health history, behavior, and screening results, such as blood pressure, cholesterol, height, and weight. These data are then compared against a database of individuals with similar characteristics, which provides a risk assessment for a number of diseases, as well as life expectancy. Individuals can detect disease or disease risk by performing other self-assessment techniques, including health assessments or health risk appraisals, breast self-examination, testicular self-examination, and self-monitoring for skin cancer (McKenzie et al., 2017).

Group:

Observations are used to gather data through direct surveillance of the population. Data collection is accomplished through watching and recording specific behaviors of the population being studied. At times, the observer becomes a part of the day-to-day activities. Examples of observations include watching factory workers for their use of safety equipment and/or precautions, observing the smoking behaviors of employees on a break, and checking food service workers' adherence to workplace health code regulations (McKenzie et al., 2017).

Community forums are public meetings. As such, people in a particular population are brought together to discuss their perceptions of the community's health problems. Important to remember is that the silent majority may not speak out, allowing more vocal individuals' views wrongly to be seen as the group's views (McKenzie et al., 2017).

Focus group techniques capitalize on communication among participants who are selected based on specific criteria. Individuals are invited to participate, and a skilled facilitator typically leads the focus group. In many instances, the facilitator encourages the participants to talk to one another, ask questions, give examples, and provide comments regarding a particular topic. Focus groups are designed so that participants share opinions and explain the reasons underlying those opinions. The number of participants for focus groups varies depending on the intended outcome; a focus group can be as small as two people or as large as the facilitator can manage. Analysis of results can be challenging. Inferring consensus may be difficult, and the results may not be generalizable (Neutens & Rubinson, 2014).

Nominal group process is a highly structured process in which a few representatives from the priority population are asked to respond to specific questions, which are based on what the health education specialist needs to know. In this process, small groups of five to seven people are involved, with each member of the group having an equal voice in the discussion and voting. All participants share their opinions by privately ranking the ideas proposed and then sharing this ranking with the groups in a round-robin fashion. This process is time-consuming and may require a large meeting space, depending upon the number of people participating (Gilmore, 2012).

Delphi panel is a group process that generates consensus by using a series of mailed or e-mailed questionnaires. The process involves individuals from three groups: decision-makers, staff, and program participants. A questionnaire containing one or two broad questions is sent to the entire group. Their answers are then analyzed. Based on the analysis of the responses, a second questionnaire with more specific questions is developed. This questionnaire is sent to the same group of respondents; their responses are analyzed; and another questionnaire is developed. On average, questionnaires are analyzed and sent out three to five times (Gilmore, 2012).

Community:

A community capacity inventory and community asset maps are tools for identifying community resources and issues. A community capacity inventory typically involves developing a written list of the skills and talents of individual community members, associations, and other resources in the neighborhood as a whole. Simple surveys, walking and windshield tours, interviews, community newspapers or directories, and other assessment methods can be used to gather information. Community members create community asset maps as they "map" local resources, abilities, and other building blocks for community growth and change. A community asset map is a visual representation of the physical assets of a community that may constitute important physical and social support structures for achieving community goals, such as libraries, playgrounds, schools, parks, and houses of worship (Gilmore, 2012; University of Kansas, 2019d).

PhotoVoice is a specific photographic technique to enable people to record and reflect on personal and community strengths and concerns. Also, PhotoVoice promotes critical dialogue and knowledge about personal and community issues through group discussion of photographs. PhotoVoice is an excellent way to reach policy makers through these discussions (University of Kansas, 2019e).

Methods

The method or strategy for collecting the primary data is based on the questions being asked, data needed, participants from whom the data will be collected, and resources needed to collect data. Health education specialists should develop a comprehensive data collection and analysis plan. The data collection and analysis plan might include multiple approaches based on program needs. For example, health education specialists should consider the feasibility of collecting data among different subpopulations to identify disparities. In addition, health education specialists should take into account potential bias results from data collection or analysis methods in the analysis plan. Refer to Sub-competency 4.2.6 Develop a sampling plan and procedures for data collection, management and security.

Data credibility can be improved by utilizing multiple methods for gathering data. Health education specialists can integrate primary and secondary data to obtain different, yet thorough, perspectives on health needs and to compare data from the priority population with data from similar populations. The combination of data can help establish the rationale for program needs.

The selection of methods will include a consideration of the resources available, population characteristics and preferences, and timeframe to conduct assessment. Health education specialists' understanding of the advantages and disadvantages of the various data collection methods assist in decision-making in the planning process. Highlights of these considerations include:

Surveys (Neutens & Rubinson, 2014)
- Mail
  - Advantages: Eliminates interviewer bias, increases assurance of anonymity, allows respondents to complete at their convenience, increases accessibility to a wide geographic region, increases accuracy because respondent can consult records, encourages identical wording for all respondents, and promotes inter-rater reliability

⊙ Disadvantages: Lack of flexibility, likelihood of unanswered questions, low response rate, inability to record spontaneous reactions or nonverbal responses, lack of control over the order of responses, no guarantee of return by due date, inability to use complex questionnaire format, strong possibility of duplicate mailing, fear of loss of anonymity, and expense

- Telephone
  - ⊙ Advantages: Cost savings compared with face-to-face survey, faster than mail survey or personal interview, accessibility to a wide geographic region, and increased monitoring and quality control
  - ⊙ Disadvantages: Call may be seen as a hoax or disruption, loss of visual component of reading the survey, interviewer has little control and respondent can hang up at any time, and low response rates due to unlisted numbers, caller ID, reduced use of land lines, "do not call" lists

- Interview
  - ⊙ Advantages: Personalization of the survey to one participant, flexibility for further probing, higher response rates, control over question order, spontaneity, no possibility of help from others, and ability to use more complex questionnaires
  - ⊙ Disadvantages: Expensive, time-consuming, increased change of interviewer bias, lack of anonymity, lack of standardization of questions, and difficulty in summarizing the findings

- Web
  - ⊙ Advantages: Quick response, low cost to administer, automated data gathering process, administered to a large number of participants, and a forced-choice format
  - ⊙ Disadvantages: Limited ability to monitor returned surveys, limited time frame within which respondent can access survey, forced-explicit choice responses, costly hardware and software

Interviews or focus group (University of Kansas Center for Community Health and Development, 2019e, 2019f)
- Advantages: Help people learn more about group or community opinions and needs have more depth, nuance and variety, nonverbal communications and group interactions also can be observed, and focus groups can, therefore, get closer to what people are really thinking and feeling
- Disadvantages: Responses may be harder to score on a scale

Observations (University of Kansas Center for Community Health and Development, 2019g)
- Advantages: A place or event, as well as situations or interactions, can be directly viewed, allowing the observer to experience the life of the community or a population
- Disadvantages: Documenting observations may be harder to analyze

Procedures

The evaluation or research design is the scheme that is used to delineate when and from whom data are collected. Methods indicate the way in which data are collected as part of the evaluation and typically consist of strategies to collect data (Issel & Wells, 2018). When conducting needs assessments, health education specialists need to be mindful of sampling techniques, basic research designs used to collect and compare data, methods of collecting data, types of data needed to answer research questions, ethical considerations, and the need for valid and reliable instruments to measure health status, behaviors, attitudes, beliefs, and so on. A key part of assessment planning is the application of proper study design with appropriate methods and instruments. Refer to Sub-competency 4.2.6 – 4.2.9 for more information on research design and methods and information regarding instrumentation and data collection.

Adequate planning and preparation are vital to successful data collection activities. The following are critical components in the data collection process: (a) data collection and instrument development, (b) data analysis plan, (c) findings or·results of assessment, and (d) written reporting of data.

As an example of the planning required for collection of primary data, the following provides steps in designing and completing a survey:

1. *Planning the survey.* This step includes determining (a) survey objectives, (b) monetary resources, (c) time resources, and (d) personnel resources.
2. *Overall design.* A survey should be designed to accomplish the objectives and should reflect data needs, data collection techniques, and resources.
3. *Method of data collection.* The method chosen should match the survey objectives and fit resource constraints.
4. *Planning data analysis.* An appropriate method of data analysis, consistent with the type of data being collected and the goals of the needs assessment, should be chosen.
5. *Drawing the sample.* From the survey objectives and design come (a) the population of interest, (b) the sample size and selection, and (c) appropriate interviewers if interviews are to be conducted.
6. *Questionnaire construction.* The questions formulated for a survey are of the utmost importance and require detailed attention. Use existing validated questions when possible. All questions should match the objectives.
7. *Pretest questionnaire.* The survey should be pretested with a sample comparable to the population of interest.
8. *Questionnaire revision.* Revisions should be based on findings from the pretest. If there are extensive changes, a second pretest should be conducted.
9. *Administering the survey.* The method chosen (e.g., mail, e-mail, telephone) should fit the nature of the data to be gathered and the objectives of the survey.
10. *Code preparation.* Data preparation includes coding the questions and responses for tabulation and designing contingent values (as necessary) to limit data entry errors.
11. *Verification.* Data entered should be tested for accuracy and for errors in coding.
12. *Data entry.* The method of data entry will vary according to resources; the key is to use a software program that is user-friendly, advantageous for analysis, and that can be watched for errors.
13. *Tabulation.* A frequency count should be conducted to ascertain how many answers are in each of the categories for every question.
14. *Analysis.* Analysis varies according to the purpose of the study, but it generally includes calculating percentages, averages, and relational indices, as well as performing tests of significance.
15. *Recording and reporting.* The report should reflect all of the previous steps outlined including the objectives, hypotheses, reliability of results, and recommendations for action. Reports often include an executive summary of the methods and major findings for the study.

(Neutens & Rubinson, 2014)

1.2.8 Adhere to established procedures to collect data.

Data collected for a needs assessment can be quantitative, qualitative, or both. Quantitative data are collected in numerical form (e.g., mortality rates or number of cigarettes smoked) or easily translated to numerical form (patient satisfaction using a 5-point scale from dissatisfied to satisfied). Qualitative data are in narrative form, collected to better understand motivation, thoughts, feelings, and behaviors (McKenzie et al., 2017). Both types of data are valuable to health education specialists throughout the program planning, implementation, and evaluation process.

To ensure quality, it will be important to find reliable, trustworthy, and skilled people to collect, enter, analyze, and manage the data. Other considerations for implementation are:

- defining roles, responsibilities, and skills needed to collect, enter, and analyze qualitative data (focus groups, interviews, and community forums), which may differ from the needs related to quantitative data (surveys)
- monitoring the data collection to ensure implementation of the process will assist in maintaining established timeframes and objectives. Identifying a committee or group should provide this oversight.
- maintaining the integrity of the data you collect and ensuring protocols address quality control measures not only on the collection but the entry of data

Refer to Competency 4.3 Manage the collection and analysis of evaluation and/or research data using appropriate technology for more information on the data collection and management process.

Operational resources are essential to any data collection effort and must be considered during the planning stage. For example, use of incentives could improve the response rates from populations/participants; access to software can help with qualitative analysis; and costs can cover use of facilities to conduct focus groups. Health education specialists also must communicate with their partners and stakeholders to inform them of the implementation of the data collection process.

1.2.9 ▲ Develop a data analysis plan.

A data analysis plan is a roadmap for organizing and analyzing needs and capacity assessment data before the collection of data (Gilmore, 2012). When developing the analysis plan, health education specialists typically include the following components:

- Scope and purpose of assessment
- Key needs assessment questions
- Description of data collection instruments (Qualitative and Quantitative) selected and why being used. Supporting documentation on databases used (e.g., methodology) can provide credibility to assessment findings
- Description of inclusion/exclusion criteria
- Description of variables to be used in the analysis
- Statistical methods and software to be used

(Issel & Wells, 2018; Neutens & Rubinson 2014)

Refer to Competency 4.3 Manage the collection and analysis of evaluation and/or research data using appropriate technology for more information on developing the analysis plan.

Competency 1.3 Analyze the data to determine the health of the priority population(s) and the factors that influence health.

Health education specialists need to identify and prioritize the behavioral, environmental, and social risk factors that are associated with health. These are called social determinants of health or the conditions in which people are born, live, work, play, and age that affect their health risks, health, daily functioning, and quality of life. Modifying these factors or determinants is pertinent to improving the health status of individuals and communities (CDC, 2018a). The types and number of risk factors are as varied as influences themselves.

People learn in different ways. What works for one individual or group does not always work for everyone. People learn by making connections with previous knowledge and experiences. Therefore, health education specialists must acknowledge learning impacts and select methods for delivering health education, health promotion, and health messages that are tailored to specific priority populations.

1.3.1 Determine the health status of the priority population(s).

The health status of those affected by the disease or illness or the one whom a program is intended to serve (priority population) is determined by an intricate mix of individual and population-based behaviors. Health status and quality of life are influenced by every aspect of a person's environment and circumstances (Doyle, et al., 2019). Health status is not merely determined by etiology, i.e., causes of diseases, but by determinants, the underlying factors, or "causes of causes" that ultimately bring about disease (Riegelman & Kirkwood, 2019). These causes are often referred to as social determinants of health. The World Health Organization (WHO) defined social determinants of health as "the conditions in which people are born, grow, live, work and age" (2019b, para. 1). These conditions are impacted by economics, social policies, and politics (Riegelman & Kirkwood, 2019). The Centers for Disease Control and Prevention (CDC) and *Healthy People 2030* have identified five categories for social determinants: 1) neighborhood and built environment, 2) health care access and quality, 3) social and community context, 4) education access and quality, and 5) economic stability (USDHHS, 2020). Social determinants of health affect health status because of the overlapping connection to health disparities and health equity. Refer to Sub-competency 5.1.1 for more information on the determinants of health.

1.3.2 Determine the knowledge, attitudes, beliefs, skills, and behaviors that impact the health and health literacy of the priority population(s).

Health education specialists need to determine factors that impact the health and health literacy of priority populations. These factors can be cognitive and behavioral. Individual factors include educational, social, and cultural characteristics of the individual. Individual factors include a person's knowledge, attitudes, beliefs, and perceptions related to health. An individual's culture, religious or spiritual beliefs as well as skill set must be considered when assessing influences on health behavior (McKenzie et al., 2017; Riegelman & Kirkwood, 2019). Behavioral (lifestyle) factors are behaviors or actions of individuals, groups, or communities. Behavioral indicators may include compliance, consumption and utilization patterns, coping, preventive actions, and self-care (McKenzie et al., 2017). Attitudes and beliefs are shaped by physical, cultural, social, and community norms. Family values, religion, and the environment also shape attitudes and beliefs. Health education specialists must understand the dynamics of priority populations to build relationships, respect, and trust, as well as to identify ways to collaborate effectively on interventions. For health education and health promotion interventions to be successful, health education specialists must acknowledge diversity in backgrounds, experiences, and cultures to effectively engage priority populations and other stakeholders in interventions.

According to ecological models of public health, behavior has multiple influences including factors at the intrapersonal, interpersonal, organizational, community, and public policy levels. Behavioral influences interact across these different levels (Sallis & Owen, 2015). Once a health behavior has been determined and factors that influence the behavior have been identified, health education specialists need to gather more information to know how these factors influence the behavior. Health education specialists need to weigh the importance and changeability of the factors against available resources for the program. Using an ecological perspective can provide a multi-level and interactive approach as health education specialists explore the relationships between risk factors. Commonly, there are five levels of influence for health behaviors:

- Individual: knowledge, attitudes, and beliefs that influence behavior
- Interpersonal: association with family, friends, and peers that define social identity, support, and role
- Institutional: rules, regulations, and policies, which may constrain or promote recommended behaviors
- Community: social networks and norms
- Public policy: local, state, and federal policies and laws that regulate or support actions/practices

Health education specialists can contribute to the impact of the program by understanding the relationships of the multidirectional flow of influence within and between levels and applying that understanding to the development of the intervention.

Once the factors that enhance or compromise health have been identified, there is a need to gather more information about how these factors impact health. Health education specialists can use data gathered from the needs assessment, data from the literature indicating risk factors and determinants of health, and data collected from surveys (e.g., YRBSS and BRFSS) to identify which factors are most important and changeable to determine the goals and objectives of the health promotion program.

1.3.3 Identify the social, cultural, economic, political, and environmental factors that impact the health and/or learning processes of the priority population(s).

A growing recognition is that, while individual behavior plays a key role, opportunities to make healthy choices are shaped by the availability of choices. Social and economic conditions created by societal norms and policies in both health and non-health sectors determine these opportunities; such opportunities are not always distributed equitably across population groups (National Association of County and City Health Officials (NACCHO), 2019). Strategies to improve population health need be developed and implemented where people live, learn, work, play, and worship.

The U.S. Department of health and Human Services (USDHHS) defined social determinants of health as "the conditions in the environments where people are born, grow, live, work, play, worship and age that affect a wide range of health, functioning and quality-of-life outcomes and risks" (2020, para. 1). These circumstances are shaped by the distribution of money, power, and resources at global, national, and local levels. In *Healthy People 2030*, five key areas of social determinants of health were revealed. They include the following:

- Economic Stability (e.g., poverty, employment, food security, housing stability)
- Education Access and Quality (e.g., high school graduation, enrollment in higher education, language and literacy, early childhood education and development)
- Social and Community Context (e.g., social cohesion, civic participation, perceptions of discrimination and equity, incarceration/institutionalization)
- Health Care Access and Quality (e.g., access to health care and primary care, health literacy)
- Neighborhood and Built Environment (e.g., access to healthy foods, quality of housing, crime and violence, environmental conditions)

Healthy People 2030 uses social determinants of health to try to reduce health disparities to achieve health equity. Health disparities are "differences among populations in health status, behavior, and outcomes" that are due to multiple influences including the determinants of health (Fertman & Allensworth, 2017, p. 428). According to the Braveman, Arkin, Orleans, Proctor and Plough (2017), health equity is "reducing and ultimately eliminating disparities in health and its determinants that adversely affect excluded or marginalized groups" (p. 2). Disparities are differences in health that are not only unnecessary and avoidable, but in addition are considered unfair and unjust.

Health is impacted by a variety of different factors. The five major factors that determine the health of a population include:

1. education,
2. economic stability,
3. neighborhood and built environment,
4. health and healthcare, and
5. social and community context.

These various components often are interrelated, and their combined effect influences the likelihood of disease, functional capacity, health behavior, and well-being. Each determinant's level of influence on population health varies, especially when applied to specific health issues.

Health education specialists conduct needs and capacity assessments to better understand influences on the health and well-being of individuals and groups. As health education specialists understand the influences on health, they can help individuals and communities make informed decisions and take the appropriate steps to enhance health.

One way to include multiple levels of intervention is to consider including system change strategies to enhance the likelihood of successful maintenance of change. Systems strategies are changes that impact all elements of an organization, institution, or system. A system is an organized collection of integrated elements that work as a whole to accomplish an overall goal. Systems can be simple (e.g., clinical reminder system) or complex (e.g., more coordination between elements, engagement of actors, and organization) (Holmes et al., 2012). A systems change is modification in how a collective unit decides upon policies, program services, decision-making, and the allocation of resources (United States Department of Justice, 2014a). Systems thinking and change requires action at multiple levels. Systems have been identified to address to address public health problems. (Holmes et al., 2012). These provide areas of leverage points for systems change. Table 1.1 provides a description of these levels.

Table 1.1
Levels for Systems Change

Level	Description
Paradigm	The mindset or beliefs of how the systems work and refer to goals, policies, and structure Change: shift or reinforcement of the paradigm
Goals	Aims of the system Change: focus or change the aims of the system
System structure	Parts of the systems, actors (e.g., leadership, staff, partners), and interconnections between the parts Change: modifying linkages within the system, system elements, or incorporating new elements
Feedback and delays	Providing information about the results of different actions by system elements to the source/administration of the actions. Change: create or change feedback loop, adding feedback loops or changing feedback delays
System elements	Actors and physical elements of the system connection through activities and information flow (communication)

Note. Adapted from Holmes et al., 2012

Examples of systems are neighborhoods, schools, communities, health systems, worksites, or health insurers. The benefit of systems change is that it impacts more than a single entity (e.g., school, worksite, clinic) and maximizes the reach of its effects. For example, the Affordable Care Act (ACA) (United States Centers for Medicare and Medicaid Services, n.d.) has a policy that all health plans under it must provide free preventive services to all enrollees; therefore, individuals enrolled in the various plans will have access and no costs for vaccines, cancer screenings, blood pressure and cholesterol screenings, and so on. Other examples of systems changes may include a state school board that has adopted healthy nutrition standards for procurement of meals for students across their school, a community health initiative that involves multiple sectors in addressing active living (e.g., faith, schools, urban planning), or a health system that employs a comprehensive patient electronic care portal from electronic medical records, telemedicine, and integrated online disease management support for all of their locations.

Systems change can take a long period of time, so impacts may be years away. Interim milestones are important to consider. Evaluations of systems change can have the same methods and impacts of those for policies, including process, context, and short-term and longer-term outcomes. Evaluation methods could include organizational interviews with leaders and staff, observations of events or structure, surveys of key informants, and patient/population-oriented outcomes for more process-oriented questions. System thinking allows planning teams to look a systems components not as separate pieces, but in terms of how they interact. Systems thinking involves looking at the system parts, including shifts in systems interdependence, communications or interactions, and system choices (e.g., attitudes about change, change fit alignment with mission). Evaluation of systems change is often more complex and involves data collection at multiple stakeholder levels (e.g., leadership, staff, partners, consumers/clients).

1.3.4 Assess existing and available resources, policies, programs, practices, and interventions.

Health education specialists can collect recommendations throughout the development and evaluation of health promotion programs and interventions, so good ideas and insights are neither lost nor forgotten. When determining the effectiveness of programs and interventions, health education specialists can use recommendations from a variety of sources, such as scientific literature, program staff, program stakeholders, and program decision-makers. At the national level, health education specialists can use systematic reviews and meta-analysis of evidence-based practices. For example, the Guide to Community Preventive Services (n.d.) (https://www.thecommunityguide.org/) provides a summary of what is known about the effectiveness, economic efficiency, and feasibility of interventions to promote community health and prevent disease. This Community Guide includes evidence-based recommendations for programs and policies to promote population-based health as well as evidence on topics, including alcohol, cancer, physical activity, obesity, and tobacco. The Community Guide has been developed and continually updated by the nonfederal Task Force on Community Preventive Services, which is comprised of public health experts who are appointed by the director of the CDC.

Health education specialists can identify gaps or overlaps in existing programs by communicating with stakeholders in the community, looking at service use by clients, and observing levels and patterns of the provided services. At this stage, health education specialists should consider potential partnerships with other agencies or organizations that have similar goals. Working with existing partners and forming new partnerships can help agencies share resources as they work toward a common goal.

Health education specialists can plan more effective interventions with a knowledge and understanding of policies related to health education/promotion. Policies are important to health promotion work. One of the core functions of public health is comprehensive public health policy development to support individual and community health efforts (McKenzie et al, 2017).

1.3.5 Determine the capacity (available resources, policies, programs, practices, and interventions) to improve and/or maintain health).

Health education specialists need to determine the health education programs, services, or policies that already exist for the priority population. Health education specialists need to use community-building processes, which are focused on the identification, nurturing, and celebration of community assets. A review of actual and potential availability of resources is essential for establishing realistic program/intervention starting points and determining how the programs/interventions can be sustained. The process of asset mapping or mapping community capacity can help the health education specialist identify available programs and interventions (Gilmore, 2012). Asset mapping also can be used to identify a community's strengths.

Assets and resources are community contributions that may prevent the health problem from occurring or assist in its solution (Issel & Wells, 2018). Community assets can be people within the community, a physical resource (such as buildings or community gathering places), services within the community, or businesses within the community (University of Kansas, 2019d) Community empowerment through capacity building helps communities solve their own problems with their own resources (Doyle et al., 2019).

Needs and capacity assessment results can be used to guide health education specialists in the planning phases of program and intervention development. Key questions that can serve as a guide for the process include:

- What is the health problem, and what are its consequences for the state or community?
- What is the size of the problem overall and in various segments of the population?
- What are the determinants of the health problem?
- Who are priority populations?
- What changes or trends are occurring?

(Gilmore, 2012)

1.3.6 List the needs of the priority population(s).

Health education specialists should identify factors during the assessment process that will guide the direction of the overall planning process. The final step in the needs assessment is validating the needs identified in the assessment. The validation process involves "double checking" or making sure that an identified need is an actual need. Multiple methods can be used to determine the validity of assessment findings. Examples of methods include a) rechecking the steps followed in the needs assessment to eliminate any bias, b) conducting a focus group with some individuals from the priority population to determine their reaction to the identified need (if a focus group was not used to gather the data), and c) getting a second opinion from other health professionals (McKenzie et al, 2017).

Competency 1.4 Synthesize assessment findings to inform the planning process.

Health education specialists should synthesize all information into a concise and useful format. This synthesized information should be used to determine priorities for planned interventions (Doyle et al, 2019).

Factors that should be identified during this synthesis include the following:

- Predisposing factors: individual knowledge and affective traits;
- Enabling factors: factors that make possible a change in behavior; and
- Reinforcing factors: feedback and encouragement resulting from a changed behavior, perhaps from significant others.

These factors may have a direct impact on health risk factors and how the health education program is planned and implemented (Green & Kreuter, 2005; McKenzie et al., 2017). Many of these factors can serve as either a facilitator or barrier. For example, knowledge that a behavior could lead to a health issue can facilitate change, but false information can be a barrier to change. These three factors (predisposing, enabling, and reinforcing) are important in combination. Knowledge regarding a health issue is an important facilitator, but the absence of knowledge, skills, or support in how to change can severely impact an individual's ability to change.

1.4.1 ▲ Compare findings to norms, existing data, and other information.

Health education specialists must validate the findings by comparisons to norms and other standards of acceptability. Common standards of acceptability include, but are not limited to, mandates (policies, statues, and laws), values, norms, comparison/control groups and the "how much" in an objective for the program. The purpose of this comparison is to improve the quality of programs and measure their effectiveness (McKenzie et al, 2017).

Norming may be comparing data found in your community group or county to the state or national level. For example, health education specialists could compare the proportion of adults who are physically active in their county to the proportion in neighboring counties as well as to the proportion listed in *Healthy People 2030* as a standard (USDHHS, 2020).

The following steps can be used to infer the need for health education/promotion from obtained data:
- Analyze primary and secondary data
- Compare data with local, state, national, or historical situation
- Consider the social, cultural, and political environment (relative needs)
- Set priorities by:
  ⊙ assessing the size or scope of the problem,
  ⊙ determining the effectiveness of possible interventions, and
  ⊙ determining appropriateness, economics, acceptability, resources, and legality of the possible intervention.

(Doyle et al., 2019, McKenzie et al., 2017)

Summary tables can be used to present metadata or to triangulate data from multiple sources. Graphs, charts, and tables are pictorial resources that can be used to summarize key results from needs assessments.

1.4.2 Prioritize health education and promotion needs.

Health education specialists must confirm that health education needs match the program needs. The needs assessment process validates the community needs and results in development of promotion efforts tailored to the specific needs within the community (Healey & Zimmerman, 2010; University of Kansas Center for Community Health and Development, 2019e).

Health education specialists can prioritize health needs by using the following criteria.
Assessing the size or scope of the problem by determining the:
- percentage of the population directly affected
  ⊙ How serious is the problem?
  ⊙ How urgent/critical is the nature of the problem?
  ⊙ How severe is the problem?
  ⊙ What is the morbidity/mortality severity, duration, and/or disability associated with the problem?
    • What medical costs are associated with the problem?
    • How many people are affected by the problem?
- effectiveness of possible interventions
  ⊙ How effective are health education interventions in addressing the problem? Are they meeting stated goals and objectives?
  ⊙ Are the potential interventions accessible to the affected population?
  ⊙ How were the needs for the potential programs determined? Are the needs of the population being met? If not, why?
- appropriateness, economics, acceptability, resources, and legality of the possible intervention
  ⊙ What health education programs are presently available to the population(s) affected?

⊙ Are the programs being utilized? If not, why?

⊙ Given the population, is the intervention appropriate and in accordance with societal/group norms?

⊙ Are there sufficient resources for implementation?

⊙ Is the intervention legal?

(Healey & Zimmerman, 2010)

Health education specialists must identify emerging health education needs and address diverse health needs. A simple approach to prioritizing health education needs is to consider whether an intervention actually can make a change in the health problem and whether the health problem is important or worth addressing. Each health problem can be rated regarding its degree of importance and changeability. Health problems classified as having both high changeability and high importance should be addressed first, as shown in Table 1.2

Table 1.2
Program Prioritization based on the importance and changeability of the health problem

	Highly Important	**Less Important**
High Changeability	High priority for intervention	High priority for intervention
Low Changeability	High priority with innovative program	No program

Note. Adapted from Green & Kreuter, 2005

1.4.3 Summarize the capacity of priority population(s) to meet the needs of the priority population(s).

Health education specialists should tailor programs to the values, wants, and needs of the priority population. This process helps to ensure that programs are readily accepted by the priority population. Programs with multiplicity (multi-components) and support, which is the appropriate built-in reinforcement components to assist participants with the expected level of involvement and/or behavior change, enhances the capacity of the priority population. Other areas that increase the priority population's capacity to meet needs include the following:

● Inclusion- the right type and number of partners

● Recruitment, reach, and response- promoting the program and ensuring that the priority population is aware of the program, has the opportunity to participate in the program, and has an adequate number actually participate in the program

● Dose- the number of units or program components that are actually delivered to the priority population

● Interaction and satisfaction- the degree to which practitioners effectively work and communicate with program participants and how satisfied participants are with the program in general or with specific components

● Context- assess the presence of any confounding factors in the environment that may affect program participation or initial results

(McKenzie et al, 2017)

1.4.4 Develop recommendations based on findings.

Health education specialists can focus on positive aspects and areas that need improving based on the results of the needs and/or capacity assessments. Health education specialists should frame recommendations so that the priority population can make decisions regarding what needs to, or can, be done and in what order of priority (Issel & Wells, 2018). For example, the Affordable Care Act (ACA) (United States Centers for Medicare and Medicaid Services, n.d.) includes a mandate for nonprofit health care organizations to conduct a community health needs assessment. The purpose of the assessment is to identify gaps in services. The health care organization then must implement strategies to address the identified gaps in service (Issel & Wells, 2018). Health education specialists should address the needs of each group of stakeholders when developing recommendations.

1.4.5 Report assessment findings.

After summarizing the findings of the assessment, health education specialists need to consider to whom they will disseminate the findings, such as the priority population, researchers, funding agencies, or other stakeholders. Health education specialists need to decide who should write the report, receive the report, as well as in what format it should be distributed and when it should be distributed (McKenzie et al., 2017). Health education specialists should use a variety of dissemination methods to present the information. Some reports are formal and/or mandated and have to be distributed through an organization's website, such as public health departments or hospitals for community health benefits assessments. Examples include the following:

- Preparing a user-friendly, easy-to-read report
- Writing a separate executive summary of the report
- Developing a press release, then holding a press conference in conjunction with the press release
- Creating a newsletter, newspaper article, or fact sheet
- Developing a PowerPoint presentation
- Making verbal presentations to community groups, the priority population, and stakeholders and using the PowerPoint, other demonstrations, or visual images to report the findings
- Constructing professionally designed graphics, charts, and displays for use in reporting sessions
- Making short videos or audiotapes for presenting the results
- Using social media to report information, such as Facebook, You Tube, or Instagram

Chapter 2
Area of Responsibility II: Planning
KEY: No symbol - entry level; ▲ - advanced 1; ■ - advanced 2

2.1. Engage priority populations, partners, and stakeholders for participation in the planning process.

  2.1.1   Convene priority populations, partners, and stakeholders.

  2.1.2   Facilitate collaborative efforts among priority populations, partners, and stakeholders.

  2.1.3   Establish the rationale for the intervention.

2.2. Define desired outcomes.

  2.2.1   Identify desired outcomes using the needs and capacity assessment.

  2.2.2   Elicit input from priority populations, partners, and stakeholders regarding desired outcomes.

  2.2.3   Develop vision, mission, and goal statements for the intervention(s).

  2.2.4   Develop specific, measurable, achievable, realistic, and time-bound (SMART) objectives.

2.3. Determine health education and promotion interventions.

  2.3.1   Select planning model(s) for health education and promotion.

  2.3.2 ▲ Create a logic model.

  2.3.3 ▲ Assess the effectiveness and alignment of existing interventions to desired outcomes.

  2.3.4   Adopt, adapt, and/or develop tailored intervention(s) for priority population(s) to achieve desired outcomes.

  2.3.5 ▲ Plan for acquisition of required tools and resources.

  2.3.6 ▲ Conduct a pilot test of intervention(s).

  2.3.7 ▲ Revise intervention(s) based on pilot feedback.

2.4. Develop plans and materials for implementation and evaluations.

  2.4.1 ▲ Develop an implementation plan inclusive of logic model, work plan, responsible parties, timeline, marketing, and communication.

  2.4.2   Develop materials needed for implementation.

  2.4.3   Address factors that influence implementation.

  2.4.4 ▲ Plan for evaluation and dissemination of results.

  2.4.5 ▲ Plan for sustainability.

Area of Responsibility II

The Role. Planning begins by reviewing the health needs, problems, concerns and capacity of the priority population obtained through the assessment of needs and capacity (Responsibility I). Early in the planning process it is important to recruit interested partners and stakeholders, such as community, religious and political leaders, representatives from community organizations, resource providers and representatives of the priority population to support and help develop the program. This planning group or committee then works to develop the mission, goals and objectives as well as create or adapt intervention strategies. The intervention strategies selected must be sufficiently robust, or effective enough, to ensure the stated objectives have a reasonable chance of being met. Cottrell, et.al. (2018) call this the "Rule of Sufficiency" (p.183). Next, the planning group must locate the resources needed to implement and evaluate the program, develop a plan for delivery, and address factors that influence the implementation of the intervention. Utilizing the objectives developed during this planning phase, the health education specialist will also begin considering the process for program evaluation (Responsibility IV) (NCHEC, 2020).

Setting: The following text is presented to describe how planning is used in different practice settings (NCHEC, 2020).

Community Setting: In a community setting where a needs and capacity assessment has been used to identify both a significant health problem and an opportunity to address that health problem, the role of health education specialists is to develop a comprehensive plan for implementation, evaluation, and sustainability. To begin, the health education specialist convenes representatives of relevant groups for the purpose of planning a health education/promotion program who will remain appropriately involved throughout the process. In identifying committee members, health education specialists may seek input and promote involvement from those who will affect, and be affected by, the program. Another key responsibility of health education specialists is to lead efforts to formulate goals and objectives and to adapt, or implement culturally relevant, evidence-based interventions that meet the needs of priority populations. If no appropriate programs exist, health education specialists are expected to develop evidence-informed programs and plans to evaluate preliminary impact. Health education specialists identify and assess community resources and barriers affecting the implementation of the program to achieve a successful program or intervention in the community setting.

School (K-12) Setting: National laws, local mandates, school boards and school administrators determine the requirement for providing health education in schools. Health education specialists employed in schools should select an advisory committee consisting of administrators, teachers, parents, and members of the community. The committee will identify objectives and age-appropriate curriculum, and materials/resources to meet the objectives outlined. Ideally the curriculum will follow a logical scope and sequence from K-12 and focus on the physical, mental, emotional, as well as the social and moral aspects of health for the whole child. A means to evaluate the effectiveness of the curriculum should also be designed during the planning stage. On more of a micro level, each health education specialist must plan lessons for their students on a daily basis that include learning objectives, teaching strategies, and evaluation methods.

Health Care Setting: Health education specialists in the health care setting often work collaboratively with a multidisciplinary planning team and/or a formalized advisory group to plan individual patient and population level health education programs. The team or advisory group may include physicians, nurses, advanced nurse practitioners, physician assistants, dieticians, pharmacists, social workers, members of the priority population and other stakeholders. This team utilizes the gap analysis, needs assessment and capacity data which has already been collected to design or modify educational resources, aids, and programs that can assist patients and their families to make informed decisions about their health, health care and/or lifestyle choices. The specific role of health education specialists during the planning phase is to identify program scope, to assist the team to establish mission, goals and objectives, and identify available resources that support the proposed program including any potential billable services. An evaluation plan must also be designed as part of planning. In addition, health education specialists offer advice about teaching tools, methods, strategies, and design promotion and evaluation tools needed to achieve the intended outcomes. They must be able to evaluate, develop, customize, and update patient education materials as needed. These materials may include brochures, posters, flyers, booklets, checklists, websites, and online resources. Further, the health education specialist may be involved in developing strategies to initiate or change policies, rules, and regulations that may impact the health of the priority population.

College/University Setting: Health education specialist faculty in a higher education setting analyze research results, current professional Competencies, certification requirements, accreditation standards, state standards and available instructional resources when planning the Health Education curriculum. Course planning is a major component of curriculum planning and health education specialists may plan courses for public health education majors as well as for the general student population. Teaching health education students how to plan programs, including the development of program goals and objectives, is vitally important. Within courses, faculty health education specialists should plan to use a variety of teaching methods, including lectures, discussions, simulations, practical experiences, and focused assignments. University health education specialists may also be given responsibility to plan class schedules, to plan budgets, and for long range program planning.

Worksite/Business Setting: Health education specialists analyze aggregate data from numerous sources that may include medical and pharmacy data, HRA data, biometric screening data, and other data sets. These data provide the basis for making a business case to key stakeholders outlining the benefits and costs of a health education program. After gaining support, health education specialists may convene an employee committee with representatives from different parts of the organization to develop a strategic plan outlining program priorities, goals and objectives, timelines, communications, incentives, and proposed budget. Health education specialists lead the team in identifying or developing evidence-based interventions and strategies to meet the needs of employees. A plan to evaluate the interventions and strategies should be developed at this point. Health education specialists also identify opportunities for new or updated policies that support employees' health and wellbeing. Examples of such policies include tobacco-free worksites, healthy vending machine and cafeteria selections, and flex time to participate in health promotion activities.

College/University Health Promotion Services Setting: Health education specialists in this setting review and utilize assessment results in collaboration with other university personnel such as practitioners in health, counseling, student life, human resources, and fitness/wellness centers. This team works together to develop program goals and objectives, as well as to select and design evidence-informed and theory-based programs and interventions that address issues and improve health within a socioecological systems perspective. Health education specialists develop partnerships with clinical practitioners, faculty members, students, off campus agencies, and other stakeholders to integrate health education into other programs, including treatment protocols and campus wide activities. Within the planning process health education specialists place emphasis on tailoring materials, methods, and technology that appeal to student preferences and the diverse and changing populations represented on a university campus. An important component of planning is to develop an evaluation process that will be utilized to determine the effectiveness of any initiated programs.

Key Terms

Programs are defined as a set of planned activities over time designed to achieve specific objectives (Green & Kreuter, 2005).

Program planning is the process of identifying needs, establishing priorities, diagnosing causes of problems, assessing and allocating resources, and determining barriers to achieving objectives (Green & Kreuter, 2005).

Vision statements are a brief description of where the program will be in the future, usually in three to five years. Among the elements considered are future products, markets, customers, location, and staffing (McKenzie et al., 2017).

Mission statements are a short statement describing the focus or purpose of a program. The mission statement underpins the development of program goals and objectives (McKenzie et al., 2017).

Goals are statements of the intent and direction of a program as well as the end results desired. The target population is identified and action words such as reduce, eliminate, or increase are used (Fertman & Allensworth, 2016).

Objectives are precise statements of intended outcomes of the program. In measurable terms, they are used to describe the changes in behavior, attitude, knowledge, skills, or health status that will occur in the intervention group as a result of the program. Objectives are small, specific steps that enable the goal to be met and serve as a bridge between a needs assessment and a planned intervention (McKenzie et al., 2017).

Community-based programs are delivered at locations considered within community boundaries rather than at a centralized location outside of the community parameters. Programs are generally delivered in libraries, local churches, schools, recreation centers, and local clinics (Issel & Wells, 2018).

Coalitions are a group of diverse organizations and constituencies working together toward a common goal (Issel & Wells, 2018).

Logic models are a tool for program planning and evaluation that shows the relationship of inputs and activities to outputs, immediate outcomes, and long-term outcomes (Issel &Wells, 2018).

Models are a mixture of ideas or concepts taken from any number of theories used together (Cottrell et al., 2018).

Pilot testing is a set of procedures used by planners to try out a program on a small group of participants prior to actual implementation (McKenzie et al. 2017).

Theories are a set of interrelated concepts, definitions, and propositions that presents a systematic view of events or situations by specifying relations among variables to explain and predict the events of the situation (Cottrell et al., 2018).

Competency 2.1 Engage priority populations, partners, and stakeholders for participation in the planning process.

Often planners need to begin the planning process by gaining support from groups of key people to ensure that planning and implementation proceed smoothly and to ensure that these key people can acquire the necessary resource support. Groups of key people, or stakeholders, include those involved in the program operations, those served or affected by the program, and the primary users of the program. When seeking support from stakeholders, the planner should be able to explain to the stakeholders why the program is necessary; that is, essentially, explaining the philosophy behind the particular program being developed (McKenzie et al., 2017). Refer to Sub-competency 1.1.5 for more information on the importance of selecting the right stakeholders in the program planning process.

2.1.1 Convene priority populations, partners, and stakeholders.

The process for knowing, understanding, and convening priority populations, partners, and stakeholders is an important component of program planning. According to Bartholomew Eldredge and colleagues (2016), convening these groups is often best accomplished by a lead agency with linkages to the community. Agencies might include health departments, hospitals, and academic institutions. This lead agency often can provide the resources for technical assistance, material support, credibility, and significant contacts. Successful coalitions consist of a highly committed core group that can be expanded to include community gatekeepers as well as a wide variety of participants (Bartholomew Eldredge et al., 2016). Structures such as formalized roles, rules, and procedures coupled with volunteer or compensated leaders will help to ensure that the program is launched and maintained effectively. Factors that are important in the convening stage include transparent and frequent communication, mutual and formalized decision-making processes, strategies to resolve conflicts, and perceptions that the value of participation is positive. Appropriate convening of priority populations, partners, and stakeholders often will result in robust member engagement, sharing of resources and effective assessment, and planning (Bartholomew Eldredge et al., 2016).

2.1.2 Facilitate collaborative efforts among priority populations, partners, and other stakeholders.

Community groups and collaborative efforts often are referred to as coalitions (Issel & Wells, 2018). Collaborative efforts provide the opportunity for program planners to bring together representatives from diverse organizations, segments, or constituencies within the community to work toward a common goal. Additionally, coalitions bring together a combination of resources and expertise (McKenzie et al., 2017).

No two coalitions or community efforts are formed or operate in the same way, though there are some common steps that are taken to form partnerships or coalitions. Olson (2010) identified the following general steps in collaborative efforts:

1. Prepare the groundwork – identify the problem, need for partnership, potential partners, draft goals and objectives.
2. Create an action plan and organize the partnership – solidify vision and goals, identify a SMART action plan.
3. Implement the action plan.
4. Evaluate the action plan.
5. Sustain the collaboration.

Ideally, the efforts and participation of a coalition will continue throughout the program and sustain community action. Health education specialists should develop a plan to encourage the coalition's participation in the entire programming process, from goal creation and resource allocation to project implementation and evaluation (Doyle et al., 2019).

Building a coalition or community-wide effort can be a complex and sometimes challenging task. A simple partnership in which your organization is paired with just one community organization may be a quick and easy strategy to enhance health education efforts. To promote this type of collaborative effort, health education specialists need to research the partner organization's mission, establish clear goals, tasks, and communication methods, and continually monitor effectiveness (Doyle et al., 2019). The drawback of this approach is that resources are limited in comparison with a coalition approach.

Identifying partners that are knowledgeable and committed to the effort, forming viable partnerships/coalitions, and working with the community to identify and/or validate issues that are important to them is critical in gaining and maintaining program support. Furthermore, establishing clear relationships between the goals in the program and the assets, capacities, and values of the community are critical (Olson, 2010).

2.1.3 Establish the rationale for the intervention.

The planning process frequently commences with planners creating a rationale to gain support of key individuals and agencies. A strong rationale helps to ensure that essential resources (e.g., personnel, financial) are obtained and that the development and implementation of the program are seamless (McKenzie et al., 2017). Key components of a good rationale include showing how the benefits of the program dovetail with decision makers' values, demonstrating the potential return on investment, and showcasing the best evidence available. According to McKenzie and colleagues (2017), four important steps are needed to write a program rationale:

1. Identify the appropriate background information.
2. Title the rationale.
3. Write the content of the rationale.
4. List the references used to create the rationale.

Establishing a planning committee consisting of interested individuals, doers and influencers, and representatives from the priority population is ideal. To maximize effectiveness, these individuals must understand and abide by the planning parameters established for the program by key decision makers (McKenzie et al., 2017).

Three important criteria, or the three Fs of program planning, are fluidity, flexibility, and functionality (McKenzie et al., 2017). Fluidity indicates that the steps in the program planning process are sequential and, therefore, build upon one another. Flexibility suggests that planning is adapted to the needs of the stakeholders and is responsive to both current and emerging health problems. Functionality means that the outcome of planning is improved health conditions, not simply the production of the program plan itself. Taking a population-based approach in which an ecological framework is used will help to articulate the rationale for the program.

Competency 2.2 Define desired outcomes.

All successful health education programs begin with the development of appropriate goals and objectives. Goals are used to measure a program's processes and outcomes. Processes might include program components, activities, delivery, and time frame, while the outcomes could include short-term changes (e.g., knowledge, attitudes, skills, behaviors) or long-term changes (e.g., behavior adherence, health status). Objectives are specific measureable outcomes that are used to guide program development and to assess program effectiveness. A shared understanding of the goals and objectives of health education programs among stakeholders, partners, and the priority audience is optimal.

2.2.1 Identify desired outcomes using the needs and capacity assessment.

Program planners use the needs and capacity assessment to identify the desired outcomes for the priority population. These are future-oriented goals based on the articulated program objectives. Desired outcomes may include reduction of risk, physiological indicators, signs and symptoms of illness or injury, morbidity, disability, mortality and/or quality of life indices (McKenzie et al., 2017).

Data collection should not be conducted in a vacuum or without an end goal in mind. Needs assessment data can help health education specialists consider the level of intervention they want to address. According to McKenzie et al, (2017) **primary prevention** is focused on protecting people from developing a disease or injury. Individuals are healthy, without signs and symptoms of disease, illness, or injury. Education about healthy diets or the importance of physical activity are examples of primary prevention. **Secondary prevention** is focused on early diagnosis of disease or potential injury. Disease, illness or injury is already present in the individual or group. For example, secondary prevention might include recommending regular preventive exams or screening tests. Finally, **tertiary prevention** is the rehabilitation after the diagnosis of a disease or injury. The goals of tertiary prevention involve preventing further deterioration and maximizing quality of life through self-management or support groups (McKenzie et al., 2017). These levels of prevention also can help health education specialists consider interventions to address their desired outcome.

Without a defined goal for use, data collection is a waste of both financial and human resources. Prior to the data collection activity, researchers and practitioners must determine the outcomes to be achieved. These may include changing behavioral risks, modifying environmental characteristics, influencing public policies, and raising awareness among the media.

2.2.2 Elicit input from priority populations, partners, and stakeholders regarding desired outcomes.

Identifying individuals willing to serve as members of a program planning committee is an important first step in ensuring programmatic excellence (McKenzie et al., 2017). The following people may be interested in being part of the program-planning process:
- Individuals who represent various groups within the priority population
- Representatives of other stakeholders not represented in the priority population
- Individuals who have key roles within the organization sponsoring the program

Among the strategies to elicit input from priority populations, partners, and stakeholders regarding desired outcomes are one-on-one interviews, mailed surveys, online surveys, community meetings, and written questionnaires consisting of forced-choice and open-ended questions. Among the questions which could be posed are as follows:

1. Can the objectives be realized during the life of the program or within a reasonable timeframe?
2. Can the objectives realistically be achieved?
3. Does the program have enough resources to obtain a specific objective?
4. Are the objectives consistent with the policies and procedures of the sponsoring agency?
5. Do the objectives violate any rights of those involved?
6. Does the program reflect the cultural characteristics of the priority population and the changes sought?

Adapted from McKenzie et al., 2017

Obstacles to obtaining input from priority populations, partners, and stakeholders regarding desired outcomes include lack of time, awareness, transportation or communication capabilities, interest/apathy, and convenient locations or times. To remove these obstacles, health education specialists should make personal contact with key representatives, provide incentives for participation, choose easily accessible meeting locations, and conduct training programs (Issel & Wells, 2018). In addition, health education specialists should use mixed methods for obtaining input, both global and specific, and vary modes of communication (e-mail, face-to-face meetings, and newsletters) to ensure widespread input about the plan.

2.2.3 Develop vision, mission, and goal statements for the intervention(s).

A **vision statement** is a brief description of where the program will be in the future, usually in three to five years. Among the elements considered are future products, markets, customers, location, and staffing (McKenzie et al., 2017).

Sample Vision Statements
- Childhood Obesity Prevention Fund: To ensure that all children are physically fit and nutritionally fed to learn, play, and grow.
- I Love Literacy Foundation: To promote reading and financial literacy among all segments of the adult population.
- Safe Seniors Campaign: To prevent injuries among older adults in traffic, at home, and in the community.

In the program planning stages, it is important to develop and express a mission statement as well as goals and objectives to provide a direction for the program and a foundation for the program evaluation (McKenzie et al., 2017). Table 2.1 provides useful information for differentiating between a mission and a vision.

Table 2.1
Comparison of Mission and Vision Statements

Mission statement	Vision statement
Statement of the purpose of organization	Statement of the desired end state
Oriented to making decision, priorities, and actions of the organization	Oriented to group meeting the results of the organization
Questions answered: • Why does your organization exist? • What is the broadest way to describe the work of the organization?	Questions answered: • What needs to be changed? • What does success look like?

Note. Adapted from Korlaar, 2019.

A mission statement encompasses the distinctive purpose and unique "reason for being" of a program. A mission statement can be a one-sentence statement or a short narrative that broadly defines the purpose. Program mission statements are used to reveal the purpose or focus of the organization or program and are enduring over time (McKenzie et al., 2017).

Sample Mission Statements
- The mission of the South County Senior Services is to provide easy access to health information and health care resources to senior citizens in South County.
- The mission of Generations' employee wellness program is to improve the health status of our employees.
- The mission of Brookside elementary school's health program is to ensure that children are healthy, safe, and ready to learn.

Goals are general, long-term statements of desired program outcomes and provide the direction upon which all objectives are based. Goals specify the priority population and often include action words such as increase, reduce, or eliminate (McKenzie et al., 2017).

Sample Goal
The goal of the program is to:
- reduce the number of osteoporosis-related fractures among elderly men and women who live in the area served by the health department.
- increase the rate of mammography screening among women ages 50 and older.
- eliminate the number of new smokers among adolescents ages 18 and younger.

2.2.4 Develop specific, measurable, achievable, realistic, and time-bound (SMART) objectives.

Program objectives are the specific actions that need to be undertaken to achieve the goal. Objectives are statements that describe in measurable terms changes in health status, behavior, attitude, or knowledge that will occur in the intervention group as a result of the program. These are the small, specific factors that enable the goal to be met. Objectives are usually written to include what will change (outcome), when or under what conditions the change will occur, how much change will occur, and who will change (McKenzie et al., 2017). SMART is the acronym for writing objectives: specific, measurable, achievable, realistic, and time-bound.

A program's objectives should be relevant to the program goal. There are many types of objectives, including process, impact (i.e., learning, behavioral, environmental) and outcome objectives. In Table 2.2, the hierarchy of objectives, including type of objective, program outcomes, and possible evaluation measures, are outlined.

Process objectives refer to the activities and tasks that lead to the accomplishment of all other levels of objective. These include the number of presentations made, the audience size, staff performance, and resources such as materials, funds, and space (McKenzie et al., 2017). These assessments lay the foundation for process evaluation.

Examples include:
- Before the start of the program, the planning committee members will place physical activity resources in each of the communities served by the health department.
- Prior to the start of the program, planners will contact ten OB/GYN physicians to gather support for the program.

Impact objectives are the second level in the hierarchy and are of three types – learning, behavioral and environmental. In these types of objectives, the immediate and observable effects of a program are described and lay the groundwork for impact evaluation (McKenzie et al., 2017).

Learning objectives are short-term, specific descriptions of awareness, knowledge, attitudes, and skills in relation to the content being taught. Health education specialists should formulate and state objectives with precision. Meaningful objectives should include implied or stated evaluation standards.

Examples include:
- The participants will be able to correctly identify three forms of weight-bearing activity after the first session.
- After the completion of the program, the participants will be able to state the importance of calorie control for weight loss.

Behavioral objectives describe the behaviors or actions that the population will engage in to resolve the problem and lead to attainment of the program goal. They are statements of desired outcomes that indicate whom is to demonstrate how much of what action and by when (Green & Kreuter, 2005).

Examples include:
- Among those attending the program, weight-bearing activity will increase by 50 percent over the following six months.
- Fast food consumption will be eliminated from the diet of all program participants after the second week of program implementation.

Environmental objectives refer to environmental or non-behavioral influences on a health problem. These factors include the social environment (e.g., peer pressure), physical environment (e.g., clean air or water), psychological environment (e.g., emotional learning climate), service environment (e.g., access to health care), and economic environment (e.g., incentives) (McKenzie et al., 2017).

Examples include:
- By 2025, the number of high air pollution alert days in the city will decrease by 10 percent.
- By 2030, the number of bicycle lanes on streets in River City will increase by 35 percent.

Outcome objectives are related to the ultimate goal(s), but are specific, measurable statements of what the educator wants to accomplish at a given time. They represent the change in health status that is the desired result of the program or intervention. These are the ends rather than the means. Program or outcome objectives include items such as changes in risk reduction, morbidity, disability, mortality, or quality of life (McKenzie et al., 2017).

Examples include:
- Within three years, osteoporosis-related fractures will decrease by 25 percent in the residents of South County.
- By 2016, the rate of sports-related traumatic brain injury among soccer players in Goodwin, Pennsylvania will decrease by 10 percent.

Table 2.2
Hierarchy of Objectives

Type of Objective	Program Outcomes	Possible Evaluation Measures
Process objectives	Activities presented and tasks completed	Number of sessions held, exposure, attendance, participation, staff performance, appropriate materials, adequacy of resources, tasks on schedule
Impact objectives • Learning objectives	Change in awareness, knowledge, attitudes, or skills	Increase in awareness, knowledge, attitudes, or skill development/acquisition
• Behavioral objectives	Change in behavior	Current behavior modified or discontinued or new behavior adopted
• Environmental objectives	Change in environment	Measures associated with economic, service, physical, social psychological, or political environments
Outcome objectives	Change in quality of life, health	Quality of life measures, morbidity data, status, risk status, and social benefits mortality data, measures of risk

Note. Adapted from McKenzie et al., 2017

When writing objectives, health education specialists should use action verbs to make the objectives specific – this process helps guide the development of the intervention and evaluation. See table 2.3 for examples of action verbs.

Table 2.3
Taxonomy and Skills Demonstrated

Event of Instruction	Skills Demonstrated	Verbs
Knowledge	• Recall of information or major ideas • Mastery of the subject matter	Define Describe Label List State Tell
Comprehension	• Understand information	Explain Outline Restate Summarize
Application	• Use information • Solve problems using knowledge or skills	Apply Construct Demonstrate Illustrate Show Use
Analysis	• Identification of components • Recognition of patterns	Analyze Distinguish Compare Contrast Explain
Synthesis	• Relate knowledge from several areas • Predict and draw conclusions	Construct Create Devise Formulate Plan
Evaluation	• Compare and discriminate between ideas • Decide based on arguments	Choose Judge Justify Debate Assess

Note: Adapted from Brookhart & Nitko, 2008

Competency 2.3 Determine health education and promotion interventions.

Designing effective health education programs requires careful planning regarding the content, process, and amount of time needed to deliver an intervention. Health education specialists need to consider their priority population's needs and interests, as well as evidence-based strategies, when planning a program.

2.3.1 Select planning model(s) for health education and promotion.

There is no shortage of planning models for health education specialists to use in designing health education and promotion programs. Advanced-level health education specialists are typically responsible for selecting planning models to be used in health education interventions and programs. Entry-level health education specialists should have knowledge of planning models that are commonly used in health education.

According to McKenzie and colleagues (2017), most existing models share common elements, and these elements are included in the Generalized Model. The Generalized Model is a simple composite of such elements and can be used in both teaching and professional practice. The five components of the model consist of assessing needs, setting goals and objectives, developing interventions, implementing interventions, and evaluating results.

Individuals often confuse theories with planning models. A theory is a"set of interrelated concepts, definitions, and propositions that presents a systematic view of events or situations by specifying relations among variables in order to explain and predict the events of the situation" (Cottrell et al., 2018, p. 365). A model is a "composite, a mixture of ideas or concepts taken from any number of theories used together" (McKenzie et al., 2017, p. 427). Planning models help lay out the program planning steps to ensure that health education specialists have anticipated potential problems in a program and developed solutions accordingly.

Three widely used models - PRECEDE-PROCEED, MATCH, and CDCynergy Lite - are described in more detail in this chapter. Other models include SMART, MAPP, MAP-IT, Healthy Communities, Intervention Mapping, among others (Cottrell et al., 2018; McKenzie et al., 2017).

The **PRECEDE-PROCEED Model** (Green & Kreuter, 2005) is currently the most often used formal planning model in health education. This model, developed as PRECEDE in the 1970s, is an acronym for predisposing, reinforcing, and enabling constructs in educational/ecological diagnosis and evaluation. The model was expanded in the 1980s to incorporate PROCEED, an acronym for policy, regulatory, and organizational constructs in educational and environmental development.

The model has eight phases:

PRECEDE

>   ***Phase 1:*** Social assessment – define the quality of life of the priority population.

>   ***Phase 2:*** Epidemiological assessment – identify the health problems of the priority population and determine and prioritize behavioral (individual) and environmental (external) risk factors associated with the health problem.

>   ***Phase 3:*** Educational and ecological assessment – determine predisposing (individual knowledge and affective traits), enabling (those that make possible a change in behavior, such as skills), and reinforcing (feedback and encouragement for a changed behavior, perhaps from significant or important others) factors.

PROCEED

Phase 4: Administrative and policy assessment – determine the resources (funding, staff, other) available for the program.

Phase 5: Implementation – select strategies and activities; begin program.

Phase 6: Process evaluation – document program implementation, feasibility, and gather feedback.

Phase 7: Impact evaluation – assess the immediate effect of an intervention.

Phase 8: Outcome evaluation – determines whether long-term program goals were met.
(Green & Kreuter, 2005)

Multilevel Approach to Community Health (MATCH). MATCH, a multi-level community-planning model, was developed in the 1980s by Simons-Morton and colleagues and consists of five phases with several steps within each stage. The phases include:

1. health goals selection;
2. intervention planning;
3. program development;
4. implementation preparation; and
5. evaluation.

MATCH is a socio-ecological planning approach. In this model, intervention planning should be aimed at multiple objectives and a variety of individuals. MATCH can be used in a variety of settings (Cottrell et al., 2018).

CDCynergy Lite. Developed by the Centers for Disease Control and Prevention (CDC) in the early 2000s, the CDCynergy community-level model is often used for health communication and social marketing. CDCynergy lite, an abridged version of the CDCynergy health communication model, has six phases of program planning as follows:

1. Describe the problem.
2. Analyze the problem.
3. Plan the intervention.
4. Develop the intervention.
5. Plan the evaluation.
6. Implement the plan.

These interrelated phases help health education specialists understand the priority population as well as the communication strategies that will best help individuals in the priority population to change their behaviors. CDCynergy lite and its more recent version are in the public domain and consist of a step-by-step guide, a reference library, and links to templates that facilitate creation of tailored plans. In addition, CDC has developed content-specific versions to address the needs of particular populations (e.g. American Indian/Alaska Natives) and disease conditions/topics including Diabetes, Cardiovascular Disease, Tobacco Prevention and Control, and many other topics (Cottrell et al., 2018).

2.3.2 ▲ Create a logic model.

A logic model is a tool for program planning and evaluation that shows the relationship of inputs and activities to outputs, immediate outcomes, and long-term outcomes. Often used by federal and foundation funding agencies, the logic model is a one-page tabular summary of the program components (Issel & Wells, 2018).

Health education programs must be carefully planned, implemented, and evaluated. The templates in basic logic models can allow evaluators to move freely back and forth among the elements of a flowchart to determine reasons for success and failure of a program (Healy & Zimmerman, 2010). Through examination of the logical sequence of inputs, activities, outputs, outcomes, and impact, health education specialists are armed with the necessary information to make recommended changes to improve programmatic effectiveness and efficiency. Programmatic effectiveness (success in achieving outcomes) and efficiency (success in using resources, both human and financial) can be easily measured through logic models.

According to Harris (2016), a logic model can be used in many ways, including to:
- map a program during the planning and evaluation phases.
- better understand the program's components and their relationship to outcomes.
- serve as a graphic to enhance stakeholders' understanding and engagement.
- be a tool to help develop and monitor programmatic benchmarks.

Refer to Sub-competency 4.1.3 for more information on the design and uses of logic models.

2.3.3 ▲ Assess the effectiveness and alignment of existing interventions to desired outcomes.

Whether the objectives are individual or behavioral change, environmental modifications, or policy shifts, it is essential to ensure that interventions or strategies that have been selected are sufficient to yield the desired outcomes or meet the desired objectives. For example, educating youth on healthy food choices to stop the prevailing trend of obesity among children will be useless if their school, home, and community environments do not make healthier options such as fruits, vegetables, and grains available to them. Alternately, the enactment and enforcement of policies within the school (e.g., removal of soda and candy machines) or social environment (e.g., tax on sugary snacks and funding for recreational areas) will facilitate the desired outcome of obesity prevention or mitigation. Promoting the use of smoke alarms in homes to protect families during a fire will not be successful unless the families know proper guidelines for installation, placement, and regular maintenance. Other criteria to consider in assessing the efficacy of strategies/interventions are fit with the organization, feasibility of implementation and costs, and acceptability to the priority population. Refer to Sub-competencies 5.1.4 and 6.2.2 for more examples of advocacy and communication outcomes.

Health education specials should use the best evidence available to demonstrate that the planned program will be successful. As health education specialists develop intervention activities that are aligned with their program objectives, they can look to existing programs that have been successful. There are multiple resources that provide information and evaluation data on effective interventions. Some examples include the following:

- Task Force on Community Preventive Services-Guide to Community Preventive Services – collection of program and intervention findings to improve the community's health.
- US Preventive Services Task Force-The Guide to Clinical Preventive Services - Recommendations on preventive services (screening, counseling, etc.) in primary care settings.
- Substance Abuse and Mental Health Services-National Registry of Evidence-based Programs and Practices - Searchable online registry of substance abuse and mental health interventions.
- National Cancer Institute- Research-tested Intervention Programs - A searchable database of cancer control interventions and program materials.
- The Campbell Collaboration – prepares systematic reviews on crime and justice, education, international development and social welfare.

(McKenzie et al., 2017)

2.3.4 Adopt, adapt, and/or develop tailored intervention(s) for priority population(s) to achieve desired outcomes.

Health promotion programs should be customized to meet the needs of the members of priority populations in terms of their age, gender, race, ethnicity, culture, literacy level, income, knowledge, attitudes, and beliefs, among other characteristics. Interventions tailored to the population's unique features are more likely to be accepted and possess greater potential for behavioral change and positive health outcomes.

People who do not want to learn can be difficult to teach. To facilitate the learning process, health education specialists should focus on increasing participants' motivation to learn. Health education specialists may use the following ten principles to facilitate the learning process (Minelli & Breckon, 2009):

- Use several senses. People may retain information differently depending on what is read, heard, and practiced.
- Actively involve participants. Use methods that enable them to be active rather than passive participants. For example, use discussion rather than lecture.
- Provide an appropriate learning environment. Keep extraneous interference and distractions to a minimum and ensure comfortable accommodations.
- Assess learner readiness. People learn only when they are physically and emotionally ready.
- Establish the relevance of the information. People tend to learn what they perceive is important to them. Knowing what is important to participants can help you make the information meet their needs.
- Use repetition. Learning is enhanced if information is repeated several times in a variety of ways.
- Strive for a pleasant learning experience. Encouragement through frequent, positive feedback about progress contributes to a positive experience.
- Start with the known and move toward the unknown. Present information that builds from the simple to the complex in an organized manner.
- Generalize the information. Learning is more likely to occur if the information is applied to more than one setting or situation.
- Appropriately pace delivery of the information. Adjust the rate at which information is covered to meet the needs of the participants.

Allowing adult learners to be part of the decision-making process when planning learning experiences is helpful. In addition, health education specialists should explain why the participants are learning a topic, as well as the immediate value of the new knowledge and skills. Educators need to approach teaching through problem solving techniques to engage the adult learner.

The type of instruction also impacts the learning process. In Gagne's Theory of Instruction, a comprehensive view of instruction is presented (Gagne et al., 2005). Through this theory, categories of learning are identified as (a) verbal information, (b) cognitive strategies, (c) intellectual skills, (d) motor skills, and (e) attitudes. In this theory, the nine events of instruction that provide conditions for learning are proposed. These nine events of instruction are hierarchical and can help with developing the sequencing of instruction (See Table 2.4).

Table 2.4
Events of Instruction

Event of Instruction	Application
1. Gain attention	• Describe why the topic is important. • Ask stimulating questions. • Present a problem to be solved.
2. Inform learners of the objectives	• Present the learning objectives.
3. Build on prior knowledge	• Associate new content with prior knowledge.
4. Present the stimulus	• Present the content.
5. Provide guidance	• Give illustrative examples, analogies, mnemonics, or basic steps in performance to help learner retain new knowledge or skill.
6. Elicit performance	• Provide opportunities to practice new skill or behavior.
7. Provide feedback	• Give immediate feedback on performance.
8. Assess performance	• Assess knowledge/skills gained.
9. Enhance retention and transfer	• Provide supplemental materials (e.g., worksheets, problem sets, case scenarios, training manual) to reinforce learning. • Discuss or ask how knowledge and skills can be applied on the job.

After identification of factors that influence the learning process, health education specialists need to use the information gathered to make program-planning decisions. As health education specialists better understand the influences on learning, they can make informed decisions and develop appropriate learning experiences for programs. Knowing barriers to learning will help health education specialists develop methods for individuals and communities to overcome barriers and learn. Barriers can include educational level, income, cultural factors, attitudes about the topics, and so on.

Health education specialists must be mindful that environments conducive to learning have both psychological and physical characteristics. Psychologically, students must feel comfortable with the pace of teaching, mix of didactic and experiential instruction, and methods of examination. Other factors that affect the learning environment include meaningfulness, openness of the community, learning aids, and consistency. Physically, the learning environment must be clean, safe, lighted, and equipped with furniture in good repair and adequate audiovisual equipment, as well as heated or cooled to the right temperature. Clients or participants in a health education program may associate comfort with the learned information. Health education specialists should strive to ensure that their students are instructed in an environment conducive to learning and should make learning satisfying.

Refer to Sub-competencies 7.2.1, 7.3.1 and 7.3.2 for more information on cultural competency as it relates to the target audience as well as staff training.

2.3.5 ▲ Plan for acquisition of required tools and resources.

Both researchers and practitioners need to give careful attention to the resources necessary to achieve the desired objectives. These resources may include individuals whom have varying skills in finance and budgeting, statistics, social and behavioral theory, communications, or administration. Human resources could include an organization's staff, partners, or community volunteers. In addition, tangible resources will require thoughtful planning. These resources can include computers, paper, writing implements, office space, and transportation, among others.

Depending on the plan or program and its complexity, certain services might be required from partners, contractors, subject matter experts, or consultants. Implementation, project, or work plans should be used to identify the services needed, and health education specialists should plan for how to procure these services. Health education specialists should work through their organization, volunteers, or partners first. Services might be available at no cost or at a reduced cost. In this situation, where services are available, a Memorandum of Understanding (MOU) may be needed. Another option is for health education specialists to work with contractors or consultants to provide the necessary services. In this situation, health education specialists should develop a written agreement in which the work needed is outlined (e.g., statement of work), deliverables/products expected, a timeline to complete the work and provide deliverables/products, and a funding amount or payment.

Few programs are planned perfectly from their inception; most need multiple modifications to enhance their effectiveness and efficiency. For example, a carbon monoxide prevention program may be initially designed for elementary school children and delivered through the classroom. As a part of the intervention, coloring books, a video, activity sheets, and stickers may raise awareness among the children of the dangers of this odorless, colorless, and tasteless gas. Yet, after initial implementation, program planners may determine that parents and caregivers need to be involved as well because they are in the best position to purchase, install, and maintain carbon monoxide (CO) alarms. Only by modifying the prevention program can health education specialists enhance the health of the entire family. When adapting an existing strategy or intervention, health education specialists should review the materials or processes to see which changes, such as content (e.g., statistics, images), delivery, or logistics, may better fit with their population of interest. Health education specialists should refer to implementation guides or protocol to see if the intervention developer has provided guidance on how to make adaptations. Health education specialists should examine how changes to existing strategies and interventions may impact the program's timeline, budget, and relationships with the funders and stakeholders before making any final decisions.

2.3.6 ▲ Conduct a pilot test of intervention(s).

Pilot testing is a set of procedures used by planners to try out a program on a small group of participants prior to actual implementation (McKenzie et al., 2017). Pilot testing sheds valuable light on whether materials, strategies, and interventions are feasible, appropriate, and acceptable to the priority audience. Although pilot testing has the advantage of a program being tested before it is launched, only a few respondents may be involved and the results may not be entirely generalizable (McKenzie et al., 2017). To minimize the drawbacks, participants should be drawn from, and be similar to, the priority population served by the health promotion program (Harris, 2016). Pilot testing may be conducted via face-to-face in focus groups, one-on-one interviews, paper-and pencil instruments, and computerized surveys.

Using formative evaluation techniques to pilot test strategies and interventions is essential to program planning. Formative evaluation is the process of assessing quality of a program during the planning and implementation process (McKenzie et al., 2017). Pilot testing can help ensure that messages and images are clear and consistent, culturally relevant, and motivational. Focus groups and self-reported knowledge, attitudes, and behavior surveys can help reveal what the priority audience understands and what barriers and facilities to behavioral change exist. Data and information gathered from a pilot test can help a health education specialist refine a program to increase the likelihood of success.

2.3.7 ▲ Revise intervention(s) based on pilot feedback.

Once the pilot testing is completed, health education specialists should make any necessary modifications to materials, strategies, and interventions. Health education specialists should view any barriers or deficiencies identified in the pilot test results as positive rather than negative because feedback allows planners to refine the program before it is launched. Necessary modifications emerging from the pilot test results should be shared with stakeholders, sponsors, and the priority population. Such transparency will reinforce health education specialists' aim to steward funding wisely and optimally improve the health status of the audience of interest.

Competency 2.4 Develop plans and materials for implementation and evaluations.

To maximize successful outcomes, it is essential that health education specialists do some initial planning to help ensure the smooth delivery of the program. In this process, health education specialists need to include theories and/or models to guide implementation, identify needed resources, use logical sequence tools to organize the program delivery, create and adhere to a timeline, develop a sound marketing plan, select the right methods to reach the priority population(s), consider integration with other programs, evaluate the sustainability of the plan, and pilot test the program.

All strategies that make up an intervention require resources for implementation. A number of additional logistical activities exist that must be carried out, such as participant recruitment, intervention development and pilot testing, or partnership development. Health education specialists must be able to assess what is needed for program creation and delivery prior to implementation.

2.4.1 ▲ Develop an implementation plan inclusive of logic model, work plan, responsible parties, timeline, marketing, and communication.

Health education specialists are responsible for deciding what and how much information will be discussed regarding specific health content during a health education program. The scope of material covered is determined by considering the following:

- Needs assessment data
- Culture of the priority population
- Literacy level of the priority population
- Priority population's previous experience regarding the health issue
- Budget constraints
- Time restrictions of program participants
- Availability of space to conduct programs

Health education programs must be carefully planned, implemented, and evaluated. The templates in basic logic models can allow evaluators to move freely back and forth among the elements of a flowchart to determine reasons for success and failure of a program (Healy & Zimmerman, 2010). Through examination of the logical sequence of inputs, activities, outputs, outcomes, and impact, health education specialists are armed with the necessary information to make recommended changes to improve programmatic effectiveness and efficiency. Programmatic effectiveness (success in achieving outcomes) and efficiency (success in using resources, both human and financial) can be easily measured through logic models.

In addition to logic models, a comprehensive work plan should be developed. In a work plan, the project deliverables, the activities that will be included, who is in charge of each aspect of the program, what resources are needed, and the timeline for tasks are outlined (CDC, 2013b). Timelines typically take the form of Gantt chart, Program Evaluation and Review Technique (PERT) chart, and Critical Path Method (CPM) (McKenzie et al., 2017). Refer to Sub-competency 3.3.1 for more detail on these methods. So that all parties involved can anticipate what to expect and when, it is essential that these sequences be determined in advance. Some funding agencies may require annual work-plan updates, especially for funded projects in which payment is "triggered" by the delivery of products and services such as interim progress and final reports. By scheduling tasks and responsible parties a priori, adjustments can be made to achieve desired outcomes. In creating this timeline, health education specialists need to consider the length of time and resources necessary to deliver an effective intervention. Health education specialists will have to make difficult decisions regarding the possible content that can be covered in the timeframe, as well as the logical sequence of it, so that the learning modules can be developed. Throughout the program, maintaining regular communication with the team through e-mails, phone calls, and mail keeps everyone updated and helps to troubleshoot obstacles to program delivery. In addition, health education specialists should schedule regular, face-to-face meetings with stakeholders to solve emerging challenges and, most importantly, celebrate successes.

2.4.2 Develop materials needed for implementation.

Information and resources that are used in any health education program should be developmentally and culturally appropriate for the priority population. During the planning process, health education specialists will need to assess whether appropriate health promotion and education materials are available, how to attain them, and how to market them. If they are not available, materials will need to be developed to meet program objectives. Information and resources should be researched early in program planning to ensure that there is time, if needed, to develop adequate materials. Health education specialists need to consider the scope (i.e., how much detail and the breadth of the material) and the sequence (i.e., the logical order of topics) when developing an intervention (McKenzie et al., 2017). Health education specialists should consider reaching out to their priority population or wider community for pro bono marketing and public relations expertise.

A literature review or environmental scan can be used to help identify existing protocols, plans, or other materials available. Existing materials that have been tested and proven successful should be considered first to possibly save time and money when resources are limited. If existing materials do not exist, a health education specialist can consider adapting or tailoring materials for the intended audience. New materials should only be created if funds and time are available, and nothing has been successfully used before with the audience. Any materials (new, adapted, or tailored) should be pilot tested before implementation. This testing will help determine if changes are needed to ensure successful implementation.

2.4.3 Address factors that influence implementation.

There are many potential barriers to the implementation of health education programs, which should be anticipated early in the planning process. Barriers might include lack of community support, agency administration support, or funding. Other barriers might be overextended health education specialists with limited time for program planning, a lack of coordination of resources within the community, or territorial issues among local agencies. A skillful planner is familiar, or becomes familiar, with the community and its potential issues. A successful planner will foresee and overcome challenges that may lie ahead. Programmatic barriers may include: reach of participants, program acceptability, retention issues with online or face to face programs, and choice of the right program incentives.

Although a program may be fully funded and perfectly designed, there may be factors that affect implementation, both negatively and positively. For example, a priority audience may be reluctant to participate in a program, such as families who refuse to allow fire fighters to enter their home to conduct a home safety check or install free smoke alarms. These families may fear scrutiny of their living situation by authority figures. In addition, there may not be enough time for health education specialists to carry out a program in its entirety due to schedule, changes of personnel, or budget cuts in an eroding tax base in a declining economy. In other instances, the audience may be highly receptive to the program, such as parents who voluntarily attend a car seat checkup event shortly after the birth of their child. Health education specialists need to seize this "teachable moment" to recognize and take advantage of the educational opportunity, in this case to ensure that parents appropriately restrain their infant. Stakeholder engagement in the design phase could include asking participants about program elements and incentives or ask the delivery team about implementation. This process may increase the acceptability and reduce participant- and staff-related barriers.

Careful planning can provide enormous benefits in ensuring that program design and implementation are sound. Often, however, real world experience indicates that the program needs to be further refined to truly be effective. In a pilot study, health education specialists might find that content could not be delivered in the specified time period, the audience could not understand certain concepts, or the method of instruction was not the most preferred method for participants. Health education specialists should take information from the pilot study and modify content or delivery method for full implementation of the program. In this way, program planners can be more effective in stewarding resources, helping the priority population change its unhealthy behaviors, and ultimately reduce morbidity and mortality. Health education specialists should consider involving new stakeholders in the implementation as needed, seek opportunities to leverage existing resources, and ask the priority audience for advice on overcoming barriers.

2.4.4 ▲ Plan for evaluation and dissemination of results.

All programs must be evaluated to measure the effectiveness in improving population health and to ensure that programmatic resources are being used efficiently. Evaluation plans (e.g., qualitative versus quantitative, levels such as process, impact, and outcome) must be built in prior to program implementation and generally require the allocation of 15 percent of the total program budget. Although uncertainty, ambiguity, risk, and control are considered "fuzzy aspects" of the planning and evaluation cycle, all efforts must be undertaken, nonetheless, to overcome these challenges to evaluation (Bartholomew Eldredge et al., 2016). In addition, an adapted evidence-based intervention must be evaluated to determine if it remains effective in a new setting with the program modifications that have been made. Elements to consider when looking at existing interventions include whom the program reached, whether it was delivered in its entirety and with fidelity to the old program, and how well accepted the changes were received by the priority population (Bartholomew Eldredge et al., 2016).

Health education specialists should develop an implementation guide, program procedural manual, project plan, or other materials to guide implementation. These "how-to" materials will ensure everyone involved understands the program and will create standards in case the program is replicated in the future (McKenzie et al., 2017).

Dissemination of results can be internal and/or external. Funding agencies will require specific reports; in addition, the agencies may require broader dissemination of the results to encourage sharing of data and knowledge. Dissemination can be either directed toward colleagues, agencies, and funders (reports, journal articles, executive summaries, presentations) or more consumer focused (infographics, websites, newsletters). Dissemination is an important step in the process as it not only allows other health education specialists to use the information to help improve development of similar programs, it can serve as important updates to stakeholders and members of the community (Issel & Wells, 2018).

2.4.5 ▲ Plan for sustainability.

Sustainability refers to the long-term operation of a program and should be a key component of planning. Seldom are all goals and objectives fully achieved in any program; therefore, it is important to continue efforts to reduce disease, injuries, disability, and death. In addition, new priority populations may emerge during the course of program implementation in any community, meaning that a health education specialist may need to adapt a program over time.

According to Fertman and Allensworth (2016), to achieve both effective and sustainable programs, priority populations, stakeholders and partners should endeavor to answer the following questions:

1. Does the health promotion program have a clear and honest understanding of its current reality?

2. Is this understanding shared throughout the health promotion program and used to sustain and improve it?
3. Is knowledge gained translated into effective action toward a desired future?

Program sustainability is often beset with many challenges. These challenges can include staff turnover, the emergence of more pressing health concerns in the community, a lack of sustained interest among members of the priority population, political upheavals, and an erosion of funding streams. To minimize budgetary shortfalls, health education specialists should maintain strong relationships with funders by keeping them informed of program achievements, keeping excellent financial records, and requesting opportunities to leverage their investment through introductions to other potential donors (Fertman & Allensworth, 2016). In addition, health education specialists should broaden and deepen their relationships with community partners throughout the program implementation, engage them in every step of the planning process from beginning to end, and plan for community adoption of the program, if applicable.

Chapter 3
Area of Responsibility III: Implementation
KEY: No symbol - entry level; ▲ - advanced 1; ■ - advanced 2

3.1. Coordinate the delivery of intervention(s) consistent with the implementation plan.

    3.1.1   Secure implementation resources.

    3.1.2   Arrange for implementation services.

    3.1.3   Comply with contractual obligations.

    3.1.4 ▲ Establish training protocol.

    3.1.5   Train staff and volunteers to ensure fidelity.

3.2. Deliver health education and promotion interventions.

    3.2.1   Create an environment conducive to learning.

    3.2.2   Collect baseline data.

    3.2.3   Implement a marketing plan.

    3.2.4   Deliver health education and promotion as designed.

    3.2.5   Employ an appropriate variety of instructional methodologies.

3.3. Monitor implementation.

    3.3.1   Monitor progress in accordance with the timeline.

    3.3.2   Assess progress in achieving objectives.

    3.3.3   Modify interventions as needed to meet individual needs.

    3.3.4   Ensure plan is implemented with fidelity.

    3.3.5   Monitor use of resources.

    3.3.6   Evaluate the sustainability of implementation.

The Role. Utilizing work accomplished in the needs/capacity assessment (Responsibility I) and in planning (Responsibility II), it is now time to implement the programs. This involves coordinating the logistics to train volunteers and staff, delivering the program, monitoring the progress, and evaluating the effectiveness and sustainability of the program. To successfully implement a program, health education specialists must have a thorough understanding of the people in the priority population: What is their current level of understanding regarding the health issue? What will it take to get the priority population to participate in a program? Do they need financial assistance or child care? What time of the day should the program be offered? What location(s) would be most convenient? and so on. For many health education specialists, implementation is one of the more enjoyable responsibilities as it may involve actually delivering the program to the priority population. It is important to note that none of the Areas of Responsibility stand alone, but are interconnected with the other Areas of Responsibility. For example, during implementation the health education specialist typically has the most contact with the public, so it is essential to act in an ethical and professional manner (Responsibility VIII). Effective communication skills (Responsibility VI) are a necessity. In most programs health education specialists will also be using population-based approaches that focus on policies, rules, regulations and laws to improve the health of priority populations. This will require advocacy skills (Responsibility V). Further leadership and management skills (Responsibility VII) are needed to actually develop and deliver a program. It is remarkable how all of the responsibilities work together and are required for a successful health education program (NCHEC, 2020).

Setting: The following text is presented to describe how implementation is used in different practice settings (NCHEC, 2020).

Community Setting: Once a health education program and plan has been designed for a priority population, health education specialists must work to identify and obtain the resources to implement the program. Information gathered from the needs and capacity assessment will inform this process. Personnel are a primary resource in implementing any such program. Health education specialists will need to train staff members and volunteers or obtain assistance from a community coalition to implement the program. Training must encompass ethics, cultural considerations, troubleshooting, and any quality assurance/fidelity processes in addition to actual delivery of the program. After launching the program, health education specialists continue to monitor progress, retain appropriate documentation, and consider various strategies for sustaining the program over time which may include transitioning program oversight to the community.

School (K-12) Setting: The health education specialist will assist youth learners in attaining, sustaining, and promoting life-long health and wellness. The K-12 curriculum should provide opportunities for the development of health literacy competencies among students and positively influence their overall well-being. The health education specialist develops age-appropriate learning objectives and activities to promote positive health behaviors. Further the health education specialist will monitor student learning to facilitate revisions in curricula and instructional methods. This includes scaffolding on student experience and prior learning; utilizing culture-responsive scenarios and materials; incorporating arts; engaging learners in meaningful simulations and cooperative learning activities; and using life skills and value-based strategies. The teacher should also use differentiated instruction in order to reach students' various needs and abilities. In addition, health education specialists should work with the established advisory committee to establish and implement school policies that support healthy behaviors.

Health Care Setting: Actually, implementing or oversight for implementing programs is often the responsibility of the health education specialist and the planning team. In the health care setting, health education specialists often serve as liaisons between patients and the health care team to enhance patient experience and help them understand the nature of their condition and its treatment. In addition, they may serve as outreach coordinators and provide programs in the community the health care system serves, or as program coordinators, and/or program managers and provide patient or staff education programs in the health care facilities. Thus, health education specialists in this setting might conduct patient and/or community education programs to improve patient outcomes, to support disease prevention, and to promote healthy lifestyle behaviors. They may facilitate and/or deliver programs and classes designed to address a specific health topic based on current medical and scientific evidence-based practice guidelines approved by specialists in the field. For example, health education specialists in this setting might conduct a program to support patients' weight-loss efforts on an individual level. They may also offer group classes, supported by presentations from health care providers and develop strategies to offer healthy alternatives in vending machines. Health education specialists might arrange opportunities to apply information learned through cooking classes or a grocery store tour to improve patients' ability to shop wisely and read food labels. It is important for the health education specialist to monitor the programs' processes and outcomes to make necessary changes to the program and its delivery as warranted. Evaluation data is typically collected during this phase.

College/University Setting: Health education specialists working in a higher education setting use their knowledge and skills to implement academic programs designed to prepare future health education specialists and/or promote personal and community health among the general student population. Health education specialists may also implement programs in a community, k-12 school or college setting as part of their research or community service that are designed to improve the health of the priority population. Implementation includes the use of a variety of instructional and assessment methods designed to promote higher-order thinking, knowledge acquisition, behavior change and/or the authentic application of requisite Competencies. It is of utmost importance for the health education specialist to provide culturally appropriate, relevant, and engaging learning opportunities for students or a priority population that ensure program success. Health education specialist faculty must also teach implementation skills to their students to ensure the Competencies and Sub-competencies of a health education specialist have been met.

Worksite/Business Setting: Health education specialists work with employers to offer programs and recommend policies that respond to employees' health and wellbeing needs. These programs and policies also have multiple aims to have a positive influence on employee recruitment and retention, morale, engagement, absenteeism, and/or healthcare costs. Health education specialists must understand the needs and interests of employees, the workplace culture, job functions, and business practices that might affect health-related behaviors. When initiating programs, it is important to monitor program fidelity and to periodically gauge how the program is being received by the priority population. Health education specialists may advocate for policies to offer healthful food choices in the company cafeteria and/or vending machines and program opportunities for physical activity, nutrition, stress management, tobacco cessation, sleep health, diabetes prevention, and others.

College/University Health Promotion Services Setting: Health education specialists in this setting work with other practitioners, stakeholders, and peer educators on campus to implement programs that address established needs utilizing a variety of evidence-informed and theory-based strategies. Health education specialists may coordinate special events, develop health initiatives, arrange for screenings by other agencies, or develop programs for priority populations within the campus community. Priority populations in this setting can include students, faculty and/or staff members. Program settings vary, and can include academic classrooms, residence halls, athletic team meeting rooms,

Greek houses, and faculty/staff members gathering places. For example, health education specialists may work with residence hall staff to offer educational sessions on several topics, including safer sex, use/abuse of alcohol and other drugs, relationship violence, stress and time management, smoking cessation, nutrition, and physical activity. They may also work with individual students, faculty, and/or staff to conduct one-on-one health coaching and motivational interviewing sessions on similar topics. Beyond group and individual programming, health education specialists may work to change campus policies, such as no smoking policies or healthy food alternatives in vending machines.

Key Terms

Award refers to funds that are approved for a recipient to complete a project or program (Health Resources & Services Administration (HRSA), 2018).

Culture involves ideas, beliefs, values, customs, and norms that are learned from family and community and passed down from generation to generation (Doyle et al., 2019).

Fidelity refers to ensuring that programs are implemented and delivered as intended per the program protocol or plan. Maintaining fidelity has implications for how the intervention is delivered, training, and evaluation (McKenzie et al., 2017).

Implementation is a specified set of activities designed to put into practice an activity or program plan.

Intervention, or program, is an activity or set of planned strategies and/or activities, delivery plan, and evaluation activities designed to achieve the desired outcomes of the program, which generally is aimed to prevent disease or injury or promote health within a population. Single or multiple strategies may be used in interventions/programs to accomplish objectives. An intervention is a specific component of a more comprehensive program (Green & Kreuter, 2005; McKenzie et al., 2017).

Intervention strategy is a specific technique or approach used in an intervention to get the desired outcome (Bartholomew Eldredge et al., 2016). Various intervention strategies can be used in combination or alone within an intervention and can include health communication, health education, health policy/enforcement, environmental change, community service, and mobilization (McKenzie et al., 2017).

Memorandum of Understanding (MOU), sometimes referred to as a Memorandum of Agreement (MOA), is a document in which the agreement and principles of that agreement between two parties is captured and outlined and is often less formal than a legal contract (McKenzie et al., 2017).

Plain language communication that allows people to "find what they need, understand what they find and use what they find to meet their needs (Fertman & Allensworth, 2017, p. 198).

Project management is the application of knowledge, skills, and techniques to execute projects effectively and efficiently (Project Management Institute, 2019).

Tailored message is a message created for an individual based on his or her specific need or interest (McKenzie et al., 2017)

Targeted message is a standardized message created for a group that has been defined by some characteristic (McKenzie et al., 2017).

Competency 3.1 Coordinate the delivery of intervention(s) consistent with the implementation plan.

When preparing to implement health education and promotion programs, health education specialists first should develop a project or work plan. The implementation phase often requires the most sustained effort among all of the phases of a health program; therefore, a well-developed plan will help in ensuring fidelity of implementation (Issel & Wells, 2018). This plan is a detailed road map for how program goals will be achieved. A planning model in which Intervention Mapping is used will assist in the development of a strong implementation (or work) plan (Bartholomew Eldredge, et al., 2016). The plan should be aligned with a logic model or broader strategic plan for the program. The plan should include goals, objectives, activities, timelines, evaluation measures, and the roles and responsibilities involved in implementing the specific aspects of the plan. A separate training protocol focused on how staff, partners, and volunteers will assist with training also may be necessary. Refer to Sub-competency 3.1.4-3.1.5). Materials created in the planning phase may help to coordinate logistics and resources (i.e., people, facilities, supplies, services) for implementation. Refer to Sub-competency 2.4.1 for more information about work plans.

3.1.1 Secure implementation resources.

Implementing health education and promotion programs requires resources. A program rarely can be implemented for little to no cost. McKenzie et al. (2017) provided the following examples of resources needed for implementation of the work plan.
- Personnel refers to the person or people who will help with implementation.
- Curriculum and instructional resources refer to the educational materials and curriculum.
- Space refers to the physical space needed.
- Equipment and supplies refers to the physical items needed.
- Financial resources refer to the monetary cost and how it will be covered (e.g., paid for by the agency/organization leading the work, participants, or a third-party [partner, sponsor, or grant funded])

Health education specialists also should consider questions about the amount of resources needed, the financial costs, and whether resources can be provided in-kind or donated. Health education specialists also might consider MOUs for partners who provide in-kind or donated resources. Refer to Competencies 7.3 and 7.4 for more information on managing resources.

3.1.2 Arrange for implementation services.

Depending on the plan or program and its complexity, certain services might be required from partners, contractors, subject matter experts, or consultants. Implementation, project, or work plans should be used to identify the services needed, and health education specialists should plan for how to procure these services. Health education specialists should work through their organization, volunteers, or partners first before looking to hire staff or procure other resources or services. Services might be available at no cost or at a reduced cost. In this situation, an MOU may be needed. Another option is for health education specialists to work with contractors or consultants to provide the necessary services or complete a set of defined tasks. Health education specialists should develop a written agreement outlining the work needed (e.g., statement of work/scope of work), deliverables/products expected, a timeline to complete the work and provide deliverables/products, and a funding amount or payment.

3.1.3 Comply with contractual obligations.

Health education specialists must follow guidelines and legal standards for their organization, as well as the organization providing funding (e.g., contract, cooperative agreement, grant). Health education specialists should always review state or local laws, rules, and regulations, as well as any funding announcements or solicitations, award notices, and/or other guidance documents. In some funding announcements, there are restrictions on how funds can be used (e.g., cannot be used for lobbying, research, patient, or clinical care, cannot substitute for existing funds, or cannot cover pre-award costs). Examples of some administrative requirements, laws, and regulations that may apply include:

- the Paperwork Reduction Act of 1995 which helps reduce the paperwork burden and maximize information collection (USDHHS, 2014c).
- section 508 of the Rehabilitation Act in which it is described that federal agencies must make websites, electronic materials, and other information technology accessible to people with disabilities (United States General Services Administration, 2018).
- the Plain Writing Act of 2010 wherein it is described that federal agencies must use "clear communication that the public can understand and use" (Plain Language Action and Information Network, 2019, para 1.). Plain language is now expected for websites, print, and other electronic materials, social media, and other materials (i.e., not just the informed consent).
- cost sharing or matching funds (e.g., in-kind funds) may be required to leverage funds.
- anti-lobbying, smoke-free worksites, and nutrition policies.
- accounting system, security clearance, data protection/release/sharing, and reporting requirements.

Health education specialists might discuss questions about applicable laws and regulations with a supervisor, organization leadership, legal counsel, and/or the funding organization to determine what legal standards apply to implementation of health promotion programs.

3.1.4 ▲ Establish training protocol.

Establishing a training protocol should include the application of best practices, as well as the development of training objectives and identification of training needs for those involved in the implementation of the program. The provision of training is a critical step to standardizing the delivery of the intervention, ensuring fidelity, and increasing morale and self-efficacy for program staff (Issel & Wells, 2018).

Health education specialists work with a wide age range of clients, participants, and organizations, with targeted initiatives specific to their identified priority population. Training programs should be accurate, credible, clear, and practical (Occupational Health and Safety Administration OHSA, n.d.). The Association for Talent Development, formerly known as the Association for Training and Development (ASTD, 2019) identified five best practices of training and development. Training developers should:

- consider the root causes of a need for training.
- conduct a systematic needs assessment and, based on that, develop a design framework.
- integrate e-learning, if appropriate.
- develop training that engages learners.
- develop an evaluation plan.

In developing a training protocol for an adult audience, it is essential to take into consideration adult learning principles, because information in literature very clearly supports that adults typically learn differently from children. Pioneering work by Friere (2000), Knowles, Holten and Swanson (2005), and Merriam & Baumgartner (2020) revealed that adult learning (andragogy) differs from children's learning (pedagogy) in several ways. Bryan, Kreuter, and Brownson (2008) described ways to integrate adult learning principles in public health training:

- Actively involve adults in helping to set the curriculum, choosing training methods, or identify training goals.
- Ask about adults' past experiences and knowledge, and use their experiences or knowledge to avoid providing redundant content during trainings.
- Use methods to help adults obtain problem solving skills rather than learning content (e.g., use problem-based learning; use broad themes that are focused on a range of challenges).
- Conduct assessments to identify ways to engage adults and learn about their goals or objectives for the training.
- Use a variety of methods, perspectives, and content because adults have diverse needs and learning styles.

These adult learning principles are the foundation for successful training with adults. Health education specialists working outside of a school setting are encouraged to incorporate these principles into their training skill set. Health education specialists also are encouraged to search the literature for proven methods of training that best meet audience needs.

Health education specialists should assess the trainees' willingness to learn. For learning to have the greatest chance of success, participant motivation and readiness must be assessed. Maslow's hierarchy of needs (Freitas & Leonard, 2011) and The Attention, Relevance, Confidence, Satisfaction (ARCS) Motivation Model (Gagne et al., 2005) described issues related to motivation. For learners to be capable of learning, certain basic needs must first be met. In Maslow's hierarchy of basic human needs, each level of needs must be met before the individual can move to the next levels. The levels of needs start at physiological needs and move up to self-actualization (Freitas & Leonard, 2011). The hierarchy of needs and its applications to training adults are presented in Table 3.1.

Table 3.1
Maslow's Hierarchy of Needs

Need	Application to Training
Physiological needs (food, water, warmth)	• Provide breaks and snacks/meals. • Set a comfortable room temperature.
Safety needs (security and safety)	• Offer safe training environment. • Permit learners to ask questions throughout.
Social belongingness (sense of belonging)	• Create a feeling of group dynamics and feeling of acceptance.
Esteem (status, achievement)	• Recognize achievements. • Positively reinforce learning.
Self-Actualization (personal fulfillment)	• Offer work or training that challenges learner. • Offer skills to make progress on long term goals.

The ARCS Motivation Model is a compilation of guidelines from many motivation theories. Causes of motivation may be either extrinsic (external to the learner) or intrinsic (internal to the learner). The intent in the ARCS Model is to provide learners with the necessary time and effort to acquire new knowledge and skills (Gagne et al., 2005). The motivational categories of the ARCS Model are presented in Table 3.2 below.

Table 3.2
Application of the Motivational Categories

Category	Application of the Motivational Category
Attention	• Capture the learners' interest. • Maintain their attention.
Relevance	• Know the learners' needs. • Provide learners with opportunities to match activities to their motives for learning. • Tie the instruction to learners' past experiences (e.g., analogies, prerequisite knowledge).
Confidence	• Build positive expectations of learning. • Provide methods for learning to achieve success in mastery of knowledge and skill.
Satisfaction	• Provide reinforcement to learners' successes. • Encourage use of new knowledge and skills.

Gagne (2005)

Agencies and organizations, such as the Centers for Disease Control and Prevention (CDC), publicize programs and interventions in which best practices are used and, therefore, may be used in training efforts (National Prevention Information Network, n.d.). Where no list can be considered comprehensive or exhaustive, the CDC provided a starting point for health education specialists. Recognized programs are grounded in a variety of Areas of Responsibilities for health education specialists. Training materials created should be created with appropriate design and deployed using instructional technology, tools, and delivery methods most appropriate for the audience being trained.

Training objectives relate to both the knowledge and skills that staff members and volunteers need to be able to implement health education/promotion interventions successfully, including those that would be useful to ensure the training protocol will be developed with defined outcomes. Objectives are worded in a way that specify content and require the ability to apply knowledge or perform a particular task at an acceptable level by the end of the training. Implementation staff may be trained on roles during the program formation, implementation, or evaluation. Objectives for training might include that the participant can demonstrate a particular learning technique (e.g., role-play), collect data for program monitoring or evaluation, provide nonjudgmental and respectful atmosphere to encourage dialogue, or dialogue with colleagues about a certain topic. As always, objectives should be Specific, Measurable, Achievable, Realistic, and Time-phased, often referred to as SMART objectives (McKenzie et al., 2017; Northwest Center for Public Health Practice, 2020). Additionally, objectives should align with goals. Refer to Sub-competency 2.2.4 for more information on SMART objectives.

When determining training needs, health education specialists must consider intervention characteristics and requirements—the skills, knowledge, and experience of individuals involved in implementation—and the setting for the training. Before delivering training, health education specialists should conduct a needs assessment to help plan the training and ensure individual needs are met (Northwest Center for Public Health Practice, 2020 OSHA, n.d.). A training needs assessment should be used to describe what the desired learning outcome is, the characteristics of the participants (e.g., age, abilities such as hearing loss or visual difficulties, intellectual abilities, language), the learning context, and the content and training expertise. The Northwest Center for Public Health Practice (2020) has an example of a training needs assessment in its Toolkit for Teaching Adults.

Health education specialists should not overlook the logistics for training when identifying training needs. For example, health education specialists might ask what type of space or special requirements the training requires. A cooking demonstration, for example, needs a space with a working kitchen. The training might be best delivered in an alternate location with a kitchen such as a home, religious institution, community center, or other gathering place.

3.1.5 Train staff and volunteers to ensure fidelity.

Depending on the magnitude of the program, health education specialists may be responsible for conducting training programs for professionals, volunteers, or stakeholders involved in delivering health education programs. Training should consist of discussion of overall program objectives and intended outcomes, the logic model, and core elements (i.e., program content and steps). In addition, health education specialists should instruct staff members on their role and offer guidance and opportunities to practice their roles (e.g., coach, group facilitator). Health education specialists may want to develop a train-the-trainer program that prepares staff members and volunteers to implement a specific training program (CDC, 2019d). The goals and objectives of training sessions should be clearly outlined, related to the implementation of health education, and include evidence-based strategies to deliver content. An evaluation of training sessions can provide feedback to help improve training sessions for future program personnel. A training manual (also commonly referred to as program procedural manual) is an invaluable tool in delivering training to staff and volunteers, because it is used to communicate the step-by-step plans for the program; also, the procedural manual is used to support program fidelity and implementation by providing background information, ideas for facilitation, and the parameters of the program (McKenzie et al., 2017).

Health education specialists must consider the best way to provide instruction to an intended audience while also considering available funds and expertise-levels of the individuals providing the training. Depending on cost, content, and instructional expertise required, a variety of methods should be used, including on-the-job training, one-on-one training, in-person group work, and distance learning techniques (e.g., video conferences, computer-based training, Internet, or conference calls). A coordinator should oversee the implementation of the training.

Competency 3.2 Deliver health education and promotion interventions.

An action plan for program implementation is used to describe how goals and objectives will be achieved, as well as identify the resources needed and how responsibilities will be assigned (Brownson et al., 2017). Health education specialists may consider using a project management plan or project management principles when implementing a plan. Building on the assessment and planning activities related to a particular health issue or problem, health education specialists should develop a plan of action in conjunction with members of the intended audience, including those who can hinder or help the implementation of the program. Additionally, Intervention Mapping is an approach used to design programs with the intention of dissemination. By using this approach, a focus on dissemination by developing an implementation plan to support adoption, implementation, and maintenance of programs is achieved (Bartholomew Eldredge et al., 2016).

In Table 3.3, five generic phases of the implementation process in health education and key components for effective public health program implementation are presented.

Table 3.3
Application of the Motivational Categories

Five Generic Phases of Program Implementation (McKenzie et al., 2017)	Six Components for Effective Public Health Program Implementation (Frieden, 2014)
• Adopt the program. • Identify and prioritize tasks to complete. • Establish a management system. • Put the plans into action (e.g., pilot or field testing, phasing, total implementation). • End or sustain a program or intervention.	• Use innovation to develop the evidence base. • Use a limited number of high priority, evidence- based interventions. • Use effective program management. • Use partnerships and coalitions. • Communicate accurate and timely information. • Obtain resources and support.

A critical first step in implementation is getting buy-in from the priority population to accept the **intervention** or **program.** To achieve buy-in, it is important to identify the individuals or organizations responsible for the delivery of the intervention. Health education specialists should use an implementation plan, project management plan, or other process to develop a detailed list of all program activities, components, and tasks along with the relationships between and among them. Careful project management includes using a system or schedule to ensure that the program progresses as planned and to monitor human, financial, and other resources. Health education specialists should use pilot testing, phasing-in, or total implementation, especially when implementing an adapted or new program (McKenzie et al., 2017). Key staff and partners should communicate throughout implementation. In addition, mass communication (i.e., sharing information on a large scale) should be used to share information and support program objectives or implementation. Health education specialists should consider health impact and how to end or sustain the program before beginning implementation (McKenzie et al., 2017). For a rigorous approach to implementation planning for adoption and sustainment, health education specialists should consider the use of Intervention Mapping, specifically Step 5 (plan for adoption, implementation and sustainability) (Bartholomew Eldredge, 2016).

3.2.1 Create an environment conducive to learning.

Critical steps to creating an environment that is conducive to learning include getting management or stakeholder support, identifying resources to support implementation, and obtaining buy-in from implementation staff and the target audience. For a program to succeed, management or key stakeholder support from the highest level is required. This support also will help with securing financial, human, or other resources to implement the program (McKenzie et al., 2017).

The learning environment should be inclusive of all learners, learner-centered, safe, and encouraging of trust and respect between the learners and the instructor (Merriam and Baumgartner, 2020; National Center on Quality Teaching and Learning, 2014). Additionally, the physical aspects of the learning environment can impact learning, including aspects such as temperature, adequate lighting, good acoustics, comfortable seating, room set-up, and good sightlines (Knowles et al., 2015). Moreover, if a key element of the intervention is skill-building, and a location conducive to skill building is not available, health education specialists must decide how or whether to adapt the intervention without compromising effectiveness.

The learning environment also should be assessed for meeting the learner's needs. Meeting the needs of the learner requires the health education specialist to have knowledge of media literacy, instructional technology, and various formats for reaching the audience.

Health education specialists should have a basic knowledge about publication layout and design, the creation process, editing of images whether printed or video, and website design to create websites and evaluate the quality of health-related websites. These factors are especially important when reaching Limited English Proficiency audiences or low health literate audiences (Plain Language Action and Information Network, 2019; United States Department of Justice, 2014).

Instructional technology is a vital tool for reaching the intended audience and achieving program objectives. For example, the computer can be used to prepare visual aids, access the Internet for instructional resources, or conduct a virtual meeting. Various multimedia formats might be useful for interactive presentations, such as Internet videos, CDs, DVDs, or other resources. Teleconferencing technology allows participants in different locations to attend discussions and lectures. Scanners and digital cameras can be used in the creation of print media and multimedia presentations.

Asynchronous training is a type of distance learning in which training occurs outside of real time (the instructor and the learners communicate at different times). On the other hand, synchronous training is a type of distance learning in which training is in real time (the instructor and the learners communicate at the same time).

3.2.2 Collect baseline data.

Prior to program implementation, health education specialists should review available quantitative and qualitative data from national, state, and local resources. Conducting this review will help in the assessment of health knowledge, beliefs, attitudes, and values of the intended audiences, as well as their psychomotor capabilities or skills related to outcomes. This identification of baseline data is important as it will provide the beginning measure for evaluating changes in behavior, practices, or skills associated with the program goals. Refer to Competencies 4.1, 4.2 and 4.3 for more information on data collection and management.

Primary data collection may be required if health education specialists want to understand the local impact of a health issue. Secondary data sources (i.e., data collected for another purpose), however, might provide the information needed. Examples of data already available may include health data (e.g., morbidity, mortality, behavior, risk factor), open government data portals (http://www.data.gov/open-gov), or other "big data" (Kaplan et al., 2014). Refer to Competency 1.2 for more information on primary data.

3.2.3 Implement a marketing plan.

Health education specialists have replaced a one-size-fits-all approach to program promotion with tailored and targeted promotion campaigns based on the ethnic and demographic characteristics and behaviors of the population being served. Health messages need to appeal to the audience's needs, preferences, and health concerns. Tailored messages are individually focused messages that appeal to a specific subpopulation, typically using information obtained from the individual themselves. Tailoring is focused on connecting an individual to information specifically focusing on his or her needs, personal data, and information through a direct communication channel. Tailored messages can include direct mail, in-person communication, the Internet, telephone or text messaging (Parvanta & Bass, 2020). Computer tailoring of messages and materials can enable a health education specialist to get the program to a larger audience (Kreuter et al., 2000). An example of tailoring is the use of a personalized application (i.e., app) on a smart phone, such as one involving smoking cessation. Through the application, an individual is guided through a series of questions to identify in what stage of change (using the Transtheoretical Model, Stages of Change constructs, for example) a person stands to assess that person's level of readiness to quit smoking. Based on the person's responses, through an application, specific content provides information and behavioral cues to support the individual at the identified stage of change. As a person interacts with the app and provides additional information, the app continues to provide personalized feedback, support, and guidance.

Targeted messages are focused on subgroups, which involves segmenting or dividing the audience into smaller groups with similar characteristics (e.g., by age, race/ethnicity, gender, geographic location) (McKenzie et al., 2017).Health education specialists can create materials using demographic targeting, a process during which planners developed print, media, and educational materials using images that reflected various ethnic backgrounds (Parvanta & Bass, 2020). Specific health messages are crafted and tailored to be culturally appropriate, relevant, and applicable. Refer to Sub-competency 6.3.3 for more information on tailoring and targeting messages.

A marketing plan is used to assist planners to indentify the audience(s), message(s), and the intended communication methods (e.g., earned media, paid media, social media (Parvanta & Bass, 2020). An important consideration in a marketing plan is to determine how the audience prefers to get their information and available financial resources. The marketing plan also should be aligned with the program goals and objectives. Numerous online tools are available, such as CDCynergy, communication plans templates, and more. The traditional principles of marketing are Product, Place, Price and Promotion. In relation to health education programming, the Product is often the target of the intervention (behavior change, policy change, etc.) rather than a tangible good. Place refers to the location of the Program, Price is the monetary or other cost (muscle soreness from exercise, difficulty adjusting to a new lifestyle, etc.), and Promotion is the sum of all avenues used to communicate messages about the program (Fertman & Allensworth, 2017). A solid marketing plan is critical for many reasons, such as increasing awareness of health issues, recruitment of the priority population, engagement of a community, garnering support for advocacy efforts, and so on.

3.2.4 Deliver health education and promotion as designed.

The implementation of a program requires a variety of skills and knowledge, including the ability to use technology, execute appropriate timelines, manage program resources, and conduct an evaluation. Health education specialists seldom have unlimited resources available to them. Most successful programs are the result of the efforts and resources of many different people and organizations. Thus, health education specialists need to have skills to collaborate with others who have similar interests and a stake in the outcomes of successful health education programs.

Before implementation, health education specialists should identify implementation issues such as staffing and training, intervention content, program delivery, and intervention participants (Pew-MacArthur Foundation, 2016). Evidence-based interventions must be implemented as designed. Failure to implement the intervention as designed may negatively affect the intervention's success (Pew-MacArthur Foundation, 2016). If the intervention is new or adapted, health education specialists should carefully follow the design and implementation plans (including any adjustments from pilot testing or phasing). The Implementation Element of the Reach Effectiveness Adoption Implementation Maintenance (RE-AIM) framework may be used to help with intervention delivery (Virginia Polytechnic Institute and State University, 2015) while the Intervention Mapping to Adapt (IM Adapt) framework may be helpful in adapting evidence-based interventions (Bartholomew Eldredge et al., 2016).

3.2.5 Employ an appropriate variety of instructional methodologies.

The scope and sequence of a program may contain many intervention strategies. An intervention may include single or multiple strategies and methods through which program goals and objectives are achieved. To implement an intervention, health education specialists need a variety of skills and knowledge (e.g., use of large-scale communication and technology, create appropriate timelines, manage program resources, and carry out an evaluation).

Behavior is multifaceted; therefore, multiple strategies are often needed to change behavior. Planners should consider strategies at various levels (e.g., individual, organizational, community, and environment) when developing interventions or programs designed to motivate behavior change. A program could include a mix of strategies that are focused on socioeconomic determinants, contextual changes, protective and clinical interventions, and counseling and education (Frieden, 2014). Intervention Mapping Steps 3 and 4 provide guidance for program design and production that is based in theory and is aligned with effective methods (Bartholomew Eldredge et al., 2016). When selecting strategies or activities, health education specialists should be sure that each strategy has evidence of efficacy. Even though the strategy may be shown to work, not all interventions that include this strategy achieve the desired outcomes. Health education specialists should look for evaluation results in the literature, program reports, or through discussion with program administrators. Refer to Sub-competency 2.3.3 Assess effectiveness and alignment of existing interventions to desired outcomes for a list of searchable databases of effective interventions.

Health education specialists should consider paid media, earned media, social media, digital media (e.g., websites, mobile phones and applications), online competitions (e.g., http://www.challenge.gov), and other technologies. Paid media refers to television, radio, print, billboards, transit, or digital advertising. Earned media involves receiving free news placement (Kreslake, et al., 2019). Social media includes collaborative projects (e.g., wikis), blogs, content communities (e.g., Flickr, Slideshare, YouTube), social networking sites (e.g., Facebook), virtual game worlds, and virtual social worlds (Zimmerman, et al., 2016). Mobile phones offer text messaging, cameras, applications, automated sensors (e.g., Bluetooth, GPS for tracking distance), and Internet access (Doyle et. al., 2018a). Health education specialists must determine the audience preference and stay abreast of continuous technological advances to make the best choice. Refer to Sub-competency 6.4.2 for more information on delivering messages using media and communication.

Competency 3.3 Monitor Implementation.

When implementing programs, health education specialists must monitor all aspects of the program, including content delivery, adherence to timelines, progress toward objectives, and use of financial resources. Data collection and record maintenance are important tasks that health education specialists must perform to ensure proper delivery of the program.

3.3.1 Monitor progress in accordance with the timeline.

Health education specialists should produce a timeline that includes major activities and outputs, as well as monitor program implementation progress. A Gantt chart is a visual representation of all the tasks that need to be completed before, during, and after the program. A Gantt chart allows health education specialists to best plan all the tasks needed to successfully deliver a program and allows health education specialists to monitor progress on all tasks (Fertman & Allensworth, 2017). Program Evaluation and Review Technique (PERT) charts also help health education specialists track progress and allows them to visually show relationships between tasks (Issel & Wells, 2018). The Critical Path Method (CPM) graphically shows timelines and relationships to tasks; in addition, CPM adds the ability to show those components that are the most important in adhering to the timeline (McKenzie et al., 2017). Each of these methods allows health education specialists to visually identify the progress for project management. Tools and resources are available online or in software packages (free or paid) to help develop the chart or model.

Health education specialists should hold regular meetings with stakeholders and implementation staff to monitor progress, receive feedback, and report progress. Health education specialists should know who receives progress reports (e.g., funders, leadership, stakeholders) and the preferred reporting methods (e.g., in-person, written). If there are delays or unanticipated events, identification and discussion of them may lead to revisions in the timeline as appropriate.

3.3.2 Assess progress in achieving objectives.

Many opportunities to track progress exist throughout implementation and through program monitoring. Program monitoring, or the ongoing collection of program related data, is a type of process evaluation (McKenzie et al., 2017). Program monitoring might be conducted by the health education specialist, a program administrator, or, in larger programs, a dedicated staff person. Health education specialists should use project meetings or other regular meetings to monitor progress through program management tools such as Gantt charts or work plans. Reviewing data sources or process evaluations also can be used to assess progress in achieving objectives. Logic models can be used to help track whether activities are producing desired outputs and if the outputs lead to expected short-term outcomes. By tracking this progress, health education specialists can identify where and when something occurred that differed from the implementation plan, providing an opportunity for the prevention or early intervention of detrimental program deviations. Keeping track of outcomes and indicators related to program objectives allows health education specialists to assess preliminary data regarding program successes, unintended outcomes, and the opportunity to refine as needed. This preliminary analysis captures descriptive data that are important to stakeholders, funders, and program staff. Monitoring progress also may help health education specialists better understand why an intervention succeeded or failed to achieve the expected results. Refer to Sub-competency 4.1.3 for more information on logic models.

3.3.3 Modify interventions as needed to meet individual needs.

Seldom is the perfect intervention already designed and ready to use. Typically, health education specialists must select an intervention that they believe will work for the audience, produce the desired outcome, and stay within the boundaries of the resources available. Health education specialists must have a flexible plan of action, know whom to involve when modifying the plan of action, and know when and from whom approvals are needed when modifying the plan. Health education specialists can evaluate the process and monitor the fidelity of implementation to identify when modifications may be needed.

Modifying the plan does not always mean the intervention is modified, but when the intervention is modified, primary attention should be focused on maintaining fidelity to the original intervention. Some modifications have been found to affect the efficacy of the intervention in the field. Conversely, adapting an intervention is a fundamental activity in implementation, as it allows health education specialists to create a common ground between the delivery of the intervention and the characteristics of the group using it. Steps in program adaptation include: (a) assess community, (b) understand the possible interventions, (c) select the intervention, (d) consult with experts, (e) consult with stakeholders, (f) decide on needed adaptations, (g) adapt the original program, (h) train staff, (i) test the adapted materials, (j) implement the adapted program, and (k) evaluate the adapted program (Escoffery et al., 2018). If adaptation to an intervention results in a form that is far from the original tested form, it is prudent to evaluate the adapted intervention for the desired outcome.

3.3.4 Ensure plan is implemented with fidelity.

Health education specialists must ensure consistency and fidelity during implementation. Activity logs, document reviews, observations, reports, surveys, Gantt charts, logic models, or interviews can be used to measure fidelity (Breny Bontempy, Fagen, & Roe, 2017). The Non-Researcher's Guide to Evidence-Based Program Evaluation, an online training from SAMHSA (2012), includes proposed questions on program delivery, dose, and quality to help measure fidelity during implementation. Program delivery refers to the overall implementation of the intervention, which is comprised of planned activities. Assessing fidelity of program involves identifying and documenting that the program is being implemented as planned in the designated order. The number of activities, referred to as multiplicity (and can be at various levels), differs from dose. Dose refers to program units delivered via the program activities. Dose, from a measurement perspective, refers to how many program components were delivered as part of the intervention for any given activity and is often tracked as part of the process evaluation and program monitoring (McKenzie et al., 2017). This tracking could include whether all activities are delivered as well as documenting common process measures such as counts related to distribution, time, and number of contacts (SAMHSA, 2012). Failure to monitor fidelity can present numerous challenges during and after the project. Poor implementation also can lead to the program not being successful.

3.3.5 Monitor use of resources.

Health education specialists must recognize the importance of monitoring resources (e.g., personnel, curriculum and instructional, space, equipment and supplies, financial) used in an intervention and the program as a whole. Several areas that require a management approach include human, financial, and technical resources (McKenzie et al., 2017).

Human resources management generally includes oversight and planning for four core functions including planning, acquisition, development, and sanction (PADS). Often these areas are guided by rules and legal decisions. Financial management includes the development and use of system processes that ensure fiscal accountability, an approach to accounting operations, reporting and regular reviews, or audits (McKenzie et al., 2017). An accounting process to carefully track the budget expenditures and income is used to help monitor financial resources, while regular internal audits and reporting provide measures for fiscal accountability, which is important especially if the program is funded by a grant or taxpayer funds. Funding agencies often require progress reports that contain information on expenses and revenues. Curriculum and instructional resources, space, or equipment and supplies should be monitored based on their volume, frequency of use, and relationship to the program or project plan. Human resources can be expensive and consume a large part of budgets; therefore, regular monitoring of human resources is critical to ensure successful implementation. Project plans and project management principles also help ensure resources are used properly. Refer to Sub-competencies 7.3.7, 7.4.3, and 7.4.7 for more details regarding managing resources.

3.3.6 Evaluate the sustainability of implementation.

The sustainability of the intervention or program should be considered from the start. Health education specialists should create an implementation guide, use a train-the-trainer model, and document lessons learned throughout project or program monitoring. Surveys, interviews, focus groups, or program documents can be used to collect data on sustainability domains or elements including leadership/political support, funding stability, collaboration/partnerships, organizational capacity, program evaluation, program adoption, communication, and strategic planning/vision (Cole & Sleet, 2016). Gathering input from partners and key stakeholders will allow for generation of ideas about how the program can be sustained after its initial implementation. Identifying partners and stakeholders who can help is necessary and should be considered at the start (not when the program or intervention is ending). Once partners are identified and data have been collected, the program implementation team can continue to develop and refine the sustainability plan to provide the best opportunity for successful continuation of the program. These activities are critical to continuing the intervention or program long-term, as well as sharing the sustainability plan with others (CDC, 2014a).

Chapter 4
Area of Responsibility IV: Evaluation and Research

KEY: No symbol - entry level; ▲ - advanced 1; ■ - advanced 2

4.1. Design process, impact, and outcome evaluation of the intervention.

4.1.1 ▲   Align the evaluation plan with the intervention goals and objectives.

4.1.2   Comply with institutional requirements for evaluation.

4.1.3 ▲   Use a logic model and/or theory for evaluations.

4.1.4 ▲   Assess capacity to conduct evaluation.

4.1.5 ▲   Select an evaluation design model and the types of data to be collected.

4.1.6 ▲   Develop a sampling plan and procedures for data collection, management, and security.

4.1.7 ▲   Select quantitative and qualitative tools consistent with assumptions and data requirements.

4.1.8   Adopt or modify instruments for collecting data.

4.1.9 ▲   Develop instruments for collecting data.

4.1.10 ▲ Implement a pilot test to refine data collection instruments and procedures.

4.2. Design research studies.

4.2.1 ■   Determine purpose, hypotheses, and questions.

4.2.2 ▲   Comply with institutional and/or IRB requirements for research.

4.2.3 ▲   Use a logic model and/or theory for research.

4.2.4 ■   Assess capacity to conduct research.

4.2.5 ▲   Select a research design model and the types of data to be collected.

4.2.6 ▲   Develop a sampling plan and procedures for data collection, management, and security.

4.2.7 ▲   Select quantitative and qualitative tools consistent with assumptions and data requirements.

4.2.8 ■   Adopt, adapt, and/or develop instruments for collecting data.

4.2.9 ■   Implement a pilot test to refine and validate data collection instruments and procedures.

4.3. Manage the collection and analysis of evaluation and/or research data using appropriate technology.

4.3.1 ■   Train data collectors.

4.3.2   Implement data collection procedures.

4.3.3   Use appropriate modalities to collect and manage data.

4.3.4 ■   Monitor data collection procedures.

4.3.5   Prepare data for analysis.

4.3.6 ■   Analyze data.

4.4. Interpret data.

4.4.1 ■   Explain how findings address the questions and/or hypotheses.

4.4.2 ▲   Compare findings to other evaluations or studies.

4.4.3   Identify limitations and delimitations of findings.

4.4.4 ■   Draw conclusions based on findings.

4.4.5 ■   Identify implications for practice.

4.4.6 ■ Synthesize findings.

4.4.7 ■ Develop recommendations based on findings.

4.4.8 ■ Evaluate feasibility of implementing recommendations.

4.5. Use findings.

4.5.1 ▲ Communicate findings by preparing reports, and presentations, and by other means.

4.5.2 ■ Disseminate findings.

4.5.3 ■ Identify recommendations for quality improvement.

4.5.4 ▲ Translate findings into practice and interventions.

The Role. The skills necessary to conduct thorough program evaluations and original health education research have much in common. Both require health education specialists to be competent in designing plans to guide their work including selecting, adapting and or creating valid and reliable data collection instruments, developing sampling plans, collecting and managing data, analyzing collected data, interpreting results, applying findings and communicating results. Evaluation is ultimately focused on determining if program objectives (Responsibility II) have been met. Evaluation must be conducted to measure the success of health education and health promotion programs. Programs not properly evaluated may be wasting valuable time, money and effort. Research is concerned with identifying new knowledge or practices that answer questions and/or test hypotheses about a health-related theory, behavior or phenomenon. Research is necessary to keep the health education profession moving forward and improving. While all health education specialists need to be competent in the basic skills of evaluation and research, much of this work, because of its complexity, is completed by those with advanced-level training and several years of work experience (NCHEC, 2020).

Setting: The following text is presented to describe how evaluation and research is used in different practice settings (NCHEC, 2020).

Community Setting: Health education specialists in a community setting must understand and interpret evaluation and research findings for use in their work. Their work may include the use of epidemiological principles to explain disease outbreaks or define high-risk neighborhoods within communities that require special program emphasis. Their work may also include evaluating policies, systems and environmental changes in the community. Health education specialists must master research principles and language to discuss any topic important to the community, such as unintentional injuries, an outbreak of measles or food poisoning, or sexually transmitted infections. They also must understand the importance of conducting and interpreting the results of sound evaluations. Evaluations provide necessary evidence to support programs when reviewed by local or state governments. In general, health education specialists working at the entry-level may be involved in data collection for both research and evaluations, as well as interpreting the results of each of these processes. Those health education specialists working at an advanced-level of practice are responsible for planning and implementing the research and evaluation processes. It is also expected that evaluation and research findings be shared with the profession so that health education specialists may learn from each other's work and the overall performance of the profession be improved.

School (K-12) Setting: Health education specialists will routinely evaluate the attainment of student learning objectives for each lesson at each grade level and assist in the data collection to assess student health knowledge, attitudes, and behaviors. Combined with current research of literature, health education specialists identify, select, and implement effective curriculum and teaching methods to enhance health education in schools. Accountability is essential to ensure that students are receiving adequate, culturally sensitive, and effective health instruction.

Health Care Setting: Research is increasingly important in addressing health issues, chronic disease conditions and the reduction of health risk behaviors for primary prevention. Health education specialists employed in health care settings, may be involved as a member of a research team that conducts research studies to improve the quality of health and patient care. They must be able to understand research studies, answer questions from patients and their families/ caregivers about the studies and interpret research findings for patients and their families. Health education specialists must be able to identify and analyze medically recommended best practices (i.e., U.S. Preventative Task Force) and incorporate them into their programs. In addition, they may collect or assist in the collection of primary, secondary, and/or tertiary data from their priority population. Health education specialists need skills to conduct summative and formative evaluation. Evaluation data is needed to support existing programs, demonstrate the need to modify existing programs, or to support future programs and program growth. Thus, health education specialists must be able to design evaluation plans to assess the effectiveness of programs and specifically the programs' ability to meet stated goals and objectives.

College/University Setting: Health education specialists in this setting are responsible for evaluating student learning as well as teaching, course and program effectiveness. In some cases, college/university faculty members have responsibilities in teaching research and evaluation skills to students. Program evaluation responsibilities may also extend to community health education and promotion programs. Depending on their faculty role and university priorities, college/university health education specialists have varying levels of research responsibilities. Research responsibilities may center on health behavior research or profession-related research. Health education specialist faculty are often expected to disseminate the findings of their research and evaluation efforts through peer-reviewed publications and presentations that provide direction for future practice and research. Evaluation and research related grant-writing may be another expectation. These efforts contribute to the scientific body of knowledge encompassing health behavior, disease prevention, and risk reduction strategies, as well as to the profession of health education.

Worksite/Business Setting: Health education specialists in this setting need both qualitative and quantitative evaluation skills to demonstrate the efficacy of health education and health promotion programs and the contributions of such programs to employee satisfaction, morale, productivity, engagement, health care costs, and to organizational goals. Health education specialists may be asked to assist in monitoring the work environment for safety compliance and injury reduction. Additionally, using evaluative research, health education specialists may be able to help determine quality ("value-on-investment") and cost-effectiveness ("return-on-investment") of various internal programs and services and external vendor programs.

College/University Health Promotion Services Setting: Health education specialists in this setting face many of the same issues as those in the business/industry and health care settings. These health education specialists need skills in all facets of evaluation, must be able to understand and interpret research findings for use in practice, and may also need to conduct research. Evaluation research skills are necessary to determine the efficacy and cost-effectiveness of programs and interventions for students, staff members, and faculty members. Health education specialists are expected to communicate findings and solicit feedback from stakeholders. Findings and feedback are incorporated into improvement and sustainability of current and new programs and interventions, as well as advocacy and strategic planning processes. Successful and even unsuccessful program efforts should be shared in the literature so that others may learn from them and ultimately improve their efforts.

Key Terms

Delimitations are decisions made by an evaluator or researcher that ought to be mentioned because they are used to help the evaluator identify the parameters and boundaries set for a study. Examples of delimitations include why some literature is not reviewed, populations are not studied, and certain methods are not used (Cottrell & McKenzie, 2011; Salazar et al., 2015).

Evaluation is a series of steps that evaluators use to assess a process or program to provide evidence and feedback about the program (Issel & Wells, 2017; Neutens & Rubinson, 2014; Simons-Morton et al., 1995).

Limitations are phenomena the evaluator or researcher cannot control that place restrictions on methods and, ultimately, conclusions. Examples of possible limitations might be time, nature of data collection, instruments, sample, and analysis (Cottrell & McKenzie, 2011; Salazar, et al., 2015).

Logic models take a variety of forms but generally depict aspects of a program such as inputs, outputs, and outcomes (CDC, 2018c). Logic Models offer a scaled down, somewhat linear, visual depiction of programs.

Research is an organized process in which a researcher uses the scientific method to generate new knowledge (Issel & Wells, 2017).

Reliability refers to the consistency, dependability, and stability of the measurement process (McKenzie et al., 2017).

Validity is the degree to which a test or assessment measures what it is intended to measure. Using a valid instrument increases the chance of measuring what was intended (McKenzie et al., 2017).

Variables are operational forms of a construct. Researchers use variables to designate how the construct will be measured in designated scenarios (McKenzie et al., 2017).

Unit of Analysis is what or who is being studied or evaluated (the individual, group, organization, or program, etc.) (Babbie, 2016).

Competency 4.1 Design process, impact, and outcome evaluation of the intervention.

An evaluation of programs is used by health education specialists to determine the value or worth of the programs. Formative evaluation is a process that evaluators or researchers use to check an ongoing process of the evaluation from planning through implementation phases. Process evaluation is any combination of measures that occurs as a program is implemented to assure or improve the quality of performance or delivery. Summative evaluation is often associated with measures or judgments that enable the investigator to conclude impact and outcome evaluations. Impact evaluation is the immediate and observable effects of a program leading to the desired outcomes. Outcome evaluation is focused on the ultimate goal, product, or policy and is often measured in terms of health status, morbidity, and mortality. Employing evaluation procedures that are explicit, formal, and justifiable is desirable for program improvement (McKenzie et al., 2017).

Data gathering instruments or scripts are used for both quantitative and qualitative data collection. Prior to developing data gathering instruments, researchers consider the type of data collection that is going to occur. Common data collection strategies include face-to-face surveys, telephone surveys, self-administered surveys, traditional mail-in surveys, and electronic platforms (e.g., SurveyMonkey). Data collection instruments are designed to answer questions that are being asked by the evaluator or researcher. Each of the various data collection instruments available has advantages and disadvantages, and the choice of an instrument depends on the goal of data collection, the population under investigation, and the resources of those trying to collect data (Windsor, 2015).

4.1.1 ▲ Align the evaluation plan with the intervention goals and objectives.

There are many reasons to evaluate health interventions. Often, and in ideal circumstances, the goal of program evaluation is to determine ways that policies or programs can be improved. When planning community health promotion and education programs, the health education specialist will select methods and strategies. If existing, evidence-based strategies that already have shown to be effective exist and apply, they should be used. Even when modeling an intervention after proven efforts, however, it is essential to ensure that the intervention remains appropriate. Evaluation is a process that health education specialists use to check to ensure they are reaching the desired outcomes. Health education specialists serving as evaluators only can know that programs are working when there are clear goals and objectives. The questions one seeks to understand through evaluation must match the stated goals and objectives of the intervention. Using adequate and appropriate evaluation methods from the outset helps allow for and encourage improved program results. A health education specialist serving as an evaluator might need to identify or establish goals or general guidelines to explain what is desirable to achieve and then determine measurable objectives related to improved health status, program implementation, accountability to stakeholders, community support, and contribution to the scientific base for community health initiatives, which inform policy and program decisions.

4.1.2 Comply with institutional requirements for evaluation.

When planning and conducting evaluation, health education specialists do so in accordance with federal and state laws and regulations, organizational and institutional policies, and professional standards. Institutions may require various levels of approval before evaluations are conducted. Some agencies might simply require review by supervisors or other levels of administration, while others might require institutional review board (IRB) review. Sometimes the level of review can depend on the intent of the evaluation. If the intent is for quality control and the results will remain internal, some agencies might require fewer levels of review and approval. If results will be shared externally, there likely will be more levels of review (including institutional review board approval in agencies with IRB panels) that are required to meet federal, state, and institutional laws and regulations.

4.1.3 ▲ Use a logic model and/or theory for evaluations.

A program logic model is a visual outline of how program components (e.g., resources, activities, and outputs) are linked to outcomes. A logic model often looks something like a flow chart. Inputs are the resources, contributions, and other investments that go into a program. Activities are the keystones of the program. Outputs are the activities, services, and products that will reach the participants of a program as a result of carefully leveraging resources through skillful planning. Outcomes are often stepwise and labeled short-term, intermediate, or long-term outcomes. Short-term outcomes – sometimes described as impact – are quantifiable changes in knowledge, skills, and access to resources that happen if planned activities are successfully carried out. Intermediate outcomes are measured in terms of changes in behaviors related to disease or health status, and long-term outcomes are measured in terms of fundamental changes in conditions leading to morbidity or mortality (McKenzie et al., 2017). When logic models are used to help guide the evaluation process, they may range from simple to complex (detailed). In Table 4.1, an example of a sample logic model template is provided.

Table 4.1
Sample Logic Model

Inputs/Resources	Activities	Outputs	Short-term outcomes	Intermediate outcomes	Long-term outcomes
Human, fiscal, physical, and intellectual resources needed to address the objectives of a program	With the resources available, the following activities will result in measurable, deliverable services and products	Activities, products and services that will influence short-term outcomes	Changes in knowledge or skills among participants of the program	Changes in behaviors or policy	Changes in morbidity or mortality

Adapted from McKenzie et al, 2017

Logic models are a dynamic "living and breathing" document, subject to change as evaluators and program specialists identify areas for improvements that likely will ensure better results. When stakeholders, implementers, and evaluators revisit and modify a logic model, all parties agree to changes in processes and expected outcomes.

4.1.4 ▲ Assess capacity to conduct evaluation.

Evaluation of all health education programming is desirable, if not essential. Evaluation will provide health education specialists with important insights that can help improve results, outcomes, and reduce costs (American Public Health Association (APHA), 2017). The feasibility of evaluation depends on the availability of human resources to staff and carry out relevant duties, physical resources such as a place to carry out the business required to conduct the evaluation, fiscal resources that provide the money, in-kind materials, and intellectual resources such as the expert opinions of stakeholders and conclusions from relevant literature. Evaluations conducted with enough resources and strong stakeholder support are used to provide feedback on both process and program outcomes.

Health education specialists considering evaluations should strive for the most rigorous evaluation design that is adequate in terms of observed evaluation standards, including utility, accuracy, and costs in time, and resources. Evaluation plans that are composed of research designs, such as randomized control trials, cohort studies, and case control/comparison studies, provide a level of confidence to the evaluator and stakeholders about the validity of the investigation. Moreover, these designs provide measurable estimates of the probability that effects are due to phenomena that should or should not be attributed to the program. Evaluation designs vary in cost, dedicated time, and outcomes; however, rigorous research designs are not always feasible. Unavoidable compromises in design are often made that jeopardize the validity, accuracy, and utility of the evaluation (CDC, 1999) but still can be used to answer evaluation questions. At times, cross-sectional, observational, and anecdotal inquiries are more feasible than more rigorous designs and can provide less expensive yet useful information.

4.1.5 ▲ Select an evaluation design model and the types of data to be collected.

As health education specialists attempt to explore, explain, or describe ideas about some phenomenon, program, or policy, they will find it necessary to develop an appropriate rationale to focus the evaluation and/or research (Brownson et al., 2017) and to craft a meaningful purpose statement that is essential in the development of evaluation questions. Health education specialists use purpose statements (also referred to as a statement of purpose) to identify in detail what health education specialists want to learn throughout an evaluation. The purpose statement is usually a sentence or two written with specificity and detail. The purpose statement helps evaluators focus and guide efforts involved with data collection and analysis. Well-developed purpose statements are used to guide the selection and/or creation of program goals. Goals are usually long-term and represent a more global vision (e.g., to reduce morbidity or mortality) whereas objectives define measurable strategies used to attain progress toward a goal.

Where program evaluation is concerned, health education specialists serve as evaluators striving to solicit answers to precise questions that carefully align with the statement of purpose, goals, and objectives of a program. These questions follow an understanding of program operations, intentions, and stakeholders (Patton, 2015). These specially developed questions are called evaluation questions.

Evaluation questions help to establish boundaries for the evaluation by stating what aspects of the program will be addressed (Patton, 2015). By creating evaluation questions, stakeholders are encouraged to reveal what they believe evaluation output should be. Negotiating and prioritizing questions among stakeholders further refines a viable focus. The question development phase also might expose differing stakeholder opinions regarding the best unit of analysis. Clear decisions regarding the questions and corresponding units of analysis are needed in subsequent steps of the evaluation to guide method selection and evidence gathering. Health education specialists use evaluation questions to monitor and measure processes, activities, outputs, and expected outcomes. Process questions help the evaluator understand phenomena, such as internal and external forces that affect program activities. Answers to output and short-term outcome questions help evaluators clearly understand how program activities, products, or associated services relate to or affect changes in behavior, attitudes, knowledge, skills, or the intentions of the participants of a program. Longer-term evaluation questions provide vital links between intervention activities, products, and services rendered, and changes in risk factors, morbidity, or mortality. Well-developed evaluation questions offer a guide for selecting appropriate data sources, which, in turn, help to guide an effective analysis plan (Patton, 2015).

At times, health education specialists will find secondary data, or data collected for other purposes, most feasible for answering evaluation questions. Sometimes secondary data is less intrusive to use for measuring differences in phenomena (e.g., emergency room or law enforcement records) than constructing new instruments to gather primary data on their own, especially where quantitative analysis can be used.

Both quantitative and qualitative evaluations, however, are used within the field of health education, and both types of evaluation have practical applications for health education specialists. Quantitative methods are focused on measuring things related to health education programs using numerical data to help describe, explain, or predict phenomena (Baumgartner, et al., 2021). Qualitative methods are descriptive with the aim of the researcher/evaluator to discover meaning or insight (McKenzie et al., 2017). Health education specialists use both qualitative and quantitative methods to obtain a deeper understanding of the program and its participants.

Often, it is advantageous to use a mixed-methods approach for data collection. Mixed methods mean using a combination of different methods and strategies to examine evaluation questions from multiple different perspectives and vantage points. This process helps a health education specialist "tell the story" and describe classifications (e.g., how many or how much) as well as to indicate why a phenomenon is occurring within a population. Doing so helps health education specialists make sound recommendations for future programming and may help them introduce new hypotheses for prospective evaluation and research purposes. Both advanced-level and entry-level health education specialists are responsible for assessing the merits and limitations of qualitative and quantitative data collection for evaluation.

Evaluation plans are often facilitated using concepts from discipline-specific evaluation models, such as those described in Table 4.2: Attainment, Decision-Making, Goal-Free, Naturalistic, Systems Analysis, and Utilization-focused. Health education specialists should consider which models will work best for a particular situation and whether evaluation approaches should be combined or used individually. Models help evaluators make data collection and analysis decisions (Neutens & Rubinson, 2014; Patton, 2011).

Table 4.2
Evaluation Model

Attainment	focused on program objectives and the program goals; serves as standards for evaluation
Decision-making	based on four components designed to provide the user with the context, input, processes, and products with which to make decisions
Goal-free	not based on goals; evaluator searches for all outcomes including unintended positive and negative side effects
Naturalistic	focused on qualitative data and responsive information from participants in a program is used; most concerned with narrative explaining "why" behavior did or did not change
Systems analysis	based on efficiency that cost benefits or cost effectiveness analysis is used to quantify effects of a program
Utilization-focused	accomplished for and with a specific population

In addition to evaluation models, evaluation frameworks have been developed to summarize and organize the essential elements of program evaluation. These frameworks provide a platform to perform and monitor evaluations. One such framework is the CDC's six-step framework that was developed to help guide program evaluation (Figure 4.2). Health education specialists should stay abreast of the availability of notable and commonly used evaluation frameworks. Evaluation standards are used as a guide to manage evaluation processes and assess existing evaluations to formulate an evaluation design. (McKenzie et al., 2017).

Figure 4.2
CDC Six-Step Framework for Program Evaluation

Elements of the Framework
Six-Step Process

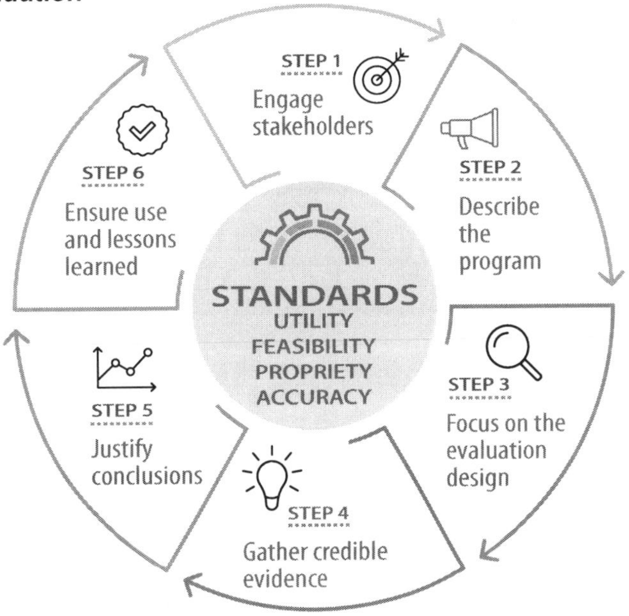

STEP 1 — Engage stakeholders
STEP 2 — Describe the program
STEP 3 — Focus on the evaluation design
STEP 4 — Gather credible evidence
STEP 5 — Justify conclusions
STEP 6 — Ensure use and lessons learned

STANDARDS
UTILITY
FEASIBILITY
PROPRIETY
ACCURACY

Steps in Evaluation Practice	**Standards for Effective Evaluation**
Engage stakeholders Those involved, those affected, primary stakeholders	*Utility* Serve the information needs of intended users
Describe the program Need, expected effects, activities, resources, stage, context, logic model	*Feasibility* Be realistic, prudent, diplomatic, and frugal
Focus the evaluation design Purpose, users, uses, question, methods, agreements	*Propriety* Behave legally, ethically, and with due regard for the welfare of those involved and those affected
Gather credible evidence Indicators, sources, quality, quantity, logistics	*Accuracy* Reveal and convey technically accurate information
Justify conclusions Standards, analysis/synthesis, interpretation, judgment, recommendations	
Ensure use and share lessons learned Design, preparation, feedback, follow-up dissemination	

Note. Adapted from CDC. Framework for Program Evaluation in Public Health, Centers for Disease Control and Prevention, 1999; 48 (No. RR-11).

4.1.6 ▲ Develop a sampling plan and procedures for data collection, management, and security.

There are two categories of sampling techniques: probability and non-probability. Both sampling techniques have strengths and limitations (Sharma & Petosa, 2014). Probability sampling techniques are those methods in which each member of the priority population has a known chance, or probability, of being selected. Random selection, which reduces the chance of sampling bias, is paramount in probability sampling. Several types of probability sampling methods exist:

1. Simple random sampling – an inclusive list of the priority population is used to randomly (such as with a list of random numbers) select a certain number of potential participants from the list.
2. Systematic random sampling – an inclusive list of the priority population is used, and starting with a random number, every nth potential participant is selected (such as every 14th participant).
3. Stratified random sampling – the sample is split into groups based on a variable of interest, and an equal number of potential participants from each group are selected randomly (such as in a simple random sample).
4. Cluster sampling – is when naturally occurring groups (such as schools) are selected instead of individuals.
5. Multistage cluster sampling – in several steps, groups are selected using cluster sampling (i.e., in a state, counties are selected at random, then schools within the county are selected at random).
6. Stratified multistage cluster sampling – in several steps, a variable of interest is used to split the sample, and then groups are randomly selected from this sample (i.e., in a state, counties are selected at random, then an equal number of elementary schools and secondary schools are randomly selected in each county).

(McKenzie et al., 2017)

Unit of analysis and sampling frame accessibility will dictate the most appropriate probability sampling method. For example, if individuals are the unit of analysis, simple random sampling may be most suitable. If the unit of analysis includes all public schools within the state of Nevada, multistage cluster sampling may be the optimal sampling method.

Non-probability sampling frames are readily assessable to the research team (Sharma & Petosa, 2014). With non-probability samples, not all units from the priority population have an equal chance of being selected, and thus their representativeness to the population is unknown. Types of non-probability sampling techniques include the following:

1. convenience – selection of individuals or groups who are available
2. purposive – researcher makes judgements about who to include in the sample based on study needs
3. quota – selecting individuals who have a certain characteristic up to a certain number (i.e., selecting 50 females from a worksite)
4. network sampling (also called snowball sampling) – when respondents identify other potential participants who might have desired characteristics for the study

(McKenzie et al., 2017)

Non-probability samples are often used in health education/promotion research as they are easier and less expensive to obtain. For instance, if a health education research team is studying the health behaviors of college students, team members may sample from classrooms that are readily accessible to them. An obvious limitation to such an approach is that the researchers cannot claim their findings are representative of all colleges or even to all students in their specific university. The findings are limited only to those students who were sampled.

Data should be collected in accordance with a well-developed analysis plan and with the evaluation questions and data sources in mind. Evaluation questions should be carefully considered, and decisions about the type, amount, and accuracy are critical. Consideration should be given to minimize the direct or indirect burden on participants, as well as other purveyors of secondary sources. Health education specialists should consider the availability of resources, sensitivity to participants, credibility, and importance of the data with regard to stakeholders (W.K. Kellogg Foundation, 2017).

Developing a data analysis plan is a crucial step for evaluation. By creating a data analysis plan for evaluation, the data that have been collected can be integrated and structured to ensure understanding and usefulness of the data to answer evaluation questions. The intended audience, often program personnel or other key stakeholders, also may influence the data analysis plan. Therefore, the intended audience may be invited to help develop or create the data analysis plan. The analysis for evaluation depends on the purpose of the evaluation as well as the availability of resources. Analysis depends on the research questions, data sources, and availability, as well as the intended audience who will use the findings. The goal of data analysis is to use statistical tests to answer the research questions. Analysis determines if outcomes were different than expected. Planning data analysis is a critical step in research (McKenzie et al., 2017. Data gathered from a research project in which problems with methods for gathering the data existed does not inspire confidence regarding the findings. Analysis planning proves helpful in minimizing errors due to inadequate or inappropriate statistical methods. Thoughts about data analysis should begin with the planning of a program and be used to guide data collection decisions. A comprehensive analysis plan is used to identify items or observations to be used for answering the research question. The analysis plan contains the level of measurement for each survey question and includes the statistical test(s) and/or descriptive data analysis that will be used to answer the research questions (Cunningham et al., 2013).

Health education specialists also need to develop a data management and security plan. Once data are collected they may need to be entered into a statistical software and checked for entry errors and missing data before being analyzed. Researchers will need to identify who will have access to the data and how it will be securely stored. Refer to Sub-competency 4.2.6 for more information on data management and security.

4.1.7 ▲ Select quantitative and qualitative tools consistent with assumptions and data requirements.

An essential initial step in data collection is to identify the types and sources of data that will be useful in answering evaluation questions. Depending on the goals and objectives set by health education specialists, a variety of methods can be used to gather data (Cottrell & McKenzie, 2011). Health education specialists may choose to use existing data collection tools. Once the evaluation questions are established, the evaluator should consider relevant existing data and use instruments already in existence, when appropriate. A myriad of data collection instruments exists for both qualitative and qualitative inquiry. Many instruments have been validated and tested for reliability and repeatedly used by national, state, and local health surveillance programs as well as some parallel ongoing programs or inquiries. Health education specialists should be familiar with the existing instruments commonly used in the field. Table 4.3 provides necessary information about some of the more common national surveys.

Table 4.3
Health Surveillance Programs

Behavioral Risk Factor Surveillance Survey (BRFSS) https://www.cdc.gov/brfss/index.html	The nation's premier system of health-related telephone surveys that is used to collect state data about U.S. residents regarding their health-related risk behaviors, chronic health conditions, and use of preventive services. In BRFSS data are collected in all 50 states, the District of Columbia and three U.S. territories. More than 400,000 adults complete BRFSS interviews each year, making it the largest continuously conducted health survey system in the world.
Youth Risk Behavioral Surveillance System (YRBSS) http://www.cdc.gov/healthyyouth/yrbs/index.htm	A national school-based survey conducted by CDC and state, territorial, tribal, and local surveys conducted by state, territorial, and local education and health agencies and tribal governments. This bi-annual survey provides data on six categories of health-related behaviors that contribute to the leading causes of death and disability among youth and adults, including • Behaviors that contribute to unintentional injuries and violence • Sexual behaviors related to unintended pregnancy and sexually transmitted diseases, including HIV infection • Alcohol and other drug use • Tobacco use • Unhealthy dietary behaviors • Inadequate physical activity
National Youth Tobacco Survey (NYTS) https://www.cdc.gov/tobacco/data_statistics/surveys/nyts/index.htm	National survey of middle and high school youth's tobacco-related beliefs, attitudes, behaviors, and exposure to pro- and anti-tobacco influences. The survey is designed to provide national data on long-term, intermediate, and short-term indicators key to the design, implementation, and evaluation of comprehensive tobacco prevention and control programs.
National Health and Nutrition Examination Survey (NHANES) http://www.cdc.gov/nchs/nhanes.htm	A series of studies used to assess the health and nutritional status of adults and children in the United States. The survey allows researchers to collect both interviews and physical examinations.
National Health Interview Survey http://www.cdc.gov/nchs/nhis.htm	The survey includes data on the health of the United States population on a broad range of health topics.

Program evaluation often is used in an internal situation, such as collecting data about specific programs, with no intent to generalize the results to other settings and situations. Program evaluations are often conducted using existing data collection instruments. Using an instrument that has been developed by someone else for different populations in different places and at different times, however, can introduce a level of internal bias that may be problematic. The evaluator should review existing instruments thoroughly and be sure that each item is appropriate and adequately can be used to examine variables of interest. Evaluators should be certain there are no extraneous items on instruments that are not relevant to the intent of the evaluation. Evaluators should be confident that the language is clear and appropriate for the population to which the instrument will be administered, as well as sure that the instrument has been tested for validity and reliability. Validity is the degree to which a test or assessment measures what it is intended to measure (McKenzie et al., 2017). Reliability refers to the consistency, dependability, and stability of the measurement process (McKenzie et al., 2017). Finally, existing instruments should be pilot tested with a sample population before use for evaluation purposes (Jacobsen, 2017).

4.1.8 Adopt or modify existing instruments for collecting data.

Developing data collection instruments can be arduous and time consuming. In many social service sectors, existing data collection instruments may be used or adapted to suit the needs of the evaluator/researcher. Depending on the respondent and method of data collection, the data collection instruments should be tested for literacy reading level. Use of a readability tool, such as SMOG (Simple Measure of Gobbledegook) or FleschKincaid, to assess reading level of the data collection tool should be performed to ensure validity of responses (McKenzie et al., 2017).

Adaptation or modification of existing data collection instruments is necessary for these instruments to be used effectively with new scenarios. Some advantages of using existing data collection instruments include previously-tested reliability, validity, direct comparison measures, reduced costs as compared to the creation of new instruments, and user familiarity. One caveat to using previously developed instruments is that, while the items on the instrument may have been extensively tested for reliability and validity, there still exists the potential for unreliable measures given different population demographics and situations (Issel & Wells, 2018). Health education specialists can find scales or instruments from a literature review, measures atlas (Agency for Healthcare Research and Quality, 2014: https://www.ahrq.gov/ncepcr/care/coordination/atlas.html) or compendiums like the Grid Enabled Measures Database (https://www.gem-measures.org/public/home.aspx), and through discussion with experts in the field.

Existing instruments are useful for investigating similar variables in contextually different investigations. Using the entire instrument is not always appropriate; however, it may make sense to use previously tested, reliable items selected from them. Scales and other aspects of the item should be retained to maintain validity, especially for research studies. The developer of the instrument can provide information to help ascertain validity and reliability information. Before using items from an existing instrument, it is important to consider:
- if the item is appropriate for the intended purpose;
- if the language appropriate for the population;
- whether a test has been performed using a sample from the intended population; and
- to whom you should give credit for using the item

(Bhattacherjee, 2012).

At times, it is appropriate to make modifications to the content, format, or presentation of any part of a question, questionnaire, or instrument. Changes are often associated with adapting to data needs and often result in a more versatile, useful instrument (Edlund & Nichols, 2019).

At times, items and survey instruments are deliberately modified. As with longitudinal inquiry, wording could be adapted/updated to reflect current nomenclature, for instance "American Indian" may have been replaced with "Native American. "Word choice also might be changed to reflect current social realities, such as adding "Facebook" as an information source in media usage questions. Modifications also could be made to accommodate new populations. Modifications such as vocabulary, updates in evidence or science, presentation style, and instructions to suit a child population rather than an adult one. Regarding multicultural projects, modification and adaptation are often necessary to translate a questionnaire into another language to research populations.

4.1.9 ▲ Develop instruments for collecting data.

When preparing a new data collection instrument for evaluation, the developer should do the following:
- Write an easy-to-understand and complete introduction to the instrument.
- Ask only questions that provide useful information in accordance with a well-developed analysis plan.
- Ask the most important questions first.
- Organize the questions in logical order.
- Use plain, easy-to-understand language.
- Avoid technical terms, jargon, and acronyms.
- Only use graphics or illustrations when they are necessary to understand the question.
- Be sensitive to the feelings and cultural beliefs of respondents.
- Thank respondents.
- Keep it as short as possible.

Evaluators must decide whether items developed for quantitative methods, qualitative methods, or mixed methods will be appropriate and adequate to answer the evaluation questions for the program. When quantitative, closed-ended items are indicated, respondents make selections that represent their knowledge, attitude, or self-reported behavior from predetermined lists, scales, or categories. Always good practice is for the evaluator to acknowledge that survey recipients may have a variety of backgrounds. Respondents should be able to understand the purpose of the question items clearly. When the question requires respondents to use a rating scale, it is best to mediate the range, so there is room for both extremes. At times, it may be helpful to relax grammatical standards if the questions sound too formal. There are several phenomena to avoid:
- Assumptions that everyone has a common basis of knowledge
- Abbreviations
- Leading questions that demand a specific response
- Questions that use two negative words
- Long lists of choices
- Recall questions over extended time frames
(Sarris, 2014)

By contrast, open-ended items solicit written or verbal responses to topics that cannot be adequately answered with a single word or phrase. The careful composition of qualitative questions is as important as with the preparation of quantitative items. Evaluators ask fewer carefully crafted questions that require people to respond freely. When composing qualitative items, the same rules apply as with quantitative questions, but evaluators also must be sure the questions provoke respondents to provide insightful information. As with quantitative item development, there are several phenomena to avoid:
- Asking a "yes/no" question or those that invite a specific (and often brief) answer
- Being too broad to capture useful information
- Being too specific with probing items
- Asking too many questions (Sarris, 2014)

4.1.10 ▲ Implement a pilot test to refine data collection instruments and procedures.

The purpose of a pilot test is to gain insights on whether a data collection instrument consistently measures whatever it should measure. For example, evaluators must have confidence that subjects responding to a survey, focus group, or interview understand the questions being asked and understand them in the same way. Reliability can be established using a pilot test by collecting data from a small sample of subjects not included in the intervention. With the pilot study complete, evaluators can be assured the data they collect will provide the consistent measures and give credibility to the validity of outcomes (Jacobsen, 2017).

Competency 4.2 Design research studies.

Although there has been much discussion about the differences between evaluation and research, it is sometimes difficult to distinguish between them as the methods are often identical. A significant difference between evaluation and research is that research can be conducted with the intent to generalize findings from a sample to a larger population. The goal of evaluation is to determine if a specific program was effective (Issel & Wells, 2018).

4.2.1 ■ Determine purpose, hypotheses, and questions.

A statement of purpose is used to clearly and succinctly define the goal of the research project (Cottrell & McKenzie, 2011; Salazar et al., 2015). Elements of a purpose statement include the following:
- Research design (quantitative study) or method of inquiry (qualitative study)
- Variables (quantitative study) or phenomena under investigation (qualitative study)
- The priority population
- Research setting (e.g., university, worksite)

A research question is an interrogative statement that reflects the central question the research study is designed to answer (Cottrell & McKenzie, 2011). Narrow- and precisely-designed research questions are more amenable to rigorous research than broadly-defined research questions (Salazar et al., 2015). The type of research question implicitly will reveal whether a quantitative or qualitative research method is most appropriate. The nature of the research question also will reflect the optimal study design for addressing the research question. Quality research questions are developed in such a way that they can be translated into testable statements, called hypotheses. To translate research questions into hypotheses, it is necessary to operationally define the variables under investigation. Operationally defining a variable entails converting the variable into a measurable quantity. For example, physical activity is defined as any bodily movement produced by the skeletal muscles that results in energy expenditure; however, in health education, physical activity for adults may be operationally defined in terms of specific intensity (e.g., moderate), frequency (e.g., five or more days a week), and duration (e.g., at least 20 minutes). A sample hypothesis in this instance may be: "No significant difference exists in the amount of physical activity in which participants engage by the end of the program." In this instance, physical activity would be measured in terms of its operational definition of adults engaging in moderately intense physical activity five or more days a week for at least 20 minutes. This operational definition could change if the research was focused on children or the elderly. Consequently, operational definitions are tailored to the purpose of the study (Sharma & Petosa, 2014).

A key feature of a scientific hypothesis is that it must be falsifiable. The concept of falsifiability is represented through the null hypothesis. The null hypothesis is a hypothesis of skepticism, in which it is stated that there is no relationship between variables. Conversely, in an alternative hypothesis, it is stated that there is a relationship between variables. An alternative hypothesis also may be directional, for instance, if the research team theorizes a program may reduce or increase the quantity of a targeted behavior. In quantitative research, inferential statistical tests are used to determine if differences or relationships exist between variables. A statistical test is a procedure that, when data are fed into, is used to either reject or fails to reject a null hypothesis.

4.2.2 ■ Comply with institutional and/or IRB requirements for research.

Human subjects' protection requirements include a standard for ethics, and details can be found in the *Belmont Report*. (National Commission for the Protection of Human Subjects of Biomedical and Behavioral Research, 1979). In the *Belmont Report*, ethical principles are outlined as respect for persons, beneficence, and justice when engaging with human subjects. In the report, the basic ethical principles and guidelines for the protection of human subjects of research are summarized. Not all health education specialists will conduct research, but all health education specialists should recognize the fundamental concepts for human subjects' protection: respect for persons (protection of individual autonomy and for those who have diminished autonomy), beneficence (protecting people from harm and working toward enhancing well-being), and justice ("equals should be treated equally") (National Commission for the Protection of Human Subjects of Biomedical and Behavioral Research, p. 5).

Health education specialists conducting research will be required to obtain informed consent. The informed consent is designed to allow participants to choose what will or will not happen to them, and the informed consent is signed by participants to indicate their choice. Informed consent includes the following information:
- Nature and purpose of the program
- Any inherent risks or dangers associated with participation in the program
- Any possible discomfort that may be experienced from participation in the program
- Expected benefits of participation
- Alternative programs or procedures that would accomplish the same results
- Option of discontinuing participation at any time

(National Commission for the Protection of Human Subjects of Biomedical and Behavioral Research, 1979)

Institutions, such as universities and hospitals, involved in conducting research that includes human subjects are required to establish an Institutional Review Board (IRB); they are also known as Human Subjects Committees (HSC), Independent Ethics Committee (IEC), Ethical Review Board (ERB), or Research Ethics Board (REB). The IRB function is to ensure physical and psychological protection of human subjects involved in research (Neutens & Rubinson, 2014). Because evaluations may have ethical considerations, an IRB review and approval is often desired or required prior to data collection (McKenzie et al., 2017). An IRB committee reviews, approves, and monitors biomedical and behavioral research involving humans. This type of monitoring and oversight is designed to protect the rights and welfare of the research participants. An IRB performs critical oversight functions for research conducted on human subjects that are scientific, ethical, and regulatory.

Health education specialists should submit IRB protocols for research through their university or organizational IRB. The IRB application typically includes a lay summary, recruitment materials, full study protocols, and research instruments (surveys, etc.). Data collection should not start until IRB approval is obtained or deemed exempt. IRB protocols may need annual renewals for longer projects. All staff involved in research should have attended human subjects training.

4.2.3 ▲ Use a logic model and/or theory for research.

Various research designs in health education research exist (Sharma & Petosa, 2014). Frequently, the research questions that the study authors are attempting to answer will dictate the optimal evaluation and research design. One evaluation tool available to health education specialists is the logic model. A logic model can be created and used as an evaluation tool to facilitate evaluation design decisions that will impact or influence the type of data and analysis available (Kellogg Foundation, 2017). An evaluative logic model is a visual outline or flowchart of how the evaluation process and its components can influence outputs related to data collection. Once this process is ascertained, the health education professional can determine what types of data can be generated, how the data will be analyzed and by whom, and how and where to share the results of the evaluation results (W. K. Kellogg Foundation, 2017). The development of the logic model is a dynamic and iterative process, subject to change as evaluators, stakeholders, and program specialists/health education specialists identify areas for evaluation. These evaluation decisions can be used to determine areas for improvements that will likely ensure better program results. Stakeholders, implementers, and evaluators should revisit and modify a logic model as part of an ongoing assessment to determine if quantifiable changes have occurred, e.g., if changes in behaviors were a result of the intervention, or if further revisions are necessary (McKenzie et al., 2017). Refer to Sub-competency 4.1.3 for more information on logic models.

4.2.4 ■ Assess capacity to conduct research.

Relevant factors to consider when gauging the feasibility of a research project include funding, staffing, time constraints, recruitment potential, equipment/material needs, and site permissions. Before undertaking a new study, the research team should determine how many participants they must recruit to address the objectives of the project or sample size calculations. For quantitative research, this process will require calculating a sample size adequate to detect statistically significant effects. Depending on the timeframe of the project and intensity of participant involvement, the sample size must account for participant attrition. Prior to planning a large-scale project, researchers should conduct a small scale, pilot study with a less rigorous research design. Often, pilot testing will uncover challenges the research team did not anticipate in their initial planning. Pilot testing also will aid in assessing a project's feasibility. If the research team intends to seek extramural funding, pilot testing can help establish evidence that a particular line of research merits financial support.

4.2.5 ▲ Select a research design model and the types of data to be collected.

A variety of research designs applied to health education exist (Sharma & Petosa, 2014). Often, the research questions that the authors of a study are attempting to answer will dictate the optimal design. For example, if the researchers are interested in gauging the efficacy of an intervention to change behavior, they likely will use some variation of an experimental design. If the research team is interested in understanding the experiences of community members living with diabetes, they may want to use qualitative interviews.

In quantitative research, designs are categorized according to the amount of control they permit (Goodman & Thompson, 2018). They are presented in the order of least to most rigorous designs. More rigorous designs are more likely to have more control over the conditions and subsequently reduce or eliminate influence of unwanted factors, which helps to strengthen internal validity. If a design has high internal validity, the researcher has more confidence that changes in dependent variables occurred because of the intervention (Salazar et al., 2015).

- Nonexperimental designs are cross-sectional in nature and do not include manipulation of any variables. Instead, the purpose of these designs is to describe features of a priority population. These are the least rigorous designs and do not control for many threats to internal validity.
- Quasi-experimental designs include manipulation of at least one independent variable and they may contain a comparison group; however, due to ethical or practical reasons, random assignment of participants does not occur.
- True experimental designs include manipulation of at least one independent variable and the research participants are randomly assigned to either the experimental or control group arms of the trial. Due to their use of both random assignment and a control group, true experimental designs can be used to control for most threats to internal validity.

If a qualitative design is required, the investigators may use one or more methods that fit with the purpose of the study. Some examples include the following:

- Naturalistic inquiry studies- experiences within an existing context
- Grounded Theory – theories are developed for existing social phenomena
- Ethnography – studies within cultural groups
- Phenomenology – specific contextual understanding of phenomena
- Action research – development of solutions to problems in a community
- Case study – in-depth study of very specific event, person, issue, etc.

(Forister & Blessing, 2020)

4.2.6 ▲ Develop a sampling plan and procedures for data collection, management, and security.

Before any data are collected, health education specialists who are engaged in research must ensure they have laid out a plan for how their research project will proceed. Central to the plan are elements such as:

- identifying how you will select research participants;
- developing a sampling plan;
- creating data collection procedures;
- following up with non-respondents; and
- establishing a data analysis plan.

The first decision in this sampling plan is how to select research participants. Researchers must develop inclusion and exclusion criteria that will restrict participant enrollment to the population they wish to prioritize (Sharma & Petosa, 2014). For example, if the research team members are seeking to study the effects of a health education tobacco cessation program, they may wish to limit enrollment in their intervention only to those adults who are current tobacco users. In such a case, the research team must determine what criteria are necessary to accurately screen participants for inclusion, as well as clearly define what constitutes a "current tobacco user." Ideally, researchers will develop inclusion criteria based on the information in the literature and/or epidemiologically-identified populations (Salazar et al., 2015). A variety of methods, including self-report questionnaire, medical records, and physiological indices, can be used to determine if participants meet the inclusion criteria of the study.

After identifying criteria for how they will define participants, researchers move forward with developing a plan to select their sample of subjects that conform to that definition. The goal of sampling is to select participants in such a way that research participants represent the population of interest (Cottrell & McKenzie, 2011). When representation occurs, it is far more likely the values obtained from the sampled participants will be generalizable to the population of interest. When representation does not happen, there is a higher risk for sampling error, which occurs when there is a difference between the observed value of a sample statistic (e.g., mean minutes of physical activity achieved by the sample) and the true value of the population parameter (e.g., actual minutes of physical activity performed by the population of interest).

The first step in sample planning is to determine the unit of analysis the research team will target (Salazar et al., 2015). Units of analyses, or sampling elements, consist of either individuals or groups. Next, the research team must identify an appropriate sampling frame. A sampling frame is an available list of people or groups that represent the population of interest. For example, if the research team is testing a school-based health education program, they may compile a list of all schools within a district from which to sample. Ideally, a sampling frame list will include all possible elements in a population; however, the existence of an exhaustive sampling frame is rarely available or may be difficult to access. For instance, if the research team intends to conduct a study related to how well patients follow post-care instructions after being discharged from the hospital, patient privacy laws may prevent the research team from accessing a complete set of patient records, only those patients who opt into the research could be assessed. Due to laws that protect individual privacy, it is often easier to achieve more exhaustive sampling frames when the sampling element is defined by groups rather than people (Salazar et al., 2015). Organizations such as churches, health agencies, schools, and neighborhood organizations often have public records of their existence or intentionally advertise their presence. If the sampling frame is comprised of individuals, accessibility to the sampling frame must be evaluated.

Once a sampling frame is identified, the research team must select an appropriate sampling technique. Ideally, the sampling technique chosen will maximize the representativeness of the sample concerning the sampling frame and, ultimately, the population that the sampling frame represents. As with most research methods, the more rigorous the sampling technique applied, the more resources and time are required. Thus, the research team must weigh rigidity against practicality. Refer to Sub-competency 4.1.6 for more information on sampling techniques.

Developing clear and precise protocols for collecting data is an essential part of the research process (Sharma & Petosa, 2014) and is particularly important if several individuals will be responsible for collecting data. Data collection procedures often are centered on ensuring that bias is not introduced into the study. For example, when explaining the purpose of a self-report questionnaire to participants, researchers should stay neutral as to not prompt participants to respond in a way the researchers would find favorable. In such a scenario, it is beneficial for the researchers to develop a script that all individuals involved in data collection will read to participants. As another illustration, if height and weight data are collected for calculating body mass index, the research team will want to ensure they are using consistent measurement procedures for all participants. One way to aid in this process is to develop a set of standardized checklists that the research team can use as they collect data from participants. For instance, a qualitative research team may want to give precise directions for transcribing participant responses. An additional issue for consideration is how the data will be stored post collection to ensure participant privacy. The research team may state that, as they collect completed questionnaires, they will be stored in a locked file cabinet for safekeeping.

An additional factor to consider when deciding on a data collection method is whether the method is practical for the population of interest. For instance, when researching the behaviors of young children, self-report is unlikely to be accurate. Elderly individuals may not be able to read questionnaires with traditional font sizes. For such individuals, structured interviews may be more suitable. Ideally, the data collection procedures should be tested in the priority population prior to full-scale implementation of the research project.

Inevitably, some participants will drop out of the research study, which can happen for several reasons, but is more likely to occur in studies that are longer in duration. Understanding why participants drop out of a program can help researchers determine if those who completed the full study differed in some important way from those who did not complete the full study. This investigation is particularly important for establishing validity of the study. A variety of strategies exist for handling non-respondent follow-up. The first step is to determine how much nonresponse is allowable. Often, researchers will inflate the total sample size they require to detect statistical effects to account for assumed participant attrition (Sharma & Petosa, 2014). By convention, a 20% attrition rate is often applied in health education/promotion research; however, this standard can be higher or lower, and the literature should be used for a guide about inflation rates.

In addition to using inflation, the research team should develop a plan to recover participants lost to follow-up. For example, the research team may plan to contact nonresponsive participants three times before giving up. If contact is established, and the participants still cannot be recovered, the research team should attempt to uncover why the participant dropped out as this information may provide invaluable insight into the structure of the study. For instance, if the research team is testing an online health education intervention, and participants find the website confusing, they may become frustrated and drop out of the study. Knowing this information would be invaluable to the research team.

Determining how the missing data will be analyzed is another crucial step for handling participants lost to follow-up. An assortment of statistical software packages exist that can be used to model missing data. Modeling missing data is essential as it can uncover patterns in the missing data. If patterns are identified, it may be possible to predict how the participants would have responded using techniques such as multiple imputation analysis.

Establishing a data management plan is critical in defining how results will be analyzed before any data are collected. A data management plan is a set of procedures for determining how the data will be transferred from the instruments used in the research to the data analysis software. Data entry is tedious, and errors can occur (Sharma & Petosa, 2014). When dealing with large data sets, it is often helpful to have two or more people independently enter the data into separate spreadsheets. Next, a cross-analysis can be conducted whereby descriptive statistics are run on the independent data sets and compared for accuracy.

4.2.7 ▲ Select quantitative and qualitative tools consistent with assumptions and data requirements.

The primary strengths and limitations of qualitative and quantitative data collection lie within the nature of the data themselves (Sharma & Petosa, 2014). Given that qualitative and quantitative paradigms exist on opposite sides of the research spectrum, the strengths of one tend to be the limitations of the other and vice versa. For instance, a quantitative researcher may be able to identify a statistical relationship between an intervention program and an increase in the number of vegetables participants consumed, but may not be able to contextualize the participants' experience of vegetable consumption. Major differences between quantitative and qualitative data are provided in Table 4.4.

Table 4.4
Differences between Quantitative and Qualitative Data

Attribute	Qualitative Paradigm	Quantitative Paradigm
View	Emic View (Reality is defined by the participants)	Etic view (Evaluator defines the reality)
Perspective	Holistic perspective (Context and values preserved)	Reductionism (Concepts reduced to context free numbers)
Role of the evaluator	Evaluator as an interactive observer	Evaluator is independent
Richness of context	Studying the rich context is encouraged	Parsimony is encouraged (ability of few variables to predict or explain)
Reality	Post positivist (Reality is multiply constructed and multiply interpreted)	Positivist (Reality can be objectively measured)
Purpose	Hypothesis generation	Hypothesis confirmation
Reasoning	Inductive (Specific to general)	Deductive (General to specific)
Design	Dynamic (No set protocol, flexible)	Fixed (Protocol once set is not modified)
Technology	People centered	Highly technocentric
Technology	Not required	Required

Note. Adapted from Sharma, M., & Petosa, R., L. (2014). *Measurement and evaluation for health educators.* Jones & Bartlett Learning.

Strengths and limitations exist in terms of how qualitative and quantitative data are collected. Qualitative researchers, for example, must be careful not to introduce bias if they are using unstructured interviews as a data collection method. Concurrently, quantitative researchers must construct questionnaire items in such a way that the responses produce data that are reliable and valid. More common currently is for health education/promotion researchers to utilize a mixed method approach to data collection. In a mixed method approach, both qualitative and quantitative data are collected (Jacobsen, 2017). One of the benefits of this approach is that it is believed to produce findings that are more insightful than either approach could produce alone.

Often health education researchers will use previously-developed instruments to collect data. To determine the suitability of existing questionnaires, the researchers must determine if the questionnaire has adequate psychometric properties and if the questionnaire was developed in a population with similar demographic features (Sharma & Petosa, 2014). If not, the instrument may not be suitable. When determining the suitability of existing data collection instruments, Kimberlin and Winterstein (2008) recommended addressing the following questions:

1. Do instruments already exist that can be used to measure a construct the same way or very similar to the desired measure?
2. How well do the constructs in the identified instruments match the construct you have conceptually defined for your study?
3. Is the evidence of reliability and validity well established?
4. In previous research, was there variability in scores with no floor or ceiling effects?
5. If the measure is to be used to evaluate health outcomes, effects of interventions, or changes over time, are there studies in which instrument responsiveness to change in the construct of interest is established?
6. Is the instrument in the public domain?
7. How expensive is it to use the instrument?
8. How much training is required to administer the instrument?
9. Will the instrument be acceptable to subjects?

An important initial step in data collection is to identify types and sources of data that will be useful in answering research/evaluation questions. Depending on the goals and objectives set by health education specialists, a variety of methods can be used to gather data (Goodman & Thompson, 2018). Health education specialists may choose to use existing data collection tools that have been assessed for reliability and validity (Souza et al., 2017). Once the evaluation/research questions are established, the evaluator or researcher should consider relevant existing data and use instruments already in existence, when available. A myriad of data collection instruments exists for both qualitative and quantitative inquiry. Many instruments have been validated and tested for reliability and used repeatedly by national, state, and local health surveillance programs as well as some parallel ongoing programs or inquiries. Health education specialists should be familiar with the existing instruments commonly used in the field. See Table 4.3 for examples of existing instruments.

4.2.8 ■ Adopt, adapt, and/or develop instruments for collecting data.

Health education specialists will have to decide if they can use existing data collection instruments in their original form, adapt an instrument so that it is suitable for the population, or develop a new instrument. In many social service sectors, existing data collection instruments may be used or adapted to suit the needs of the researcher. To adapt or modify existing data collection instruments to be used effectively with new scenarios can make sense. Some advantages include:

- previously tested reliability,
- direct comparison measures,
- reduced costs as compared to the creation of new instruments, and
- user familiarity.

Not all instruments, however, can be used in all populations. Sometimes adaptations must be made for a specific population. Additionally, sometimes specific items can be used, but care must be taken to retain subscales for validity purposes.

Common for health education specialists is to create new items or all-new instruments to be used for data collection, especially regarding program activities, outputs, and short-term outcomes. New instruments may include survey questions, behavior assessment items, and interview questions/guides for face-to-face interviews or focus groups, among others (Couper, 2008; Davidov et al., 2018). Refer to Sub-competency 4.1.8 Adopt or modify existing instruments for collecting data for more information on adopting, adapting, or creating new instruments.

4.2.9 ■ Implement a pilot test to refine and validate data collection instruments and procedures.

As with evaluation, the purpose of a pilot test is to gain insights about whether a data collection instrument consistently measures whatever it should measure. Data gathering processes and instruments should be pilot tested to ensure they are correctly measuring the concepts under investigation (Brownson et al., 2017).

When considering an instrument's validity, the researcher should consider content, criterion, and construct validity (Jack, Jr. et al., 2010, Souza et al., 2017). Content, or face validity, is a concept that involves the instrument's items of measurement for the relevant areas of interest. Review of an instrument by topical experts or researchers could be a method to assess content validity. Criterion validity refers to a measure's correlation to another measure of a variable. Establishing construct validity ensures that the concepts of an instrument relate to the concepts of a particular theory (Jack, Jr. et al., 2010, Souza et al., 2017).

Reliability indicates the accuracy or precision of the measuring instrument. Reliability is an issue of concern for observational data collection as well as with data gathering instruments (Simons-Morton et al., 1995). Specific procedures are performed to estimate instrument reliability among data gathering instruments. Internal consistency is a method used to investigate the intercorrelations among items within an instrument. Selecting a reliability test such as internal consistency, test-retest, split half, and alternate form depends on the type of data (i.e., nominal, ordinal, interval/ratio). To assess the reliability of questions measured on an interval/ratio scale, researchers should use internal consistency. To assess the reliability of knowledge questions, researchers should use test-retest or split-half (Bhattacherjee, 2012, Bolarinwa, 2015).

Test-retest reliability is evidence of stability over time. Rater reliability is the difference among scorers of items and controls for variation due to error introduced by rater perceptions (McKenzie et al., 2017). Existing data collection instruments should be reviewed thoroughly, and each item should appropriately and adequately be related to variables of interest. Researchers should be certain to exclude useless or superfluous items that are not associated with the intent of the research.

As with critiquing instruments for evaluation, researchers should be sure that the language is clear and appropriate for the population to whom the instrument will be administered. Precaution needs to be taken to ensure that language bias has not been introduced into the instrument (Tolley, 2016). One example of language bias in data collection instruments relates to binary response options. Binary response means giving respondents just two options to respond, where there may be more than two clear answers. Consider gender, a binary option would include just two options, male and female, where people may identify as something other than male or female. Another example of binary response options that may not allow all respondents to answer in a way that reflects their situation is marital status, married and unmarried, but some people might identify with some other marital status. Binary options limit the ability of research participants to self-identify. Other examples include heteronormative terms (marriage between heterosexual couples) and non-inclusive personal pronouns (she/he). Instead provide an exhaustive list such as she/her, they/

them, he/him, and an "other" option for the participant to self-identify. Another common example of language bias on surveys is ethnicity. Consider how a respondent might feel when asked to identify their ethnicity and the instrument forces them to choose just one option from a list, but the respondent identifies as multiracial. In this scenario, inclusivity is missing and is, therefore, biased.

A second form of language bias is when one assumes the reader or speaker are native English speakers. This type of bias can lead to miscommunication or alienation of study participants. Unique populations require sensitivity to provide an inclusive survey, such as engaging a respected community member to review the material for appropriateness of the language and tone (e.g., slang, local dialects, and non-verbal language).

A third form of language bias data collection involves the deaf and hearing-impaired communities. Provide alternative means of communication, such as written communication, TTY (Teletype Terminal), text messages, or an American Sign Language interpreter or another appropriate sign language interpreter (Tolley, 2016).

Health education specialists should assess a data collection instrument for language and other bias prior to the data collection phase. Pilot testing a data collection tool with members of the priority population is an essential step in validating a data collection instrument. Pilot testing also provides an opportunity for members of the community to make comments and suggestions to minimize bias in data collection instruments, including language bias. The results of the pilot test will allow for modification of items based on feedback prior to using in the study (Jacobsen, 2017). During the pilot testing phase, the community can comment on cultural appropriateness, language bias, and other stigmatizing concerns that affect data collection instruments.

Competency 4.3 Manage the collection and analysis of evaluation and/or research data using appropriate technology.

Once the data gathering instruments have been developed and reviewed, health education specialists carry out the evaluation or research plan. The plan may be simple or advanced, depending on intended uses and the needs of the program, as well as the expectations of the program planners, funding agencies, and end-users (Cottrell et al., 2018). Usually desirable is to utilize the most rigorous evaluation model or research design available. Ethics, cost, as well as political and resource realities, however, sometimes indicate a lesser approach to evaluation and research designs. Fortunately, these less rigorous approaches and designs are feasible and adequate to answer some research questions when precision might not be as valuable. The researcher is always professionally and ethically bound to provide the most rigorous design and scientifically sound data information to the audience of interest.

4.3.1 ■ Train data collectors.

Health education specialists train personnel and stakeholders regarding appropriate data collection methods to ensure the quality of data. Standardizing the procedure of data collection with frequent monitoring of the process will help ensure collection of data is accurate, complete, and conforms to program requirements.

Data that have been collected is subject to a variety of bias and error. Controlling for researcher bias can be accomplished in part by making sure that trained specialists collect all data. Health education specialists should provide data collectors with clear instructions on how to use instruments and to conduct interviews, focus groups, and other data collection activities. The following steps help reduce error in findings that may be due to issues regarding inter-rater reliability.

1. Walk through the instrument with data collectors to point out specific instructions.
2. Provide an example of a completed instrument or interview transcript for data collectors.
3. Provide clear instructions and/or a script (for phone surveys or interviews) for data collectors to follow.
4. Allow data collectors to practice with a "standard" data set or example to make sure everyone is getting the same answers, when consistency is desirable.
5. Allow interviewers and focus group facilitators to practice in a "role play."
6. Give feedback to data collectors or offer fidelity checks to improve their methods. (Boyce & Neal, 2006)

4.3.2 Implement data collection procedures.

Data collected for evaluation or research can be quantitative, qualitative, or both. Quantitative data are used to numerically describe what is happening (Baumgartner et al., 2021). Qualitative data are not numerical and are usually descriptions of what is occurring or why it is occurring (Baumgartner et al., 2021). Both types of data are valuable to health education specialists throughout the program planning, implementation, and evaluation processes.

It is helpful to formally map each piece of data collected to the analytic plan or reporting requirements and make sure that the data collection will supply everything needed. At times, it seems reasonable to collect as much data as possible, but more is not usually better. When searching for intriguing new discoveries unrelated to the research or evaluation questions, researchers focusing on extraneous data find it is extra work to extract and manage that data, and that, ultimately, the extraneous data produces spurious undesirable results and associations. Another reason to avoid collecting too much data is that trying to manage too many data elements makes it easy to overlook tiny critical errors in the most significant data.

Find reliable, trustworthy, and skilled people to collect, enter, analyze, and manage the data, to ensure quality results. Other considerations for implementation are:

- defining roles, responsibilities, and skills needed to collect, enter, and analyze qualitative data (focus groups, interviews, and community forums), which may differ from the needs related to quantitative data (surveys).
- monitoring the data collection to ensure the implementation of the process will assist in maintaining established timeframes and objectives. Identifying a committee or group would provide this oversight.
- maintaining the integrity of the data collected and ensuring that protocols address quality control measures not only on the collection but also on the entry of data.

Operational resources are essential to any data collection effort and must be considered during the planning stage. For example, the use of incentives could add value to the response rates from populations/participants, access to software to support qualitative data analysis, and budget to cover the cost of facilities to conduct focus groups. Health educations specialists also must communicate with their partners and stakeholders to inform them of the implementation of the data collection process.

4.3.3 Use appropriate modalities to collect and manage data.

Data are used to investigate or track progress toward one or more program objectives. Data also can be used to assess the effectiveness of organizations, services, programs, and policy. Data collection must be carefully monitored and managed to ensure optimal utility. Prior to the administration of data collection instruments, health education specialists should decide about incentives for participants, respondents as proxies for other people, acceptable response rates, and what documentation or information should be provided to the respondent. Field procedures for carrying out data collection include the following:

- Protocols for scheduling initial contacts with respondents
- Introducing the instrument to the respondent
- Keeping track of individuals contacted
- Following up with non-respondents when appropriate

Data should be organized in such a manner that they may be analyzed to interpret findings, which often requires statistical understanding and extensive training to get optimal use from the collected data. Data collectors should follow all protocols and engage quality control measures when necessary to assure usability of the data collected. Computer assisted data collection requires up-front effort, but can greatly expedite data collection, monitoring, and quality control. Of importance is that all data are carefully coded and organized into a useable format (McKenzie et al., 2017). Research and evaluation data can help not only to record what changes have occurred, but also to identify what led to those changes (Aday & Cornelius, 2011).

Managing data is an integral part of the research/evaluation process. How the data are managed depends on the type of data, how the data are collected, and how the data are used throughout the project lifecycle. Effective data management helps the researcher/evaluator organize files and data for access and analysis, which helps ensure the quality of research and supports the published results of said research.

Increasingly popular is to use online survey platforms to collect and manage evaluation and research data. Electronic data collection has gained in popularity with the increase in Internet penetration and comes with unique strengths and limitations. Several strengths of this method are its cost-effectiveness, versatility, potential reach, convenience, and anonymity of the respondents (Cottrell & McKenzie, 2011). Web-based data collection also offers convenience to participants as they can complete the survey where and when it is best for them. From a monitoring perspective, most survey software will allow the evaluators to download the responses and import them directly into statistical software. In doing so, the risk of data entry errors from transcribing data from paper-and-pencil surveys into statistical software is dramatically reduced.

Another advantage to online survey platforms is participant reach. Reach through targeted advertisements on online social media, such as Facebook, helps connect participants potentially interested in the subject matter, such as pregnant mom research, based on the potential participant's recent search history. Although, it is still important to provide a compelling reason to entice participants to complete the online survey or questionnaire, or provide an incentive (e.g., discounts, gift cards). The potential reach of online surveys through targeted recruitment significantly increases the range and population pool far more effectively than previously possible, particularly for the cost (McRobert et al., 2018; Wright, 2005).

Despite its strengths, electronic data collection also has shortcomings. These shortcomings include lower response rates, language barriers, not feasible for all populations (lack of or limited internet access), and the risk for multiple response rates (Couper, 2008). When determining whether to use Internet surveys, the evaluation team should consider the audience's computer literacy and accessibility to high-speed Internet.

Selecting the best method for survey dissemination requires extensive research on the population of interest (e.g., pregnant smokers in their twenties). Members in this group often have preferences for anonymity, and convenience would support the selection of an online tool for dissemination to target this population. Electronic data from online platforms are susceptible to server crashes, as well as hackers. Hackers are individuals who "break into" servers to steal data. Evaluators using commercial survey companies need to investigate the security of the vendor of the platform they are considering. Additionally, the evaluation team should routinely check and download the data to ensure integrity.

4.3.4 ■ Monitor data collection procedures.

Data collection must be carefully monitored and managed to ensure optimal utility. Prior to the administration of data collection instruments, health education specialists should decide about incentives for participants, respondents as proxies for other people, acceptable response rates, and what documentation or information should be provided to the respondent.

Field procedures for carrying out data collection should include protocols for scheduling initial contacts with respondents, introducing the instrument to the respondent, keeping track of individuals contacted, and following up with non-respondents when appropriate. Data collectors should follow all protocols and engage quality control measures when necessary to assure usability of the data collected. This process includes organizing data in such a manner that they may be analyzed to interpret findings. All data must be carefully coded in a useable format (McKenzie et al., 2017). Computer-assisted data collection and analysis software are available to assist with these tasks; however, these systems require up-front effort, statistical understanding, and often extensive training to get optimal use from the collected data.

4.3.5 Prepare data for analysis.

Preparing data for analysis will primarily involve adhering to the data management plan developed during the data analysis planning stage. The data management plan should include procedures for transferring data from the instruments to the data analysis software. The data analysis plan is also used to detail how data will be scored and coded, missing data will be managed, and outliers will be handled. For questionnaires, a scoring guide will tell the research team how to code the variables. The scoring guide also will be used to detail if any items are filler items that should not be included in the scoring calculations, as well as provide scores for any items that need to be reverse coded.

Another important part of the data analysis plan is data screening. Data screening may include assessing the accuracy of data entry, how outliers and missing values will be handled, and if statistical assumptions are met. Outliers can be identified through statistical software; however, the research team often decides how to handle outliers. Problematic outliers are outliers that are not representative of the population. These outliers can arrive from implausible data or biased data. Beneficial outliers are outliers that are representative of the population. Interpretation of whether outliers are beneficial or problematic is often based on the expertise of the research team. Many inferential tests are sensitive to outliers, especially multivariate outliers. Multivariate outliers are unusual combinations of scores on different variables. Multivariate outliers are difficult to detect without the aid of statistical tests. Prior to deleting outliers, the research team should double check to make sure the data are accurately entered. Researchers also will have to deal with missing data (Ponto, 2015; Sharma & Petosa, 2014). Missing data are observations that were intended to be made but were not made. Handling missing data depends largely on how much is missing and if there are patterns to the missing data.

Parametric tests are rested upon many assumptions, which, if not met, can compromise the integrity of the study results. The research team should determine which assumptions they will need to test and how they will be tested during the data analysis planning phase. During the preparation phase, the research team should test the assumptions of the statistical tests they will use to assure they are able to use that statistical test.

4.3.6 ■ Analyze data.

Health education specialists acting in an evaluation or research capacity must consider and plan for the methods and strategies they will use to analyze data before collecting any data. The plan used for analysis is directly related to the methods used to collect data. For example, qualitative data collected from a focus group will require much different analysis than quantitative data collected on a survey about health behaviors.

Analyzing data using qualitative methods helps evaluators or researchers become more experienced with the variables or phenomenon of interest. Hence, evaluators or researchers use qualitative analysis methods to achieve a deep understanding of the issues surrounding items or variables of interest. Qualitative research has a unique value for investigating complex and sensitive matters. As one might expect, it is extremely beneficial to achieve a deep understanding of how people think about specific topics and can be especially helpful when the researcher is willing to trade generalizability for contextual detail. The qualitative analysis enables the researcher to describe the phenomena of interest in detail and in the original language of the research participants (Brownson et al., 2017).

Qualitative research methods include a wide range of data collection strategies (Patton, 2015). The type of qualitative method researchers use depends on the purpose of the evaluation, resources, and use of other techniques. Following are common qualitative approaches often used in health education:
- Observation/audit
- Participant observation
- Document study
- Interviews
- Focus groups (Patton, 2015)

Sample sizes in qualitative data are generally small. Sound qualitative research and evaluation are controlled and systematic. Most analyses involve systematically analyzing the content of the data, breaking it into meaningful pieces, and organizing these pieces in a way that allows the characteristics and meaning to be better understood. There are several steps involved in qualitative data analysis.

1. Data reduction: This step involves selecting, focusing, condensing, and transforming data. The process should be guided by thinking about which data best answer the evaluation questions.

2. Data display: This display involves creating an organized, compressed way of arranging data (e.g., through a diagram, chart, matrix, or text). The display helps to facilitate identifying themes, patterns, and connections that help answer evaluation questions. This step usually involves coding or marking passages in a text (or parts of images, sections of a video, etc.) that have the same message or are connected in some way. An accompanying explanation of what the selected passages have in common is created.

3. Conclusion drawing and verification: During this last step, the data are revisited multiple times to verify, test, or confirm the themes and patterns identified.

(Jeanfreau & Jack, 2010; Miles et al., 2019)

Qualitative analysis is a cyclical and iterative process with many rounds of investigating evidence, modifying hypotheses, and revisiting the data from a new light. Evaluators and researchers reexamine data repeatedly as new questions, themes, and connections emerge. Evaluators and researchers examine qualitative data to identify the following:

- Patterns, recurring themes, similarities, and differences
- Ways in which patterns (or lack thereof) help answer evaluation questions
- Deviations from patterns and possible explanations for the divergence
- Interesting or particularly insightful stories
- Specific language people use to describe phenomena
- The extent to which patterns are supported by past studies or other evaluations (and if not, what might explain the differences)
- The extent to which patterns suggest that additional data need to be collected

(Malterud, 2012)

Qualitative data are coded using words that describe the content or a process. Researchers can look for themes, or patterns, based upon these codes. There are multiple data analysis approaches in qualitative research. For example, researchers can use a narrative analysis approach, where they are using theory to assist them in drawing conclusions or a discourse analysis approach; a discourse analysis approach, where they use linguistics to interpret verbal and nonverbal communication; or a grounded theory approach where they are using data to develop theory, among others (Jacobsen, 2017).

By contrast, quantitative data can be analyzed using descriptive analysis with the aim that characteristics of the group of people or the program being studied are summarized (Aday & Cornelius, 2011; Ponto, 2015). Descriptive analysis is exploratory and designed to describe phenomenon specific to a population using descriptive statistics such as raw numbers, percentages, and ratios. Descriptive statistics are used to show what the data reveal, as well as provide simple summaries about what the samples' measures. A variety of ways exist to represent descriptive data numerically. Two such classifications include continuous data that have the potential for infinite values for variables or discrete data that are limited to a specific number of values to represent variables. Descriptive data also may be classified as nominal, ordinal, interval, and ratio. Nominal scores cannot be ordered hierarchically, but are mutually exclusive (e.g., male and female). Ordinal scores do not have a standard unit of measurement between them but are hierarchical. Interval scores have common units of measurement between scores, but no true zero. Ratio scores represent data with common measurements between each score and a true zero (Porta, 2014). Mean, median, and mode are measures of central tendency that can be used depending on the type of data collected. Variance, range, and standard deviation can be used to describe the dispersion of the data.

Analytic analysis is explanatory, and both descriptive statistics and inferential statistics may be used to explain the phenomenon. Inferential statistics, such as t-test, analysis of variance (ANOVA), analysis of covariance (ANCOVA), regression analysis, and many of the multivariate methods like factor analysis, multidimensional scaling, cluster analysis, discriminant function analysis, and so on are used when researchers or evaluators wish to draw conclusions about a population from a sample (Neutens & Rubinson, 2014). This process involves making inferences about central tendency such as mean, median, mode, or any number of other aspects of a sample distribution of a population. A variety of sampling methods is common to research and program evaluations to a lesser degree. Health education specialists are responsible for knowing terms that relate to using inferential and other statistical methods.

A variety of computer software technologies are available to support data analysis. Some data analysis software is open-source software. Open-source software is in the public domain and may be used free of charge. The majority of data analysis software is commercial, meaning it is designed to meet the needs of a specific customer base. Consequently, commercial software may vary in the types of statistical analyses packages they offer. If the research team would like to perform specialized analyses, team members should consult with the vendor prior to purchasing a software license. Software learning curves can range from easy to very difficult. Many software companies provide training and tutorials on how to use their software, and some offer certification programs. Although computer software, when used correctly, can assist with the analysis of both qualitative and quantitative data, health education specialists must know how to use the software and be familiar with the basic principles of data analysis, statistics, and the standards of evaluation and research. Depending on the sophistication of the analyses, a statistical consultant might need to be hired to perform data analysis.

Popular software for analyzing quantitative data include the following:
- *Microsoft Excel* for comprehensive statistical analysis
- *SPSS* for comprehensive statistical analysis
- *SAS* for comprehensive statistical analysis
- *Stata* for comprehensive statistical analysis
- *R* open-source software containing a variety of statistical packages

Popular software for analyzing qualitative data include the following:
- *ATLAS.ti* for visual analysis of data
- *Ethnograph* for analysis of textual data
- *HyperRESEARCH* for analysis of textual and multimedia data
- *QSR Nvivo* for assisting in code-based theorizing
- *MAXQDA* for analysis of text-based data from focus groups, unstructured interviews, case histories, field notes, observation protocols, and document letters

(Sharma, & Petosa, 2014)

Competency 4.4 Interpret data.

Health education specialists often collect, analyze, and interpret data. The research and evaluation questions and the level of measurement of the data, whether for evaluation or research purposes, should be used to guide data analysis. Expert consultants in qualitative or quantitative data analysis can guide the process if the research or evaluation questions are complex or if the health education specialist is unfamiliar with the specific analysis tool or software.

Health education specialists' ability to interpret results from their own and others' evaluations and research is essential. Uncovering facts regarding a program's performance is not enough to draw evaluative conclusions. Correlates can be derived through the interpretation of data, reach and effectiveness or size of the effect can be measured (CDC, 1999). According to Brownson et al. (2015), health education specialists need to incorporate an evidence-based practice approach to their evaluation and research findings and scientific evidence into decision-making, policy development, and the implementation of programs. Evidence comes from reviews of literature, research, and evaluation processes. Programs steeped in the principles of evidence-based practice have gained favor among professionals practicing health education. In an evidence-based practice approach, the best available scientific evidence and data are combined, program-planning frameworks are employed, community engaged, programmatic evaluation employed, and results disseminated (Brownson, et al., 2017). Evidence must be interpreted to determine the significance and draw relevant inferences to plan future programs or interventions. Data interpretation is strengthened with the inclusion of key stakeholders and incorporating community perspective during the evaluation inquiry process (CDC, 1999).

4.4.1 ■ Explain how findings address the questions and/or hypotheses.

Health education specialists conducting research or evaluation should compare the results of their investigations against previously developed research/evaluation questions. The questions asked to reflect the values held by stakeholders provide a basis for forming judgments concerning program performance. In practice, when stakeholders articulate and negotiate their values, these negotiations become the standards for judging whether a given performance of a program will be considered successful, adequate, or unsuccessful. The evaluation and research questions generated early in the process reflect the stakeholders' values. When operationalized, these standards are used to establish a comparison by which the program can be judged. The use of which data collection methods and analyses determines the probability that findings are not due to chance. The results of the evaluation/research can provide a narrative of experiences, as well as the strengths and weaknesses of the investigations. Sometimes helpful is to have the main results addressing the key research/evaluation questions listed first and then present the additional findings. Accurately interpreting results will put valuable information in perspective, enabling evaluators and/or researchers to compare results and findings to the expected outcomes of stakeholders.

In evaluations in which multiple methods are used, health education specialists detect evidence patterns by isolating important findings (analysis) and combining different sources of information to reach a larger understanding (synthesis). When agencies, communities, and other stakeholders agree with the synthesis of analyzed data, they are more inclined to use the evaluation results for the program. The five steps in data analysis and synthesis are straightforward:

1. **Enter the data into a database and check for errors:** If health education specialists are using a surveillance system, such as BRFSS or PRAMS, the data have already been checked, entered, and tabulated by those conducting the survey. If health education specialists are collecting data with their own instruments, they will need to select a computer program for entry and analysis of the data, as well as determine who will enter, check, tabulate, and analyze the data.
2. **Tabulate the data:** The data need to be tabulated to provide information, such as a number or percentage for each indicator. Some basic calculations include determining the number of participants achieving the desired outcome or the percentage of participants achieving the desired outcome.
3. **Analyze and stratify the data:** Health education specialists analyze and stratify the data by various demographic variables of interest, such as participants' race, sex, age, income level, or geographic location.

4. Make comparisons: When examination of health education specialists' program includes research as well as evaluation studies, health education specialists should use statistical tests to show differences between comparison and intervention groups, geographic areas, or the pre-intervention and post-intervention status of the priority population. They should present data in a clear and understandable form. Data can be displayed in tables, bar charts, pie charts, line graphs, and maps.

4.4.2 ▲ Compare findings to other evaluations or studies.

Health education specialists serving as researchers/evaluators should describe the results of data analyses clearly in writing so their results can be compared to results of other programs or studies. Results and statistical data that are appropriately presented provide health education specialists with comparable findings. Findings might be compared to previous reports on the same priority population or with similar programs through parallel studies, systematic reviews, surveillance data, online databases, and investigations reported in peer-reviewed articles. A variety of techniques can be used to compare data from different sources (Neutens & Rubinson, 2014). Data comparisons can be presented graphically in tables, figures, bar or line graphs, and pie charts. Comparing findings with findings in other published literature creates useful information for stakeholders and evaluators to consider.

4.4.3 Identify limitations and delimitations of findings.

In research, **delimitations** are parameters or boundaries placed on the study by the researchers that help to manage the scope of a study (Connelly, 2013; Cottrell & McKenzie, 2011). Delimitations differ from limitations in that **limitations** are boundaries placed on a study by factors or people other than the researchers (Connelly, 2013; Cottrell & McKenzie, 2011). Delimitations often involve narrowing a study by geographic location, time, and population traits. Subsequently, findings must be analyzed within the context of the specific delimitations of the study.

Even under the best of circumstances, the findings from evaluation and research are subject to systematic error in the sampling, design, implementation, or analysis that compromises the results to some degree. Often this error is referred to as bias. Confounding variables (or factors) are extraneous variables outside the scope of the intervention that can impact the results (Jack, Jr. et al., 2010; Lehmann et al., 2017). In other words, some variables affect results and are not accounted for in the study design. Health education specialists need to be able to evaluate sources of error in evaluation or research critically to make sense of scientific reports, as well as popular media. Health education specialists should be able to identify research errors such as sampling errors, lack of precision, and variability in measurement. They also should be able to spot systematic errors such as selection bias, instrumentation bias, and other internal threats to validity (Friis & Sellers, 2014; Lehmann et al., 2017).

4.4.4 ■ Draw conclusions based on findings.

After analyzing the data, the research team can evaluate the findings from the study and draw conclusions. Keeping conclusions grounded in the research questions and hypotheses will prevent unwarranted extrapolation. Furthermore, conclusions should be constrained by a study of delimitations and limitations (e.g., the sampling technique used). The research team members must be careful to interpret conclusions considering the specific delimitations and limitations of their study.

4.4.5 ■ Identify implications for practice.

Implications are often the focus of future research or evaluation and suggestions for health promotion practice. The results of new research on a health issue or topic should be used to guide decisions about how an intervention could be refined, expanded, or translated for widespread use in practice (a less controlled environment). For example, if researchers conducting a study about teen tobacco use prevention concluded that the audience is more likely to respond favorably to peer-based social media messages compared to traditional media messages with celebrity spokespersons, a health education specialist should recognize that the best strategy for a new intervention would be to recruit teens in the community to post messages on their social media channels, while avoiding investments in billboard and radio advertisements in which the local quarterback is featured. In this example, the intervention channel would change based on findings from the study.

Similarly, evaluation results offer insights about how an intervention could be modified to improve outcomes. Perhaps in earlier research studies, it was suggested that a particular strategy would be effective, but an evaluation did not yield expected outcomes. Health education specialists should be able to examine those results and make decisions about how best to modify the program to optimize desired results.

The results of research and evaluation efforts are only the starting point. Health education specialists must consider multiple other factors when deciding how best to implement or modify an intervention. The list of factors that affect program decisions is seemingly endless. Common considerations include the following:

- **Political environment**. Perhaps an assessment or evaluation demonstrated a need for comprehensive sexuality education, but in a political election year, this subject is a controversial one. The politics in this situation must be factored into decisions about how best to address the health needs identified.
- **Cultural barriers.** In an assessment, for example, it was determined that many young mothers in a refugee settlement are not breastfeeding their babies. Through research about the culture, a health education specialist learns that breastfeeding is considered taboo. Being sensitive to the culture of the community must be factored in decision making about the intervention.
- **Funding limitations.** Many times, it is common for the most desirable solution to an issue determined through research and evaluation to be out-of-reach economically. Health education specialists must not only consider the best option through research and evaluation, but also the cost-to-benefit proposition, return on investment, and propose an intervention that is within the constraints of available funding.
- **Shifting and variable leadership priorities.** Often health education specialists work within an organization or system where other individuals, e.g., administrators, political appointees, elected officials, or other high-level decision-makers have their own priorities, which may compete with time, attention, and resources.

Health education specialists must be skillful at presenting the results from their research and evaluation to inform and influence decision-makers. Health education specialists also should provide insights into implications for future research. For example, what knowledge gaps were filled and what additional questions could be addressed by future work? What were some of the limitations and how could those be addressed in future research or evaluations (e.g., population(s) sampled, sample size, measurements)?

4.4.6 ■ Synthesize findings.

Refer to Sub-competency 4.4.1 for the steps in data analysis and synthesis.

Lessons learned throughout the course of an evaluation or research study do not automatically translate into informed decision-making and appropriate action. Deliberate effort is needed to ensure that the processes and findings are used and disseminated appropriately. Understanding and being able to clearly articulate the findings of an evaluation/research investigation provides stakeholders the perspective necessary to make judgments concerning its merit, worth, or significance. Five elements are critical for ensuring use of an evaluation. They are:

- design, which refers to how the questions, methods, and overall processes are constructed;
- preparation, which refers to the steps taken to rehearse eventual use of the findings;
- feedback, which is the communication that occurs among all parties;
- follow-up, which refers to the technical and emotional support that users need during the evaluation and after they receive evaluation findings; and
- dissemination, which is the process of communicating either the procedures or the lessons learned from an evaluation to relevant audiences in a timely, unbiased, and consistent fashion (CDC, 2013; Issel & Wells, 2017).

4.4.7 ■ Develop recommendations based on findings.

Recommendations are actions for consideration resulting from evaluation or research. These recommendations can be short, intermediate, or long-term in nature. They help program staff improve programs, make decisions about program operations, and move toward program goals. Forming recommendations is a distinct element of program evaluation that requires information beyond what is necessary to form decisions regarding program performance. Suggestions for continuing, expanding, redesigning, or terminating a program are separate from judgments regarding a program's effectiveness. To make recommendations, information concerning the context, particularly organizational context in which programmatic decisions will be made, should be used to guide the process. Proposals that lack enough evidence or those that are not aligned with stakeholders' values can undermine an evaluation's credibility. By contrast, an evaluation can be strengthened to anticipate political sensitivities of intended users and highlight areas that users can control or influence. Sharing draft recommendations, soliciting reactions from multiple stakeholders, and presenting options instead of directive advice increase the likelihood that recommendations will be relevant and well-received (CDC, 2011b; Issel & Wells, 2017).

4.4.8 ■ Evaluate feasibility of implementing recommendations.

Robust evaluation designs in which randomized control trials, cohort studies, and case control/comparison studies are used provide evaluators and stakeholders with confidence in the validity of the evaluation. Recommendations used in these evaluation designs may be used to generalize to other similar scenarios. Most recommendations derived from program evaluation, however, will be specific to the program itself and directed at program planners and stakeholders either involved in the effort or affected by it. The feasibility of implementing recommendations from evaluations depends on cost, resources, time, politics, and other contextual factors. Programs planned with an evaluation plan and developed with provisions for flexibility allow for early adjustments in programming that may have the potential for desired effects or minimize costs to be maximized. With enough time and strong stakeholder support, feedback on program processes and impacts can serve to improve programming and the feasibility of implementing recommendations. Health education specialists can use a similar importance and feasibility matrix as the one used in a needs assessment process. Refer to Sub-competency 1.4.2 for an example matrix to assist with this process.

Competency 4.5 Use findings.

Findings from evaluation and research can be applied based on the intention of the user. Health education specialists and/or evaluators should make certain that stakeholders have an opportunity to carefully review and discuss research or evaluation findings before applying recommendations to programs or policy. Evaluators translate recommendations to action plans, including who is going to do what about the program and by when. Stakeholders will likely require various reports that may include an executive summary with an explanation of the evaluation goals, methods, and analysis procedures, listing of conclusions and recommendations, and any relevant attachments, including evaluation questionnaires, interview guides, and so on. Evaluators may deliver the results in the form of a presentation accompanied by an overview of the report. Evaluators should be sure to record details of the evaluation plan that can be referenced as needed in the future.

4.5.1 ▲ Communicate findings by preparing reports, and presentations, and by other means.

Reporting or communicating research involves detailed documentation. Research is often prepared with the intention of publishing findings in professional peer-reviewed literature for use by other investigators. Although a report may be developed to meet the needs of stakeholders, typically the first part of the report includes an introduction. This introduction may include the front matter (such as the title of the program, names of the evaluators or researchers, and date of the report) and the executive summary. Also included in the introduction should be an explanation of the background of the program and the health-related and/or other problems addressed by the program (Issel & Wells, 2017; Neutens & Rubinson, 2014).

The second part of the report, the literature review, may include an explanation of relevant studies and an understanding of the background for the study. The literature review also will relate to the purpose of the study, research questions, hypotheses, and the priority population. In the literature review, a theoretical orientation will be provided, which also may provide the framework for the review (Murphy et al., 2017; Neutens & Rubinson, 2014).

The method section is used to describe how the evaluation or research plan was carried out. This section includes an overview of the procedures, subjects, and data gathering instruments used in the research (Murphy et al., 2017; Neutens & Rubinson, 2014). The data analysis plan is often described within the method section.

In the results section, evidence tested against the stated hypotheses or research questions is presented along with the statistical findings and includes a discussion of what the findings mean. Findings should be presented in factual and descriptive terms to meet the needs of the intended audience. The results are often communicated in words, numbers, and statistics. The discussion of the data findings typically provides interpretation, implications, and applications to practice (Murphy et al., 2017; Neutens & Rubinson, 2014).

The final portion of the written report may include conclusions, recommendations, or a summary (Murphy et al., 2017; Neutens & Rubinson, 2014). This section is the part of the report most likely to be read by the stakeholders, in addition to the executive summary (Jack, Jr. et al., 2010; Murphy et al., 2017). The conclusions indicate whether the analysis supports the hypothesis and often includes recommendations for future research and new research questions. In the summary, problems, procedures, and principal findings may be briefly restated. (Murphy et al., 2017; Neutens & Rubinson, 2014).

4.5.2 ■ Disseminate findings.

Dissemination is the process of communicating procedures, findings, or lessons learned from an evaluation to relevant audiences in a timely, unbiased, and consistent fashion. Like other elements of the evaluation, the reporting strategy should be discussed in advance with intended users and other stakeholders. Such consultation ensures that the information needs of relevant audiences will be met. Planning effective communication also requires considering the timing, style, tone, message source, vehicle, and format of information products. Health education specialists should consider dissemination audiences (e.g., research/program participant, organization, community) and the best format to reach them. Regardless of how reports are constructed, the goal for dissemination is to achieve full disclosure and impartial reporting. Developing a checklist of items to consider in creating a tailored evaluation report may help to direct the report content for the audience by explaining the focus of the evaluation, its limitations, strengths, and weaknesses (Issel & Wells, 2017).

Health education specialists contribute to the profession and to the professional development of other health education specialists by sharing their research/evaluation findings. A common way to disseminate research findings is through presentations at local, state, national, and international health-related conferences. Through presentations, dialogue about the processes and outcomes related to evaluation/research are encouraged. Often, the abstracts and objectives of the presentations are required to facilitate a peer-reviewed process for selecting the presentations that appear in conference programs. Conference sessions may include poster sessions, breakout sessions (i.e., session time shared with other speakers), concurrent sessions (i.e., session time dedicated to one presentation), and keynote sessions.

An evaluation or research report is the typical form of communication used to disseminate the outcome of the plan set forth by the evaluation or research planners (Issel & Wells, 2017). Although reports take on different styles, these documents need to provide user-friendly information to the stakeholders involved (CDC, 2013a). Other dissemination methods for more public consumption or community audiences may be writing newsletter or news articles, creating an infographic, short PowerPoint presentations, or one page brief with key highlights of the purpose, methods, key results and implications.

4.5.3 ■ Identify recommendations for quality improvement.

Recommendations are actions for consideration resulting from evaluation or research. They help program staff improve programs, make decisions about program operations, and move toward program goals. Forming recommendations is a distinct element of program evaluation that requires information beyond what is necessary to form judgments regarding program performance. Recommendations for continuing, expanding, redesigning, or terminating a program are separate from judgments regarding a program's effectiveness. To make recommendations, information concerning the context, particularly organizational context in which programmatic decisions will be made, should be used to guide the process. Recommendations that lack sufficient evidence or those that are not aligned with stakeholders' values can undermine an evaluation's credibility. By contrast, an evaluation conducted by a health education specialist can include recommendations that anticipate political sensitivities of intended users and highlight areas that users can control or influence. Sharing draft recommendations, soliciting reactions from multiple stakeholders, and presenting options instead of directive advice increase the likelihood that recommendations will be relevant and well received (CDC, 2013a).

Program evaluation and research studies provide important information for the incorporation of recommendations that will help improve programs based on their evaluation. Forming recommendations requires information beyond just what is necessary to form judgments. For example, knowing that a program can increase the services available to battered women does not necessarily translate into a recommendation to continue the effort, particularly when there are competing priorities or other effective alternatives. Thus, recommendations about what to do with a given intervention go beyond judgments about a specific program's effectiveness. If enough evidence does not support recommendations or if they are not in keeping with stakeholders' values, they can undermine the credibility of an evaluation.

4.5.4 ▲ Translate findings into practice and interventions.

The health promotion process is cyclical. Health education specialists begin with an assessment, then plan, implement, and evaluate interventions based on the needs that were identified in a community. In many ways, the evaluation that occurs at the end of a project can serve as a renewed assessment of the community. An evaluation report likely offers new insights and perspectives about the population that were assessed earlier. If the evaluation showed that knowledge, attitudes, or behaviors within a community were shifted positively because of the intervention, the health education specialist knows efforts were successful. If the evaluation did not yield the desired results, however, it becomes necessary to modify the intervention, make midcourse corrections, or do something different. Research findings are similar in that the results of the research study can be used to make decisions about how and when an intervention should be administered; the difference, in this case, is with timing. Research results should be used to inform the development of new interventions, while evaluation reports can be used to support decision-making about how to modify a program.

Chapter 5
Area of Responsibility V: Advocacy
KEY: No symbol - entry level; ▲ - advanced 1; ■ - advanced 2

5.1. Identify a current or emerging health issue requiring policy, systems, or environmental change.

5.1.1   Examine the determinants of health and their underlying causes (e.g., poverty, trauma, and population-based discrimination) related to identified health issues.

5.1.2   Examine evidence-informed findings related to identified health issues and desired changes.

5.1.3   Identify factors that facilitate and/or hinder advocacy efforts (e.g., amount of evidence to prove the issue, potential for partnerships, political readiness, organizational experience or risk, and feasibility of success).

5.1.4   Write specific, measurable, achievable, realistic, and time-bound (SMART) advocacy objective(s).

5.1.5   Identify existing coalition(s) or stakeholders that can be engaged in advocacy efforts.

5.2. Engage coalitions and stakeholders in addressing the health issue and planning advocacy efforts.

5.2.1   Identify existing coalitions and stakeholders that favor and oppose the proposed policy, system, or environmental change and their reasons.

5.2.2   Identify factors that influence decision-makers (e.g., societal and cultural norms, financial considerations, upcoming elections, and voting record).

5.2.3 ▲   Create formal and/or informal alliances, task forces, and coalitions to address the proposed change.

5.2.4   Educate stakeholders on the health issue and the proposed policy, system, or environmental change.

5.2.5   Identify available resources and gaps (e.g., financial, personnel, information, and data).

5.2.6   Identify organizational policies and procedures and federal, state, and local laws that pertain to the advocacy efforts.

5.2.7   Develop persuasive messages and materials (e.g., briefs, resolutions, and fact sheets) to communicate the policy, system, or environmental change.

5.2.8   Specify strategies, a timeline, and roles and responsibilities to address the proposed policy, system, or environmental change (e.g., develop ongoing relationships with decision makers and stakeholders, use social media, register others to vote, and seek political appointment).

5.3. Engage in advocacy.

5.3.1   Use media to conduct advocacy (e.g., social media, press releases, public service announcements, and op-eds).

5.3.2   Use traditional, social, and emerging technologies and methods to mobilize support for policy, system, or environmental change.

5.3.3 ▲   Sustain coalitions and stakeholder relationships to achieve and maintain policy, system, or environmental change.

5.4. Evaluate advocacy.

5.4.1   Conduct process, impact, and outcome evaluation of advocacy efforts.

5.4.2   Use the results of the evaluation to inform next steps.

The Role. Health education specialists are expected to advocate for and support initiatives that promote the health of priority populations. This means they should initiate and promote legislation, laws, rules, policies and procedures that are designed to enhance health. Whether it be federal health care legislation, a state law to require motor cycle helmets, a league rule mandating mouth guards in youth basketball, or corporate policy to restrict smoking in common areas, health education specialists should have the skills to initiate and promote such initiatives. Further, health education specialists should advocate for their profession, health education certification, and accreditation of professional preparation programs. They need to educate potential employers about the benefits of hiring professionally trained, degreed and certified health education specialists. It is important that health education specialists talk to legislators, decision makers, personnel directors, allied health workers, coworkers, family and friends about the value of health education and health promotion (NCHEC, 2020).

Setting: The following text is presented to describe how advocacy is used in different practice settings (NCHEC, 2020).

Community Setting: Health education specialists act as advocates for community health needs using sound evidence and ethical principles. They may advocate for policies, laws, rules and/or regulations that promote the health of the priority population. For example, health education specialists may support, encourage or lobby the local government to use funds to develop bicycle paths or for a youth sports program to create a policy that requires all participants to require mouth guards. Health education specialists also advocate for their own agency/department and for the health education profession as a whole. Advocacy can take place as part of one's employment or as the civic responsibility of a private citizen.

School (K-12) Setting: In the K-12 setting, health education specialists may promote the WSCC model, which emphasizes the relationship between educational attainment and health by putting the child at the center of a system designed to support both health and education. Health education specialists may provide expert assistance to administrators in examining state and local mandates and recommending placement of health education programs in the overall curriculum scope and sequence plan. The K-12 health education specialist must be prepared to advocate for the school's health education program as well as laws, policies, rules and regulations that support youth health. The development of health councils or student health ambassador groups should also be encouraged to assist the health education specialist in advocacy efforts.

Health Care Setting: In the health care setting, the health education specialist must advocate for the health of patients and their families. In a patient-centered health care system, this could involve promoting patient engagement with health care professionals, including patients in creating and developing patient education programs and materials, or advocating for organizational policy, rule or system changes that may improve the patient experience and ultimately patient health. Like health education specialists in other settings, health education specialists in the health care setting need to advocate for the health education profession and the hiring of certified health education specialists (CHES®). This may involve educating allied health professionals, staff and patients about the specific skills of a health education specialist. For example, the health education specialist may advocate for health educators to be given the responsibility to complete Medicare's Annual Wellness Visit in the clinical setting per the recommendations of the Centers for Medicare and Medicaid Services.

College/University Setting: Health education specialists in the college/university setting may be charged with being advocates for health education programs at the campus level or for the health education profession at the campus, state, national or global level. In addition, the health education specialist in the college/university setting may also engage in advocacy for public health actions such as policy change or legislative action. These advocacy situations may be intended to influence campus colleagues and administrators, community members, decision-makers, and other stakeholders. Interaction with these individuals may take place in "one on one," small group or large group situations. The actions may occur in formal or informal settings, and may be planned or incidental (i.e., "the elevator speech"). Advocacy actions may also require the development of advocacy informational materials or the use of traditional or social media. Beyond engaging in advocacy, the health education specialist working in a professional preparation program may have responsibilities in preparing prospective health education specialists in the planning, implementation and evaluation of advocacy efforts.

Worksite/Business Setting: Health education specialists may act as advocates for health education and health promotion with other functional units within the worksite including occupational health, safety, work/life, employee assistance, benefits, and other business units and functions. Health education specialists identify, organize, and advocate for resources needed for the implementation, continuation, and evaluation of programs. Health education specialists may also advocate for new policies and/or for changes to existing policies related to health and wellbeing, e.g., tobacco-free policies. They also identify data and present to key stakeholders to ensure that activities match the stated goals, objectives, outcomes, and budget. These metrics may be called key performance indicators (KPI). This often supports health education specialists' future advocacy for additional resources to modify and expand their programs. Health education specialists also need to advocate for their profession and support professional initiatives that will further the profession such as certifications and accreditations.

College/University Health Promotion Services Setting: Health education specialists in this setting advocate for support and acceptance of health education and promotion services, programs, and resources for the campus community and its members. They also advocate for policies that support health and well-being, and systems changes that ensure efficacy of health promotion services from a socioecological perspective. Health education specialists in this setting need to stay apprised of local, state, and national health issues, proposed laws/regulations, and opportunities that may impact the campus community's health. Another important advocacy role is to promote the health education profession and seek opportunities to showcase the health education specialist's important role on campus.

Key Terms

Act is a bill or joint resolution that has passed both chambers of the US Congress, been signed into law by the president, and has become an individual law (United States Senate [USS], n.d.).

Activism is engaging in activities such as peaceful protests, civil disobedience, or boycotting (Parvanta et al., 2018) to gain attention for a specific cause.

Advising refers to when an organization or individual shares information without indicating a preference for which way a specific policy or legislation may go (Parvanta et al., 2018).

Advocacy occurs when individuals or non-governmental organizations work together to build coalitions, inform public opinion, set agendas, or communicate through the media about a specific topic (Parvanta, et al., 2018).

Agenda is a proposed order of business for a political meeting or party (Baumgartner, 2016).

Constituent is a citizen residing in the district for which a specific legislator covers (National Conference of State Legislatures [NCSL], 2019).

Cultural Inclusion refers to ensuring all individuals, especially those historically excluded, are included in the process of decision-making (National Council on Nonprofits [NCN, 2019).

Health Equity is a state wherein everyone has the same opportunities and access to attain optimal health (Wilensky & Teitelbaum, 2020).

Legislator is an elected member of a legislative body (NCSL, 2019).

Legislature is the branch of government responsible for enacting laws (NCSL, 2019).

Legislation is a bill or joint resolution of the US Congress (USS, n.d.).

Lobbying is an action of an organization wherein someone is paid to persuade elected officials to vote or take action on a specific topic or piece of legislation (Parvanta et al., 2018).

Lobbyist is a person who is paid by a specific special interest group (a body of people who hope to receive benefits) to influence legislation (NCSL, 2019).

Media Advocacy occurs when an individual, coalition, or organization uses the media to advance a specific initiative (Parvanta et al., 2018).

Media Relations refers to when an organization creates a management plan to share information with the larger public (Parvanta et al., 2018).

Public Policy is a multifaceted approach to solving issues of public funding and is also seen as the "output" of government (Theodoulou & Cahn, 2013).

Policy Maker is anyone who makes decisions that impact others such as members of the US Congress (Parvanta et al., 2018).

Political Action Committees (PACs) are established and administered by corporations, labor unions, and other membership organizations with the purpose of soliciting funds from individuals associated with the sponsoring organization (United States Federal Election Commission, 2020).

Resolution is a document to express opinions or intent of a specific organization or legislative chamber (NCSL, 2019).

Upstream Factors is a focus on the cause of the problem at the broadest or initial occurrence (Parvanta et al., 2018).

Competency 5.1 Identify a current or emerging health issue requiring policy, systems, or environmental change.

The health education specialist needs to identify and prioritize health issues or behaviors for policy, systems, or environmental change. Some examples of these topics are increasing access to healthy foods, tobacco cessation, or access to places for physical activity. This process includes exploring social determinants of health that influence an issue for future advocacy efforts. These determinants could include characteristics of the community member to environmental and policy factors. Understanding these social determinants can assist health education specialists in defining their advocacy and policy change goals and objectives.

5.1.1 Examine the determinants of health and their underlying causes (e.g., poverty, trauma, and population-based discrimination) related to identified health issues.

The health education specialist should examine determinants of the health issue by applying a socio-ecological and social determinants of health perspective. These determinants could include individual (e.g., knowledge, attitudes, skills), interpersonal factors (e.g., provider recommendation), organizational, community (e.g., media campaigns, transportation), and policy factors. Health education specialists may need to conduct a literature review or read about issues on government websites to collect this information. Refer to Sub-competency 1.3.1 for more information on social determinants of health.

Tracking life expectancy by census track or zip code can be used to describe wide ranges of mortality between areas within a defined geographical area (Boothe et al., 2018; Robert Wood Johnson Foundation, 2018). Using this analysis of life expectancy as an example, addressing these disparities by assessing the extent to which inequities exist among populations allows health education specialists to consider upstream factors in the social, physical, and built environments that are the root cause for differences in disease distribution and health outcomes among populations of different racial, ethnic, age related, and socioeconomic backgrounds.

5.1.2 Examine evidence-informed findings related to identified health issues and desired changes.

The health education specialist needs to find evidence-based information about the health issues, impacts of health issues, and potential solutions for background information to prepare for advocacy efforts. They can search through computerized reference databases for this information for published articles on evidence-based interventions or solutions to health issues, which are accessible at most universities and public libraries. In addition, information about health issues for advocacy efforts can be found in many reference databases and are accessible to the public such as the National Library of Medicine's PubMed, Google Scholar, Journal Storage (JSTOR), and the Education Resources Information Center (ERIC). Fact-based information on a health issues, who is affected by health issues (epidemiology) and health consequences also can be accessed at no cost on governmental websites such as the National Institutes for Health (NIH) and the Centers for Disease Control and Prevention (CDC). Moreover, current facts can be accessed from topic-specific non-profit health organizations such the American Liver Foundation, American Cancer Society, or the American Heart Association. Finally, health education specialists can find evidence-based solutions or interventions in Cochrane review databases, Community Guide to Preventive Services (https://www.thecommunityguide.org/), and national policy clearinghouses (i.e., What works https://ies.ed.gov/ncee/wwc/).

Health education specialists examine evidence-informed findings related to identified health issues and desired changes. Health education specialists should use evaluation and research findings in policy analysis to inform health policy debates and to help address decision-makers' information needs regarding longstanding critical issues, such as people who lack access to healthcare, efficient operation of government health insurance programs, effective care delivery, chronic disease and long-term care, health care financing, and public health. Further, the utilization of evaluation and research findings can help health education specialists assess needs of their stakeholders that remain unmet (McKenzie et al., 2017). Use of evaluation and research findings in policy analysis will serve as a key resource to help health education specialists remain current with reported policy implications, identify solutions, and translate effective policy and media advocacy techniques to influence decision-makers into practice.

As professionals, health education specialists interact with a variety of individuals ranging from legislative correspondents, health care providers, and patients. The health education specialist has to be skilled in written and verbal communication, as well as in understanding and interpreting mass media (Parvanta et al., 2018). Conceptually, health policy includes factors and forces that affect the health of the public (Wilensky & Teitelbaum, 2020). Policies play a major role in delivering and financing health care and public health efforts in the United States; policies influence or structure health care, communities, and society.

The following forces affect the organizing, financing, and delivery of health-related policy: congress, federal health agencies, states, health care providers, businesses, and local communities (Wilensky & Teitelbaum, 2020). For example, congressional members could bring health-related legislation forward for a vote, while health care providers and communities can advocate or promote education for policy change. Because health policy is an ever-changing endeavor, it is essential for health education specialists to stay abreast of developments for advocacy work and policy change through their organization, advocacy partners, and state legislation agenda.

5.1.3 Identify factors that facilitate and/or hinder advocacy efforts (e.g., amount of evidence to prove the issue, potential for partnerships, political readiness, organizational experience or risk, and feasibility of success).

For health education specialist, simply being trained in advocacy skills is not sufficient. Even seasoned advocates are affected by various factors that hinder or promote their efforts. For example, during the 2010s, many states implemented medicinal marijuana policies, and advocates were at a loss for accurate and evidence-based support to advocate against such an effort. The same was true during the 2019 JUUL (vaporized nicotine device) usage epidemic among middle- and high-schoolers in the U.S. Other potential factors that could hinder advocacy efforts include (Buchar, 2011):
- lack of awareness of current issues or legislation.
- lack of advocacy skills.
- positions that prohibit the ability to advocate during work hours.
- lack of time.
- lack of funding.
- lack of self- or collective-efficacy.

While there are some barriers to being an advocate, there are also many ways in which the health education specialist is supported and encouraged to advocate. For example, the professional competencies for health education specialists includes advocacy as a key area of work (NCHEC, 2019). Other recognized opportunities for advocacy include the following:

- **Training** in advocacy skills and issues such as the annual Health Education Advocacy Summit, in which there are scholarships to support attendance (Society for Public Health Education [SOPHE], 2019a), or the SOPHE advocacy webinar series.
- **Participating** in national action such as the SOPHE Action Center (SOPHE, 2019b), the APHA Legislative Action Center (APHA, 2019), and NACCHO Policy and Advocacy Activities (NACCHO, 2019) all of which do important research and connect health education specialists with their legislators.
- **Collaborating** among organizations through coalitions and other partnerships.
- **Training programs** at the undergraduate and graduate levels wherein courses are focused on advocacy, creating advocacy tracks in programs, and even creating certificates in public health advocacy.

5.1.4 Write specific, measurable, achievable, realistic, and time-bound (SMART) advocacy objective(s).

Objectives are statements in which changes in policy, for example, are described in measurable terms. SMART is the acronym for writing objectives: specific, measurable, attainable, realistic, and time-sensitive. Refer to Sub-competency 2.2.4 for more information on SMART objectives. Below are some examples of advocacy objectives.

- By March 2022, 65% of US congress persons will vote "yes" on the CARE Act.
- By August 2022, 70% of US senators will receive a briefing kit.
- After the 2020 Health Education Advocacy Summit, congress will hold votes in both houses for the CARE Act.

5.1.5 Identify existing coalition(s) or stakeholders that can be engaged in advocacy efforts.

To ensure advocacy efforts are effective, the health education specialist must engage stakeholders in the community who often are also gatekeepers to grass roots mobilization. By conducting key informant interviews, holding focus groups, reviewing case studies, and conducting surveys of people in different settings that are specific to political context, health education specialists begin the process of building a stakeholder base for their advocacy efforts. Health education specialists also find advocacy champions through local topical coalitions (e.g., obesity), health departments, social services agencies, community organizations, and community members.

Once an advocacy issue is identified, the health education specialist can ask the following questions when engaging stakeholders (University of Kansas, 2019a):

- What community resources are available?
- Who are the allies and adversaries on this issue?
- Who else shares the problem?
- What would those groups who share the problem gain or lose by joining the campaign?
- Would you be willing to help with advocacy efforts?

Competency 5.2 Engage coalitions and stakeholders in addressing the health issue and planning advocacy efforts.

Coalitions, formal, long-term alliances among organizations, can be powerful change agents for policy, system, or environmental change. Coalitions represent large numbers of individuals and groups, and decision-makers are aware that coalitions may include their constituents. Coalitions can be strengthened and resources expanded by identifying existing coalition and stakeholder allies who share similar advocacy interests or have the resource capacity to assist an advocacy initiative (Hampton & Lachenmayr 2019). The health education specialist can conduct an environmental scan of agencies or coalitions working on a similar health issue through reviews of initiatives in local papers or health-related newsletters, or when attending professional meetings. They can locate state or local affiliates of national organizations or advocacy groups.

5.2.1 Identify existing coalitions and stakeholders that favor and oppose the proposed policy, system, or environmental change and their reasons.

To identify existing allies already working on similar issues, making sure to survey their strengths and resources, the health education specialist should use a local resource directory or asset inventory of associations and institutions. Potential allies may support the initiative if benefits of achieving the advocacy goal for them outweigh their coalition costs in time, money, and effort. The more benefits potential allies receive by achieving the advocacy goal, the more likely they will join the initiative. In bringing forward state legislation about increasing physical activity (e.g., minutes of activities daily) for students, the health education specialist could seek partners in stakeholders such as a state-wide coalition for Physical Activity and Nutrition, schools of public health or community health programs, non-profits focused on health, and regional cancer coalitions. The health education specialist will analyze each groups' bene-fit-to-cost to prioritize groups for recruitment and to strategically emphasize the benefits of supporting the initiative, and look first for those coalitions and stakeholders who possess unique expertise that the coalition presently lacks (University of Kansas, 2018a). Once identified and on-board, the health education specialist should encourage assistance with activities in which benefits are emphasized to their organization, such as contributing their data/statistics and using their established media contacts/experts as well as drafting organizational resolutions and signing-on to letters.

The health education specialist can identify coalitions and stakeholders in opposition to the proposed legislative or policy action and can assist the advocacy group with strategy and argument creation to attempt to persuade them on the issue or find common ground (Hampton & Lachenmayr, 2019). To identify existing or potential opponents, the health education specialist can develop a list of those individuals and groups that may have something to lose if the advocacy goal is achieved. Health education specialists can determine what they may lose, what influence they may have, and possible strategies and tactics they may use in opposition. Opposition is issue-dependent, and sides may change over time. Health education specialists can identify potential opponents to the proposed legislation and can listen to their arguments, redirect resources, and craft targeted persuasive messages to counter resistance (University of Kansas, 2018b). Once identified, health education specialists can engage potential opponents who may have something to lose and encourage their assistance, when possible, through listening sessions, issue education, and the opportunity for negotiated strategies and resource leverage.

5.2.2 Identify factors that influence decision-makers (e.g., social and cultural norms, financial considerations, upcoming elections, and voting record).

Advocating is adding a value judgement about the need for policy change while educating decision-makers about the issue. Decision-makers can be influenced by the actions and messages of strong, visible coalitions, the parties of which may want to be associated with health-promoting changes (Butterfoss, 2019). The health education specialist can learn decision makers' level of previous knowledge and awareness of the health issues and influence decision-makers using health advocacy communication messages crafted to emphasize the importance of the issue to their constituents (Matteson & Lam, 2016). For example, in recommending that a legislator vote for the Comprehensive Addiction Resources Emergency (CARE) to fund opioid and substance services in states and community, a health education specialist can present numbers of people affected by opioid addiction in a senator's state, its health and economic effects, and what voting for the act would provide constituents such as more funding for education about the harms of opioid use and treatment and public health services to address the addiction.

Health education specialists can conduct research and analyze factors that influence their decision-making about how the proposed policy, system, or environmental change may affect their constituents. They can research credible information sources as well as the level of public support for the change. To demonstrate the level of public support, community and community leader opinion surveys, focus groups, and interviews can be used (Friedman & Schwartz, 2016).

Health education specialists should determine if the decision-makers are supportive of the proposed policy by examining if they or their family have been affected by the issue, who their influencers are, what similar issues they support, and other self-interests related to the proposed policy. Health education specialists can use state legislative tracker systems (e.g., govtrack.us) or scan state or local newspapers to learn about these areas. In addition, they can analyze and chart the decision-makers' political capital such as amount of money and donors, their communications capacity, and number of supporters they can organize. To identify additional factors that influence decision-makers, research their voting record, the issues the decision-makers are passionate about, their future political ambitions and upcoming elections, their organizational relationships and memberships, and their values and ideals (Fresina & Pickles, 2013). For example, as a part of its funding, the 21st Century Cares Act has the Beau Biden Cancer Moonshoot initiative to support cancer research. Former Vice President Joe Biden and President Obama launched this initiative and the Act was approved in 2016. It was named for Biden's son who died from brain cancer.

5.2.3 ▲ Create formal and/or informal alliances, task forces, and coalitions to address the proposed change.

Health policy advocacy can affect and sustain large population health behavior change by modifying the surrounding environment. For example, health education specialists can work with a community coalition to be a part of community organizing to increase green spaces in a city to promote walking, biking, and playing outside for physical activity. Groups of interested, motivated stakeholders, not just decision-makers, can influence policy, system, or environmental change (Eyler & Brownson, 2016).

The health education specialist can develop strategic alliances, collaborative relationships between groups or organizations, assist all parties to mobilize and share resources and expertise to attain a common goal and speak with one voice. A high level of strong community participation is a key element in a health policy advocacy campaign. Groups, formally or informally, who organize a community around a health issue require strong leadership and a dedicated core of individuals who are willing to intentionally mobilize their resources for a common goal. Whether recognized formal alliances (i.e., coalitions) or informal alliances without legal recognition, alliance membership increases coalition capacity. Alliance benefits include demonstration to decision-makers of widespread support of the issue, maximization and leverage of power and resources, resource-sharing, and diverse approaches to manage the issue. On the other hand, health education specialists should realize drawbacks to working in alliances include more complex decision-making, possible workload inequalities, and difficulties in sustainability (Cole & Sleet, 2016).

Types of alliances for advocacy efforts can include task forces and coalitions. A task force is an action-oriented and time-limited group convened for a specific purpose. Coalitions, a "group of groups" formed to share information and resources around a common issue, are formal and long-term. A coalition is created for sustainability and possess formal structures and written agreements for leadership, communications, and finances (Cole & Sleet, 2016). Coalition collaborative efforts can range from pooled resources and negotiated strategies to taking supportive roles such as signing on to letters to decision-makers or sharing membership lists.

Whatever the format, alliances help build advocacy capacity. First, the health education specialist should decide if an alliance is the best approach to take and, if it is, communicate with and enlist as many groups such as businesses, health agencies, or educational leaders necessary to demonstrate a coordinated approach to decision-makers. Health education specialists can help identify the goal of the group and needed resources, and recruit potential members at community events or service club meetings. The health education specialist can look for organizations with similar interest in the issue, specialized skill sets, experience in the advocacy field, and those who represent the diversity of the community (Hampton & Lachenmayr, 2019). In planning to advocate for a tobacco ordinance to limit smoking in outdoor spaces such as parks in a county, a health education specialist could work with local tobacco coalition and American Cancer Society Cancer Action Network (CAN) advocacy organization in which members have experience in educating and advocating for cancer-related policy change. The health education specialist can request participation in the task force or coalition early in the process to let the coalition members know ahead of time the level of commitment and involvement expected of them. The coalition members should create a coalition structure, meet regularly, and continually evaluate operations. Possible coalition members may include (Prevention Institute, 2014):

- policy-makers,
- experts,
- organizations with a similar focus,
- community influentials, and
- the target audience.

5.2.4 Educate stakeholders on the health issue and the proposed policy, system, or environmental change.

Once a policy, system, or environmental change has been identified and an educational campaign has been determined to be the best strategy for change, a health education specialist can conduct a review of the relevant literature to find a description of the health issue, effects of the health issue in terms of epidemiology, health consequences or costs, and potential interventions or solutions to address the issue. The health education specialist can obtain factual information derived from scientific and evidence-based research to educate the public and decision-makers about the issue and citations from government agencies, peer-reviewed journals, and the coalition's program evaluation results. For example, in assisting with advocacy efforts for raising the age of use of tobacco products to reduce teen smoking initiation, the health education specialist can present data about current rates of smoking cigarettes and e cigarettes among adolescents, the harmful effects of smoking related to cancer, heart disease, and emphysema, and present data that legal age laws do restrict and reduce teen smoking and that other states also are trying to pass or have passed similar laws. Armed with appropriate data, resources, and their personal stories, coalition members can be mobilized to educate decision-makers. Educating refers to providing information on an issue without asking for action on that issue. Coalition members can educate decision-makers on behalf of the coalition, as long as no value judgement or specific bill number is mentioned. Credible evidence gathered can be presented in various ways such as personal contact, legislative briefings, and formal reports. The health education specialist should build a continuing professional relationship with decision-makers and consistently provide them with credible information on health issues (Hampton & Lachenmayr, 2019; Kwon & Nelson, 2016).

Health education specialists can build traditional health communication campaigns to increase awareness and educate a priority population about disease-preventing and health-promoting information, attitudes, and behaviors. Health education specialists may employ a variety of mass media, multi-media, and inter-personal communication channels and strategies tailored to their interests. Health communications campaigns are used to influence a population's health behaviors (Kreps et al., 2019). Health communications campaigns can be used as a strategy to educate the public and decision-makers about a proposed policy, system, or environmental change. In media advocacy, decision-makers with the power to affect change are the priority audience, and the public is the secondary audience (Dorfman & Bakel, 2019). For policy changes, health education specialists should focus their advocacy efforts primarily with decision-makers such as organizational leaders, school boards, health plan leaders, county administrators or state leaders.

5.2.5 Identify available resources and gaps (e.g., financial, personnel, information, and data).

Health education specialists can conduct an asset inventory to identify advocacy campaign resources and gaps. Community assets mapping is a strategy to list and categorize resources that the advocacy coalition could use during the advocacy campaign to make policy or environmental changes as well as resource gaps within a community. Refer to Competency 1.2.7 – Determine primary data collection needs, instruments, methods, and procedures to learn more about community assets mapping. The health education specialist can gather data around strengths of coalitions, presence of individual advocates, community support, and other indicators of community assets through interviews, surveys, or community discussions. Using primary data collection techniques such as interviews or windshield tours (walking or driving through the community), mapping helps the coalition determine the best locations, audiences, and community networks to target (Matteson & Lam, 2016).

Obtaining these necessary campaign resources requires funding. The health education specialist should analyze the coalition's commitment to fundraising and identify any gaps in funding for advocacy activities by projecting costs for all advocacy efforts planned and assessing the current available funds. The coalition should attempt to obtain funds from a variety of sources. Possible funding opportunities and fundraising methods may include grant applications, donor solicitations, or special events. Also, coalition members should evaluate the campaign budget for materials and staffing costs as well as any income expected from fundraising. A comprehensive fundraising plan, including activities, strategies, timeline, and evaluation, will assist in identifying appropriate approaches to obtaining funds to fill budget gaps (Fertman et al., 2019). For example, the health education specialist can outline different campaigns with potential donors throughout the year in the fundraising plan, and what activities would be conducted for that campaign such as fun run, dinner function, or telethon to raise funds. The asset inventory can be used to identify skill gaps in coalition membership, and potential members with expertise related to the health issues and/or advocacy skills (e.g., community organizing, writing briefs). After skill gaps are identified, individuals can be asked to join the coalition to help fill those gaps (Friedman & Schwartz, 2016).

Because data and evidence are the foundation of strong advocacy campaigns, the health education specialist should describe the problem and its distribution such as how many people are affected by a health issues. Moreover, the health education specialist should research factual information and the most localized data to present to local administrators or legislators, because they are concerned for their constituents. Background data collected should include socio-economic costs of the policy, barriers to the advocacy campaign (i.e., need for more stakeholder support, policy opponents, advocacy window), and issue history. Any data gaps about the health issue should be filled in using primary data collection techniques. In addition to background information and data, health education specialists can detail all of the resources needed to meet the goals and objectives including facilities, funds, advocates, media and community contacts, and access to other resources (Matteson & Lam, 2016).

5.2.6 Identify organizational policies and procedures and federal, state, and local laws that pertain to the advocacy efforts.

Health education specialists should be aware of advocacy policies and procedures for the setting in which they work. For example, employees in non profit agencies can perform lobbying as long as that lobbying meets the federal guidelines and does not exceed a certain percentage of the activities in that nonprofit organization. Lobbying is any attempt to influence specific legislation according to federal law. Lobbying can be direct via communications with a member or employee of the legislature, while grassroots lobbying attempts to influence public opinion with respect to the legislation or issue and encouraging the policy-maker to act (Internal Revenue Service, 2019). Lobbying is different from advocacy in that it involves asking decision-makers to pass or dismiss a certain policy or piece of legislation. Advocacy tends to take a more general form of creating awareness or mobilizing the communities. It should be noted that health education specialists working for some state and federal agencies are not allowed to conduct lobbying activities. Health education specialists should know polices that govern them in their workplace to avoid any potential violations. (Galer-Unti et al., 2016; IRS, 2019; Parvanta et al., 2018). They can check with their human resources, governmental affairs, or communications offices about rules related to policy and advocacy for their employer.

5.2.7 Develop persuasive messages and materials (e.g., briefs, resolutions, and fact sheets) to communicate the policy, system, or environmental change.

In creating health communication campaigns, the health education specialist aims to shape the discussion on issues through messages told from the public health point of view. Steps in creating a campaign include: determine media goals and objectives, state priority audiences for the message, craft the message, and evaluate the message (Doyle et al., 2019a). Media advocacy, with its focus on the health communication processes for advocacy issue awareness, can assist in influencing health policy through wide information dissemination. To develop an effective message, the health education specialist creates a health communication team including health issue and communication experts and coalition representatives to plan the approach and determine a position statement. Advocacy needs are assessed, and strategies are implemented and evaluated (Mattson & Lam, 2016).

Once the advocacy goal and key stakeholders are defined, a clear, specific, message needs to be developed to per-suade decision-makers to act. Specifically, effective media advocacy, used in conjunction with policy advocacy, starts with a persuasive message strategy. The strategy includes: the message (what is said to the public and decision-makers, the messenger, the mass media, and the target audience, the public and decision-makers) (Dorfman & Bakel, 2019). The most effective messages grab decision makers' attention, address obstacles, and are culturally competent (Mattson & Lam, 2016). For example CHIP [Children's Health Insurance Program] is the US campaign website (http://www.CHIPisUS.org/); supporters are invited to learn about the impact of the CHIP program and contact decision-makers to say "Yes to funding CHIP." The health education specialist should craft messages that are simple and compelling and supported by credible evidence. In the message, the health education specialist defines the health problem, provide a solution, and directs the message towards those decision-makers who can implement the change (Parvanta et al., 2018).

The health education specialist can synthesize the research into clear, easy-to-understand persuasive messages using metaphors, personal stories, and charts and graphs (Kwon & Nelson, 2016). For example, if the message demonstrates to the decision-maker how the policy will positively affect constituents, it may be more persuasive. The health educa-tion specialist can frame the message, integrating new information with existing understanding. In addition, effective, attention-getting messages are most likely to be persuasive and influence decision makers' behavior if they are repeat-ed, offer a reward or benefit, are consistent with values or norms, have low cost or risk involved, and come from a cred-ible authority (University of Kansas, 2018c). Multiple methods can be used to communicate the persuasive message to decision makers including briefs, resolutions, and fact sheets.

Briefs

In the CDC, four types of briefs are listed as follows:
1. Information briefs in which research on policy approaches is summarized.
2. Issue briefs in which all available evidence, when policy solutions are unknown to-date, is summarized.
3. Policy impact briefs contain the most information on an issue, having large amounts of existing evidence as well as potential impact of policy implementation.
4. Policy briefs are used to summarize best practices and policy options and are used in policy development and implementation

(CDC, 2018b; Kwon & Nelson, 2016).

A policy brief is focused on one topic and backed by credible, evidence-based data. A brief provides a decision-maker with a description of an issue as well as implications of policy enactment to address the issue (Parvanta et al., 2018; Uni-versity of Iowa Prevention Research Center, 2017). Authors of the policy brief attempt to convince the decision-maker to take a specific action on the issue; therefore, it needs to be especially persuasive.

Policy briefs cover, in about six pages or less:
- the defined public health problem and its importance,
- relevant evidence and data analysis,
- policy options and recommendations, and
- limitations and conclusions.

(Bhattacharya, 2013)

Resolutions

Professional associations adopt policy resolutions, written statements of support of, or opposition to, legislation to express the group's formal opinion and desired actions. In a resolution, the problem or issue is defined, and rationale and background are described using statements prefaced by "Whereas" clauses. A "Resolved" statement or description of recommended action completes the resolution (National Conference of State Legislatures, 2019).

In 2020, a resolution about Addressing the Health Impacts of Climate Change was created through the Society for Public Health Education. The following are some of the "whereas" statements in the resolution:
- Whereas, extreme weather events can directly harm human health and impact health indirectly through outcomes such as food insecurities and malnutrition.
- Whereas, climate change has affected food security due to warming, changing precipitation patterns, and greater frequency of some extreme events (Climate change has negatively affected crop yields in some areas and led to lower animal growth rates).

Source: (SOPHE, 2020) https://www.sophe.org/wp-content/uploads/2020/05/Final-SOPHE-Climate-Change-Resolution-5.4.20-2.pdf

Fact sheets

Health education specialists can create one-page, easy-to-read fact sheets for coalition members to distribute to decision-makers and the public. Focusing on the most important and up-to-date relevant information about the issue, fact sheets include a statement of the issue, who is affected by the issue, and recommendations to solve the issue (Hampton & Lachenmayr, 2019). The health education specialist should format the fact sheet on colored, letter-sized paper, create a headline or title, use bulleted lists with plenty of white space, and use charts or other simple illustrations to emphasize key points (Parvanta et al., 2018).

5.2.8 Specify strategies, a timeline, and roles and responsibilities to address the proposed policy, system, or environmental change (e.g., develop ongoing relationships with decision makers and stakeholders, use social media, register others to vote, and seek political appointment).

Once the health education specialist has collected and analyzed all pertinent evidence and data about a health issue and potential interventions to address it, health education specialists can determine the campaign objectives, identify the priority policy solution, and create a strategic plan. A first step to address the proposed policy change is to set an advocacy agenda to inform the advocacy plan. The health education specialist should determine a clear action to shape the advocacy plan, identify decision-makers who can implement the change action, and create an effective, persuasive advocacy message that comes from credible influencers (Galer-Unti et al., 2016).

The health policy advocacy plan should reflect identified community health issues about which community members have deep feelings. The issue, though, needs to be winnable, specific, affect many community members, be supported by evidence and data, and involve coalition and community members in important ways as part of a comprehensive program plan. Community health needs assessments and asset inventories can assist in helping the coalition members focus their efforts and identify an issue (Hampton & Lachenmayr, 2019).

Promoting a health issue can be in the form of a voluntary policy, a local ordinance or law, or a state or federal law. When first choosing the health issue of interest for the community, it is necessary for a coalition to consider what:

- could be gained by supporting the issue,
- is the stage of readiness and commitment of the coalition to address the issue,
- other groups are affected by the issue, and
- policies are already in existence to deal with the issue.

(Hampton & Lachenmayr, 2019)

In general, planning for health policy advocacy is similar to health education program planning. Just as with program plans, health policy advocacy plans must be created in advance of taking advocacy action, conducted with a coalition or partners, and include goals/objectives, asset assessment, community support analysis, change targets, strategic style, and action steps. On the other hand, health policy advocacy planning differs from traditional program planning as hidden agendas, differing values systems, and actions within a political system are important parts of the process. Also, advocacy planning and advocacy action happen simultaneously instead of in a linear manner, making assessment a continual task. Planning phases generally include some type of:

- political/organizational analysis,
- issue identification and framing,
- goal creation,
- information gathering,
- and actions,
- evaluation.

The health education specialist should create and monitor an advocacy plan. In that plan are found not only goals, actions, timelines, responsible personnel, and resources needed but also assets, allies/opponents, targets and agents, strategies and tactics used, and specific action steps that can be evaluated (Doyle et al., 2019b; Friedman & Schwartz, 2016).

Some specific strategies that may be included in an advocacy plan include talking points, newspaper editorials, letters/e-mail/phone calls, public service announcements, press conferences, websites and blogs, and face-to-face meetings with decision-makers. When meeting with decision-makers, the health education specialist can prepare background materials, prioritize the most important points, and be professional in the advocacy presentation (Galer-Unti et al., 2016). Social media, used in behavior change interventions, is also used in policy advocacy campaigns. Social media messages communicated from social media channels can be used to inform the public as well as assist in gaining supporters to the cause (Brownson & Eyler, 2016; Friedman & Schwartz, 2016; Galer-Unti et al., 2016). Complementing traditional media, using social media may increase awareness among a decision-maker's constituent, who, in turn, may address the issue with the decision-maker (Mattson & Lam, 2016). For example, the #MeToo movement, where women share their stories of sexual harassment, has spurred awareness about the issues and also changes in terms of removal of individuals who were guilty of harassment, and more education about harassment of women. The movement also has led to changes in state and organizational policies around workplace harassment in legislation on statute of limitations on sex crimes. The health education specialist can encourage citizens to register and vote on policies, systems, or environmental changes that promote health or become deputy registrars in a county to register others to vote. In addition, they may serve on councils and boards that can lead to the health education specialist holding public office themselves (Galer-Unti et al., 2004).

Competency 5.3 Engage in advocacy.

The health education specialist may engage in advocacy or work with community members or coalitions to affect change and can employ many types of media for advocacy such as public service announcements and social media. Many potential techniques that can be used either by health education specialists or community members to influence decision-makers to make changes that affect public health. These strategies can involve direct advocacy through a meeting with a local city official or legislator, media advocacy, or educating groups to vote or organize a health issue.

5.3.1 Use media to conduct advocacy (e.g., social media, press releases, public service announcements, and op-eds).

Advocacy initiatives are designed to influence policy and law and often include working with the media (Parvanta et al., 2018). These communications for these initiatives can include interviews, press releases, media alerts, backgrounders, public service announcements, op-eds, or letters to the editor. The health education specialist should include multiple media advocacy strategies into the plan.

5.3.2 Use traditional, social, and emerging technologies and methods to mobilize support for policy, system, or environmental change.

There are many types of strategies to include in an advocacy plan. Examples include traditional, social, and emerging technologies. Traditional advocacy strategies involve the following:
- Voting behavior (i.e., register to vote and encourage others to do the same)
- Electioneering (i.e., contributing to the campaign of a candidate supportive of public health and health education)
- Direct lobbying (i.e., contacting a policy maker)
- Grassroots lobbying (i.e., town hall meetings, door-to-door petitions)
- Media advocacy (i.e., responding to members of the media for health-related information)

(International Centre for Policy Advocacy, 2014)

Not all advocacy should be face-to-face interactions. Some advocacy techniques include sharing a link on a social media platform of a credible article. Examples of social advocacy techniques include (International Centre for Policy Advocacy, 2014):
- social media platforms (e.g., Facebook, Twitter, and blogs).
- signing online petitions through platforms like Change.org or We the People.

Internet action networks are vital resources for health education specialists to use when working on advocacy issues and considered emerging methods in technology (International Centre for Policy Advocacy, 2014). A brief list of public health action networks follows:
- APHA has *Legislation Updates* that contain information about health-related legislation, a Media Guide that allows members to send electronic letters to local media, and the Legislative Action Center that has regular updates posted on legislation and allows members to e-mail local political representatives (APHA, 2019).

- BALLOTPEDIA, an online encyclopedia of American politics and elections, has lifetime voting records for US Senators and Representatives.
- Capwiz, a site where elected officials by location are listed, can be used to connect constituents with the appropriate elected officials based on zip code.

In addition to Internet action networks, mobile technologies are emerging solutions for advocacy. These technologies can include any device and/or application in which mobile technology to communicate with people across great distances is used (Hall & Ireland, 2016). TakeAction! is one such example (Developing New Leaders (DNL) Media, 2019). After arranging personal settings, an alert is sent on a cellular phone for specific issues for which the person is interested in advocating. Two other emerging technologies for advocacy are the following:

- SMS advocacy platforms (e.g., phone2action)
- Advocacy software (e.g., DNL or Salsa)

5.3.3 ▲ Sustain coalitions and stakeholder relationships to achieve and maintain policy, system, or environmental change.

Sustaining coalitions and stakeholder relationships are necessary to maintain, improve, and promote policy, system, or environmental change. The health education specialist should sustain coalitions by having a large group of passionate advocates, having strong relationships, including diverse viewpoints, and seeking and carefully using funding. Butterfoss (2019) recommended eight steps to build and sustain effective coalitions:

1. Clarify or reaffirm vision and mission.
2. Engage the community.
3. Solidify collaborative infrastructure and processes.
4. Recruit and retain active, diverse partners.
5. Develop leaders.
6. Market the coalition.
7. Focus on action.
8. Advocate.

To accomplish the work of coalition building as it relates to advocacy, the health education specialist must create a specific advocacy plan. An advocacy plan includes five elements (University of Kansas, 2019f):

1. Goals
2. Organizational considerations
3. Constituents, allies and opponents
4. Targets
5. Tactics

In the first two steps of coalition building, health education specialists should identify the goals of the advocacy effort and identify organizational issues that can be used to facilitate or impede efforts. Next, health education specialists should begin to identify their allies, constituents, and opponents. Allies are a critical part of any campaign and, therefore, play an essential part in the implementation of advocacy efforts. Allies connect health education specialists to their advocacy objectives.

Once the health education specialists know the campaign goals, organizational issues, and has developed a list of allies and opponents, a list of the targets for their campaign needs to be developed, such as a city board who can vote on a health issue. Health education specialists must identify which individuals can make the final decision about that health issues and should keep good records regarding whether these identified individuals are considered a target, supporter, opponent, or undecided on the issue. As a final step to the development of an advocacy campaign, health education specialists need to begin to strategically think about the tactics that they can use with their allies to influence their targets and help them to achieve their campaign goal. A good resource to use in the development and implementation of advocacy plans is the Community Health Toolbox available at https://ctb.ku.edu/en/table-of-contents/advocacy/advocacy-principles (University of Kansas, 2019d).

As health education specialists plan action steps, it is useful to ask themselves the following questions (University of Kansas, 2019h):
- What will be the scope of this action?
- Who will carry it out?
- When will the action take place and for how long?
- Do we have the resources to make it happen?
- What resources are available?
- Which allies and constituents should be involved?
- Which individuals and organizations might oppose or resist?

The developers of policy make changes at one or several levels. At the national level, congress and federal health agencies have prominent roles in developing health policy (Parvanta et al., 2018). Federal programs such as Medicare and Medicaid impact the financing and delivery of care for Americans. At the state level, states can enact legislation and set guidance for professional licensure for health care providers and professionals. At the community level, businesses and their health plans, hospital systems, medical centers, and health departments policies can be implemented at the community level to affect the local community (Baciu et al., 2017).

Many techniques exist that can be used to help influence policy makers. Policy makers are held accountable to their constituents and as civil servants. Many people do not exercise their right to influence policy makers, so those professionals who do choose to advocate or lobby can be extremely effective. The following is a list of potential techniques that health education specialists or their community coalition can use either by themselves or in combination to influence decision-makers (International Centre for Policy Advocacy, 2014):
- Vote.
- Have legislative meetings with staffer or policy maker.
- Develop policy tool kits or resolutions that can be disseminated to others with whom to advocate.
- Use policy makers to help influence other policy makers.
- Hold town hall meetings with policy makers present.
- Write an opinion piece for the local newspaper.
- Send a tailored advocacy letter with a clear "ask" to the policy maker.

Certain ways are available to influence policymaking depending on the stage of the process (University of Kansas, 2019i). For example, during policy formulation, the health education specialist could help set the agenda by defining the problem and evaluating policy solutions, as well as recommending content and evidence to draft the policy or legislation. During policy implementation, health education specialists can offer public comment on draft rules or policies and serve on advisory bodies. After enactment, they can recommend changes based on operational experience, evaluations, or new health evidence.

Before contacting an elected official to inform or advocate for a health issue, it is important to be knowledgeable about the issue being discussed. To become more knowledgeable, a health education specialist can review bills, resolutions and other legislation that are found at Congress.gov (Library of Congress, n.d.). This website has all federal legislative information and is maintained by the Library of Congress. The health education specialist can prepare brief and clear "talking points" in which the problem, proof of the problem, and the solution being advocated are stated (Parvanta et al., 2018). Many individuals contact their elected officials by phone, e-mail, fax, letter, or in-person. E-mailed or faxed letters are a preferred written method, because, unlike mailed letters, these correspondences do not have to go through a bioterrorism screening process. Because of the changing dynamics of the mail screening processes, individuals should check for the best way to contact an elected official through their website or aides or individuals who work as staff to support the offices of members of congress.

Prior to a first meeting with a legislator to discuss a legislative proposal or pending legislation, it is vital for the health education specialist to discover facts about the legislator (University of Kansas, 2019j). The health education specialist could locate how the legislator has voted in the past on health issues, committees or subcommittees on which they serve, and special interests (National Council, 2017). This process will help identify personal and professional information about the legislator, as well as endorsers, committees, sponsors, and influencers of the legislator. In the meeting with the legislator, the health education specialist should share views on an issue, asking him or her to vote a specific way on a bill or support a new legislation.

After contacting a legislator, advocacy efforts are not over. For example, it is important to take the time to show appreciation with a "thank you" and to follow-up with the representative or an appropriate staff person. The health education specialist can find others who support the issue and encourage them to make a phone call, write a letter, sign a petition, or schedule a meeting. By using a variety of strategies to advocate for health issues, health education specialists have the potential to shape and change policy to impact the health of many people (University of Kansas, 2019j).

The health education specialist conducts media advocacy by following some basic steps to improve the effectiveness of the advocacy efforts. A strategy is to develop a particular media channel, understand the media, develop messages for that channel, and attract journalists' attention and trust (Parvanta et al., 2018).

The health education specialist and/or individuals involved in advocacy work and policy change often question their impact on the system. Evaluating the progress of policy change created by advocacy efforts can be challenging. The following are recommended steps in a policy advocacy evaluation (Parvanta et al., 2018):

1. Adopting a conceptual model for understanding the process of policy change
2. Developing a theory about how and why planned activities lead to desired outcomes

3. Selecting benchmarks to monitor progress
4. Measuring progress toward benchmarks and collecting data

The use of theory is helpful when a health education specialist plans for evaluation efforts to identify successes and weaknesses. For example, the use of the Transtheoretical Model Stages of Change (Simons-Morton et al., 2012) is a theory that can be used for evaluating advocacy efforts. See Table 5.1.

Table 5.1
Example of the application of the Stages of Change Model to Public Health Advocacy.

Construct	Specific Progress
Precontemplation	The legislator or community does not see the use of JUULs (e-cigarette) by high-school students as threatening their health.
Contemplation	With the use of the media, more legislators and community members are concerned about high-schoolers using JUULs.
Preparation	Congress creates a new caucus to end the youth vaping epidemic and begins to plan their meetings and communication strategy.
Action	The caucus contacts the media to discuss the caucus, research findings, and legislation. This caucus meets until legislative success is achieved.
Maintenance	Legislation is enacted and enforced across the US.

Research results regarding the effects of healthcare policy provides evidence-based information that affects healthcare outcomes. In addition, reliable and valid results from research influence quality, cost, use, and access to public health and health care (Wilensky& Teitelbaum, 2020). The research background on health issues and impacts of different policy or legal approaches helps public health stakeholders make informed decisions and improve the quality of health education and public health efforts.

Competency 5.4 Evaluate advocacy.

Advocacy campaigns are focused on an overall goal (e.g., policy to change) and specific objectives or secondary goals necessary to accomplish the overall goal (e.g., media access, coalition capacity expansion). Advocacy effort evaluation allows coalitions to monitor and track progress, gains, changes, and resource allocation (CDC, 2011b). The health education specialist can use qualitative and quantitative methods to collect data to assess if the advocacy goals were met.

5.4.1 Conduct process, impact, and outcome evaluation of advocacy efforts.

In advance, health education specialists should clarify their advocacy goals, create timelines and benchmarks to monitor progress, and determine how the results will be used. They should set realistic, measurable goals and monitor progress on not only the primary goal (most important advocacy goal) but also any secondary goals (Dake & Jordan,

2016). Compared to health education program evaluation, advocacy evaluation poses some interesting challenges because of a campaign's long duration, a coalition's sustainability level over the life of the campaign, the types of evaluation designs necessary, and the need for tracking "small steps" in the progression of the campaign. The evaluation focus, therefore, is on acquiring the best information to guide future decision-making on the way to a policy change (Friedman & Schwartz, 2016; Lloyd et al., 2002).

Advocacy evaluation starts with evaluation planning. For example, the health education specialist and coalition's evaluation team should first establish the purpose and audience for the evaluation. Next, they define the goals, objections, and actions for the short and long term, similar to traditional program planning and evaluation and prioritize primary and secondary goals. Primary goals may include policy adoption, placement, or maintenance. Secondary goals are important to help determine if progress is being made towards the primary goal and may include partnership formation and co-sponsorships, issue support, outreach efforts, strategies and tactics, coalition capacity, and change in community norms (Lloyd et al., 2002).

The health education specialist can use qualitative and quantitative methods to evaluate advocacy efforts. Qualitative methods may include case studies, stories, and opinion pieces, while quantitative methods include surveys or polls of communities. Health education specialists also can track meetings with decision makers about issues, media spots or social media posts (and impressions) of their messages, and meeting notes of different advocacy campaigns.

The health education specialist should match measures and data collection strategies to goals and objectives before collecting and analyzing data. Next, the process evaluation during the campaign is conducted. Process indicators for implementation can include campaign reach, activities and tactics counts, and other products tracked. The impact evaluation is next and is used to measure policy awareness or public attitude change. Finally, the health education specialist conducts the outcome evaluation to measure if the policy was adopted (Dake & Jordan, 2016; Lloyd et al., 2002). Similarly, the health education specialist can conduct outcome evaluation to measure media advocacy campaign effect on decision-makers and the public. The health education specialist can conduct a process evaluation in the implementation phase to monitor media message reach and influence and monitor the media advocacy strategy to improve efforts and revise messages as necessary (Hampton & Lachenmayr, 2019; Lloyd et al., 2002; Mattson & Lam, 2016). Examples of outcome and process measures in evaluating advocacy are found in Table 5.2.

Table 5.2
Example of the application of the Stages of Change Model to Public Health Advocacy.

Indicators	Outcomes
Awareness	• % of people who are aware of a health issue
Exposure/Engagement	• # of people who saw a campaign • # of times people like a message/tweet • # of people who went to website for more information
Policy change	• New policy was enacted. • Number of policy changes related to a health issue in a community

Process	• Number of policy briefs on an issue(s) • Number of campaigns conducted by the coalition in a year • Number of media outlets used for a campaign • Number of legislative meetings • # of signatures of a petition • Opinions or attitudes shifts toward an issue • Steps taken in a grassroots advocacy effort

5.4.2 Use the results of the evaluation to inform next steps.

To measure the primary goal, the health education specialist should compare the advocacy outcome with the coalition position statement that includes the priority issue and goal. For example, if the goal was to raise the age of legally smoking from 18 to 21 in a state, and, subsequently, the law is passed, the goal was met. However, if the bill was not passed, the health education specialist and the coalition members should review what processes they took and re-evaluate their advocacy activities for the next year. If the advocacy outcome and coalition match, and the campaign is ended. The public, especially the priority population, is then notified through media by the advocacy team. If the coalition determines the campaign was not successful but wishes to move forward, members will assess weaknesses of the campaign and, to improve future strategy efforts, determine why the advocacy message did not resonate with the intended audience (e.g.., decision-maker, leader). If the coalition decides not to move forward, the health education specialist may evaluate any progress made toward secondary goals. Again, the public and priority population should be notified as well as a report written to guide other coalitions working on similar issues (Mattson & Lam, 2016).

The health education specialist and the evaluation team should review and analyze the data given to the advocacy team or coalition. The team can work together to draw conclusions and discuss implications of the findings in relation to strategy and work plan changes that need to be made. Advocacy evaluation results can be used to:
- determine if the campaign is making a difference,
- modify activities and strategies,
- secure grant funding and other resources, and
- communicate and publicize campaign successes.
(CDC, 2011)

The results of the evaluation can help coalitions justify funding, demonstrate accountability to decision-makers and funders, show outcomes over time, and enhance coalition image. For health advocacy media campaigns, evaluation can bring about adjustments to campaign goals and be used to inform strategies for the next campaign influence (Friedman & Schwartz, 2016; Hampton & Lachenmayr, 2019; Lloyd et al., 2002).

Chapter 6

Area of Responsibility VI: Communication

KEY: No symbol - entry level; ▲ - advanced 1; ■ - advanced 2

6.1. Determine factors that affect communication with the identified audience(s).

6.1.1   Segment the audience(s) to be addressed, as needed.

6.1.2   Identify the assets, needs, and characteristics of the audience(s) that affect communication and message design (e.g., literacy levels, language, culture, and cognitive and perceptual abilities).

6.1.3   Identify communication channels (e.g., social media and mass media) available to and used by the audience(s).

6.1.4   Identify environmental and other factors that affect communication (e.g., resources and the availability of Internet access).

6.2. Determine communication objective(s) for audience(s).

6.2.1   Describe the intended outcome of the communication (e.g., raise awareness, advocacy, behavioral change, and risk communication).

6.2.2   Write specific, measurable, achievable, realistic, and time-bound (SMART) communication objective(s).

6.2.3   Identify factors that facilitate and/or hinder the intended outcome of the communication.

6.3. Develop message(s) using communication theories and/or models.

6.3.1   Use communications theory to develop or select communication message(s).

6.3.2   Develop persuasive communications (e.g., storytelling and program rationale).

6.3.3   Tailor message(s) for the audience(s).

6.3.4   Employ media literacy skills (e.g., identifying credible sources and balancing multiple viewpoints)

6.4. Select methods and technologies used to deliver message(s).

6.4.1   Differentiate the strengths and weaknesses of various communication channels and technologies (e.g., mass media, community mobilization, counseling, peer communication, information/digital technology, and apps).

6.4.2   Select communication channels and current and emerging technologies that are most appropriate for the audience(s) and message(s).

6.4.3   Develop communication aids, materials, or tools using appropriate multimedia (e.g., infographics, presentation software, brochures, and posters).

6.4.4   Assess the suitability of new and/or existing communication aids, materials, or tools for audience(s) (e.g., the CDC Clear Communication Index and the Suitability Assessment Materials (SAM)).

6.4.5   Pilot test message(s) and communication aids, materials, or tools.

6.4.6   Revise communication aids, materials, or tools based on pilot results.

6.5. Deliver the message(s) effectively using the identified media and strategies.

6.5.1   Deliver presentation(s) tailored to the audience(s).

6.5.2   Use public speaking skills.

6.5.3   Use facilitation skills with large and/or small groups.

6.5.4   Use current and emerging communication tools and trends (e.g., social media).

6.5.5   Deliver oral and written communication that aligns with professional standards of grammar, punctuation, and style.

6.5.6   Use digital media to engage audience(s) (e.g., social media management tools and platforms).

6.6. Evaluate communication

6.6.1   Conduct process and impact evaluations of communications.

6.6.2 ■   Conduct outcome evaluations of communications.

6.6.3 ▲   Assess reach and dose of communication using tools (e.g., data mining software, social media analytics, and website analytics).

The Role. Communication is fundamental to all of the other seven responsibilities associated with being a health education specialist. Health education specialists must interact with a variety of people from various backgrounds including other health professionals, consumers, students, employers, employees, patients, and fellow health education specialists. One must be able to effectively communicate in both oral and written forms to establish and maintain successful health education programs. Whether through individual, small group, social media or mass communication strategies, health education specialists use their professional training to create, tailor, pilot test, deliver and evaluate communication messages. The ability to communicate effectively provides health education specialists with the foundation to advocate (Responsibility V) for health issues and the health education profession (NCHEC, 2020).

Setting: The following text is presented to describe how communication is used in different practice settings. (NCHEC, 2020)

Community Setting: Communication is needed in nearly every aspect of a health education specialist's work within the community setting. In a community setting, health education specialists assist in developing health communication campaigns designed to bring about behavioral change among priority audiences and influence health policy issues at the local, state, and national levels. Health education specialists develop communication messages to be delivered through a variety of channels and utilize program materials developed in the language of and at appropriate reading levels of the priority population. This requires strong written and verbal skills including public speaking and the ability to identify/incorporate those communication channels used by priority populations. Competency in traditional methods of communication (i.e., radio, television, newspapers, posters, pamphlets) and social media platforms (i.e., Twitter, Facebook, Instagram) as well as newsfeeds, webinars, and other new/emerging media platforms is especially important. Health education specialists might be asked to serve on various community-wide coalitions to help identify and implement communication strategies to improve health. Those health education specialists practicing at an advanced-level may serve as communication advisors or consultants for a variety of community organizations.

School (K-12) Setting: The health education specialist must interact and communicate with a broad range of individuals including but not limited to students, parents, fellow teachers, administrators, advisory boards and the community at large. Effective communication is essential to the work of a school health education specialist. Evidence of successful implementation of the health education program should be communicated and celebrated throughout the school and community. This may involve the use of traditional communication channels such as newspapers, TV and radio as well as electronic media such as e-mail, Web-sites, and social media. Open forums or discussion boards should be conducted to allow for input from interested stakeholders.

Health Care Setting: In health care settings, health education specialists may serve as navigators and/or consultants assisting patients, families, caregivers, and health care providers to find evidence-based health information from reliable sources. They must have core communication skills, show empathy, be reflective listeners, and practice teach-back as they respond to patients' specific needs. They must have strong verbal and written communication skills and utilize those skills when disseminating information to patients, their families, caregivers, staff, stakeholders, and the public. When delivering health education messages and/or programs, they must be skilled in communicating scientific and medical information in an understandable format based on the learners' health literacy and health numeracy levels. Health education specialists must be leaders and foster an inclusive workplace that promotes an environment of respect and trust through open and clear communication with all stakeholders. For a specific example, the health education specialist in the health care setting may be responsible for developing a patient-focused diabetes education communication platform for an outpatient primary care office. Upon approval, the health education specialist will then deliver the diabetes materials to the patients in multiple forms such as telephone calls, patient health portals, webinars, or via in-person sessions. As the health messages are delivered, the health education specialist evaluates the campaign to determine its effectiveness.

College/University Setting: Health education specialists in this setting communicate formally and informally with students, campus and professional colleagues, administrators and other stakeholders. The communication can occur in an instructional setting, as a member of a committee or specially designated group, at a professional conference, a public meeting or other venues. The purpose of the communication might be instructional, informational, to provide feedback or input, or for advocacy. This communication might be provided in-person, online, via e-mail, or through traditional or social media. Health educators working in professional preparation programs may also have responsibility for preparing prospective health educators to utilize communication skills. Health education specialists in a college/university setting use communication skills to disseminate evidence-based best practices and approaches for health education and health promotion. A health education specialist in this setting will use written communication to publish scholarly papers, informational papers and health education materials based on current research. Persuasive communication techniques are used by health education specialists to secure funding for grant proposals, to encourage healthy behaviors in priority populations, and to persuade decision makers to adopt policies, laws, rules, and/or regulations to support health.

Worksite/Business Setting: Health education specialists identify and communicate unmet employee needs (e.g., insufficient opportunity for physical activity) to management and key internal stakeholders. Using their background in behavioral and biological sciences, they interpret the problem for management and articulate effective ways of addressing the problem, such as offering a program or screening or changing organizational policy. In doing so they must understand management concerns and communicate ways in which a specific health education program or policy might benefit both the organization and employees. In addition, health education specialists develop communication strategies and messages to be delivered to priority populations through a variety of channels and program materials in the style and frequency that matches the culture of the organization and supports the organization's mission, vision, values, and business practices. In this capacity health education specialists need to communicate with a variety of people (top management to hourly workers) in a variety of ways (oral, written, social media, newsletters, posters, etc.). This work may be done in conjunction with internal and/or external communications and marketing specialists.

College/University Health Promotion Services Setting: Health education specialists in this setting utilize a variety of communication strategies and channels to develop and deliver messages to priority populations, colleagues, partners, stakeholders, and administration. Communication skills are critical in assessment, program and intervention planning, marketing, implementation, and evaluation, as well as advocacy, leadership, and management. Strategies and channels used are situation specific, tailored to the audience and often include social media and digital communication for programs, interventions, and marketing with priority populations. Traditional print (e.g., posters and bulletin boards), electronic communications (e-mail, conference calls, webinars), and face-to-face communication (e.g., motivational interviewing and presentations) are also requisite skills. Health education specialists must use professional written and oral strategies when communicating with partners, stakeholders and administration. Effective communication is essential when gaining support for programs and interventions, sharing evaluation results, and advocating for resources, policies, and system changes on campus.

Key Terms

Communication goal is the overall health improvement an organization or agency strives to produce, and a communication program should be designed to support and contribute to achieving the specific desired improvement (National Cancer Institute [NCI], 2008).

Communication objectives are the communication outcomes aimed to support the overall communication goal; these should be attainable, measureable, and time specific (NCI, 2008).

Communication strategies are the overall approaches taken in the program to achieve communication outcomes to impact health and contribute to, achieving defined goals and objectives (NCI, 2008).

Cultural sensitivity is understanding, valuing, and respecting the similarities and differences between culturally-based attitudes, beliefs, and behaviors (Diaz-Cuellar & Evans, 2013).

eHealth literacy is the ability to locate, understand, exchange, and evaluate online health information in the presence of dynamic contextual factors (both online and offline) and apply the knowledge gained to maintain or improve health (Paige et al., 2018).

Health communication is the exchange of information used to inform and influence practices, behaviors, or policies to improve individual or community health (Schiavo, 2014).

Health literacy is the degree to which an individual has the capacity to obtain, communicate, process, and understand basic health information and services to make appropriate health decisions (CDC, 2014d).

Health marketing is the creation and delivery of health promotion programs using multidisciplinary, evidence-based strategies to motivate the public toward positive health practices (CDC, 2011a).

Persuasive communication is targeted or tailored health-related messages to meet audience members needs and persuade them to adopt healthy attitudes and behaviors (Doyle et al., 2019).

Policies are sets of rules and objectives to guide activities (Doyle et al., 2019).

Segmentation is the process of categorizing diverse populations into subgroups, which have similar backgrounds, demographic and psychological characteristics, as well as experiences, among other differences (Institute of Medicine (US) Committee on Communication for Behavior Change in the 21st Century: Improving Diverse Populations, 2002)

Social marketing is the method of using marketing principles in planning, implementation, and evaluation of health education programs designed to bring about social change. The ultimate objective of marketing is to influence action (Resnick & Siegel, 2013).

Social media are activities and behaviors among people who are online to share information, knowledge, and opinions using social media (Bensley et al., 2019). Examples of social media include blogs, videos, image sharing, and social networking sites like Facebook, Twitter, and LinkedIn.

Competency 6.1 Determine factors that affect communication with the identified audience(s).

Communication plays a fundamental role in motivating and supporting individuals to change and sustain health behaviors. Moreover, health communication is used to encourage policymakers to adopt health promoting policies and/or practices and enables healthcare providers to adequately care for, and communicate to, diverse populations. Effective communication in health education and promotion involves an in-depth understanding of factors influencing communication among an identified audience.

Health education specialists need to understand, for example, the factors influencing communication, such as the lifestyles, concerns, attitudes, beliefs, social norms, barriers to change, and sources of gaining health information of the intended audience. In addition, communication approaches are impacted by the cultural, social, and political environments to which the intended audience is exposed. Understanding these factors prior to developing any type of communication is key to best promote behavioral and social change among specified audiences. Methods used to determine these factors are similar to the data collection processes and procedures used in the needs assessment phase of program planning, including summary of a literature review or past report on a population (Schiavo, 2014).

6.1.1 Segment the audience(s) to be addressed, as needed.
Health education specialists should begin a communication program or campaign by identifying the intended audience(s) for specific health communication strategies and/or approaches. Defining specific subgroups of a larger population is called segmentation. Identified populations are oftentimes broad (e.g., men over the age of 55); whereas, the intended audience or segment of the broader population for which the communication is intended is more narrowly defined and based on various characteristics (e.g.,behavior, demographics, attitudes, geographic area). A segment of the audience may include those most at-risk for a specific health concern (e.g., African-American men with chronic obstructive pulmonary disease (COPD) living in the southeast region of the U.S.); health education specialists should determine how to segment the audience to effectively communicate to that audience. The motivation and capacities of the intended audience for making a desired behavior change will impact the communication objectives of any health education program.

Segmentation is used to assist in ensuring health education materials, communication messages, and activities are relevant for the intended audience's specific preferences, needs, behaviors, beliefs, attitudes, and overall knowledge. Appropriately segmenting the audience also allows for selection of the best communication channels to reach the intended groups. Given the vast differences and diversity within a broader population, it is often difficult to reach the general public with one communication message or strategy; therefore, segmenting the audience, as needed, helps the health education specialist to reach the intended subgroups in a more effective manner (National Cancer Institute [NCI], 2008). Example characteristics for population segmentation are described in Table 6.1.

Table 6.1
Example characteristics for population segmentation (NCI, 2008)

Characteristic	Examples for Segmentation
Behavioral	Levels of readiness to change a behavior, health-related decisions/activities, information-seeking behavior, lifestyle choices, use of various types of media
Cultural	Language preferences and proficiency, religious/spirituality beliefs, ethnicity, family structure, and lifestyle characteristics (such as specific activities or special foods)
Demographic	Education level, income, occupations, geographic location, place of work
Physical	Age, sex, gender, health risks, health status, and family history
Psychographic	Values, beliefs, attitudes, personality, self-efficacy

Health education specialists can segment the intended population based on characteristics relevant to the health behavior being targeted for change.

6.1.2 Identify the assets, needs, and characteristics of the audience(s) that affect communication and message design (e.g., literacy levels, language, culture, and cognitive and perceptual abilities).

Assess needs for health-related information

Health education specialists can define the information needs of a population, which may include statistics for community assessment, educational materials, evidence-based programs or strategies for planning for health communications, survey tools for data collection or evaluation, or topic-specific health information. Data to be collected can include audience media preferences and use, information-seeking behaviors, trust in different message sources and psychographics. Health education specialists can use a variety of software and/or Web applications to save and retrieve data and/or literature necessary for program planning, assessment, implementation, or evaluation. Health education specialists can start with the BEHAVE framework to plan their communication project. Within the BEHAVE framework, the audience, behavioral change, motivation, and mechanism of change are described (Parvanta & Bass, 2020). Questions to ask themselves include the following:
- Who is the audience to reach?
- What behaviors or actions should the audience do?
- What factors contribute to their behaviors?
- Which actions should be taken to effectively address the factors? (Parvanta & Bass, 2020).

Health education specialists need to know where to obtain the resources and materials needed to effectively implement programming. Resource materials can be used to increase awareness and enhance learning. Health education specialists should select the most appropriate materials and resources from credible, reliable sources that match audience needs. Regardless of where health information originates, the following are steps for identifying the information needed for dissemination:

1. Identify the need.
2. Match the need to likely source.
3. Pursue the lead.
4. Judge the quality and quantity of the information found.
5. Organize the available material in a format most useful to the user.

Identify level of literacy of intended audience

Health education specialists should assess the literacy and health literacy levels of their audience before developing materials and messages. About half of adults have limited literacy skills, which means that they struggle with basic reading and writing tasks. Approximately nine out of ten adults have limited health literacy skills, which means they struggle with complex health information, including navigating the United States healthcare system. Many factors contribute to a person's literacy status, including age, education, income, health status, and stress (U.S. Department of Health and Human Services [USDHHS], 2010).

Health literacy is defined as the extent to which individuals have the ability to obtain, process, and understand basic health information and health care services to make appropriate health decisions (CDC, 2016a). Several factors impact health literacy including a person's receipt of appropriate written health communication materials, ability to accurately interpret written health-related information, and communication with providers (USDHHS, 2014a). Some consequences of poor health literacy are inappropriate or no usage of health care services, improper use of medicines, poor health outcomes, or poor self-management of chronic conditions (Zarcadoolas et al., 2006).

eHealth literacy is the ability of an individual to locate, understand, exchange, and evaluate online health information in the presence of dynamic contextual factors (both online and offline) and apply the knowledge gained to maintain or improve health (Paige et al., 2018). People with low eHealth literacy are less likely to actively seek health information on the Internet, and they are less likely to engage in health promoting behaviors, including healthy diet, exercise, and secondary prevention (e.g., cancer screenings) (Paige et al., 2018).

Many people struggle with accessing and comprehending health information delivered from expert and peer sources that is available on both online and offline environments. Health education specialists should apply universal precautions when developing and communicating content for a priority audience. Health literacy universal precautions are used to assist in reducing the complexity of language so that people can understand the recommendations, communicated both verbally and in written text, to make informed decisions (Agency for Healthcare Research and Quality [AHRQ], 2019). Readability formulas like SMOG, Fry Readability formula, or Flesch-Kincaid readability tests are used to evaluate the reading grade level of a text. Readability formulas, however, cannot be used to predict how well the intended audience will understand the material. Applying universal health literacy precautions and testing the comprehension of educational materials with a priority audience are imperative.

In verbal communication with their primary population of interest, health education specialists should:

- speak slowly.
- focus on and repeat key messages.
- explain things in plain language (i.e., avoid jargon).
- avoid using statistics.
- allow time for questions.
- use the "teach back" technique in which individuals have a chance to show that they are understanding the messages.
- use other communication materials or strategies to compliment the interaction.

(AHRQ, 2019)

In written communication, health education specialists should do the following:

- Use short sentences (no more than 25 sentences) in which everyday language is used.
- Use paragraphs (if necessary) that are no more than 250 words and 8 sentences.
- Define acronyms and use them minimally.
- Use the active voice.
- Highlight, bold, or create text-box to display important main points.
- Supplement text with image, video, or other multimedia.

(AHRQ, 2019)

Numeracy is the ability to access, use, interpret, and communicate numeric information in a wide range of situations in life (CDC, 2016b). An individual's numeracy level also affects individual's health care decisions and behaviors (Peters et al., 2007). Some strategies to assist people in their numeracy processing is to:

- present fewer health statistics.
- reduce the need for inferences and calculations.
- use visual cues or displays to show numbers.

Other strategies to increase health literacy include focusing on one numeric idea at a time (i.e., one point of data per sentence), using analogies or physical items to represent quantity (e.g., using the fist as a serving size for fruits), or teaching with stories. For example, in teaching about walking two times a day for 30 minutes, health education specialists might talk about a man who takes a long walk around his neighborhood after breakfast and again at dinner.

Cognitive abilities have been significantly correlated with measures of health literacy. Specifically, cognitive function, such as the ability to actively process, remember, and apply information learned to a variety of health concepts, can significantly impact overall health literacy levels of individuals (Seper et al., 2014). Moreover, both cognitive function and health literacy independently are used to predict mortality rates (Baker et al., 2008). Therefore, it is important for health education specialists to understand that health literacy involves individuals' ability to manage their health, which is related to cognitive function, and health communication strategies should be used in consideration of both health literacy level and cognitive demands of communication materials.

6.1.3. Identify communication channels (e.g., social media and mass media) available to and used by the audience(s).

Health education specialists should select the best method of delivery to effectively reach a priority audience with a desired message. These communication methods can include the following:
- Interpersonal (e.g., health care professionals, family, friends)
- Social Group (e.g., neighborhood associations, work sites, houses of worship, social clubs)
- Communal Group (e.g., meetings, conferences, events)
- Mass media (e.g., radio, television, newspapers, magazines)
- Social media (e.g., webinars, blogs, e-mail, text messages, social networking websites)

(NCI, 2008)

The preceding method(s) must be strategically selected and appropriate for the audience and situational healthcare context. Specifically, health education specialists should make sure the intended audience, message, and channel align. For example, mass media (e.g., radio or television) can be good for raising awareness among general audience members; social media is good for delivering targeted persuasive messages on which people can act and share with other network members; and one-on-one counseling can be good for didactic instruction and self-efficacy building experience. In addition, health education specialists should consider the source of the message.

Selecting the source of the message is just as important as determining the channel to reach the priority audience. Sources of health information include health education specialists and healthcare organizations, but they also include peers, family members, healthcare providers, and key community stakeholders. Health promotion specialists place emphasis on how to reach the priority audience from a physical perspective (e.g., what social media they are using), but it is also important to consider the psychosocial aspects of health information reach and accessibility (e.g., who the best agent is to deliver the message so that it is received by the audience). Socio-demographic segments of the population trust certain online channels and sources more than others (Paige et al., 2017), making both features important in selecting the method of message delivery.

When choosing a delivery method, health education specialists should consider the following questions:
- Where does the priority audience go for health information (online vs. offline vs. combination)?
- What technological devices (smartphones, tablets) and programs does the priority audience use for health information (apps, social media, informational websites)?
- What is the nature of the message? Is it sensitive or embarrassing, complex, time sensitive?
- Who does the priority audience want to deliver this message (peer, family, organization nurse, and/or physician)?

6.1.4 Identify environmental and other factors that affect communication (e.g., resources and the availability of Internet access).

Just as factors related to the person or factors outside of the person (intrinsic vs. extrinsic) contribute or hinder the implementation and evaluation of health education programs, these factors also influence the success of reaching communication goals. Health education specialists must be aware of the individual, social, cultural, and environmental contexts that motivate this communication related to health education and promotion.

At the **individual level,** communication is determined by information needs (e.g., information, social support), as well as the channels and sources of health information that are preferred or to which are subscribed. At the **relational level,** communication can be motivated in a multitude of ways, including the method that the message is delivered (verbal or non-verbal; text-based or multimedia-based) and the relationship among communicators (e.g., acquaintances, patient-provider, community membership) who are delivered and received the message. For example, health recommendations about medication may have a greater degree of credibility and acceptance if it is delivered by a healthcare provider, but generic coping recommendations may be better received from a patient or similar other who has first-hand experience. Although healthcare providers are the most trusted source of health information (Chen et al., 2018), health education specialists must remember that there are alternative sources that can affect, for better or for worse, the communication of health information.

Environmental or system-level factors exist that affect communication, specifically from the perspective of accessibility. A common topic of consideration is Internet access, which is a powerful and low-cost tool to implement health promotion interventions and to quickly reach priority populations with health education resources. Nearly 10% of the U.S. population does not have Internet access, which includes older adults (27%), people residing in rural geographic regions (15%), and those with a high school (16%) or less than high school (29%) education (Anderson et al., 2019). Once people have physical access to communication, they must be able to navigate the information to effectively benefit from it. In the healthcare system, for example, health literacy universal precautions (e.g., improve verbal interaction, improve written communication, link to supportive systems, engage patients as partners in care) are encouraged for use to facilitate patients' access to health information and to optimize productive patient-provider communication that resulted in both informed and shared decision-making (AHRQ, 2019).

Competency 6.2 Determine communication objective(s) for audience(s).

Health education specialists should identify communication objectives to set priorities regarding the specific activities and the messages used for the activities. These objectives serve as the contract or blueprint for what will be accomplished, and they are used to determine evaluation outcomes to be measured. Communication objectives are used to articulate what the health education specialist aims to do; therefore, they should be:
- supportive of the program goals.
- realistic and achievable.
- specific to desired change, the intended audience(s), and the timeframe for the change to occur.
- measurable to track progress.
- prioritized for resource allocation.

(NCI, 2008)

6.2.1 Describe the intended outcome of the communication (e.g., raise awareness, advocacy, behavioral change, and risk communication).

The intent of health communication is to promote knowledge and change attitudes, beliefs, and actions through the use of social influence and behavior change theoretical approaches. Oftentimes, however, health communication is relied on by a communicator as the sole strategy/approach for achieving unrealistic expectations for what can be accomplished. For example, it is not feasible for communication to cause sustained behavior changes for complex behaviors or compensate for lack of resources, products, and services in any setting. Communication is a powerful tool, however, to strengthen health education efforts. To optimize its value, it is vitally important to identify the specific, desired outcomes of the communication, when creating the communication objectives. In determining the desired outcomes, it is important to think specifically about the health problem or issue, the audience(s), and the ability of communication to impact the health issue with the selected audience(s). Communication alone feasibly can contribute to creating supportive environments for change by strategically influencing the attitudes, beliefs, and/or polices of intended audience(s) in that environment. Specifically, communication contributes to community activation by enhancing social support systems and reinforcing socially normative behaviors. Communication that is both effective and appropriate for a given population can enhance message recall, ultimately promoting awareness and increasing knowledge around specific health issues to predict intended behavior change. Moreover, communication is effective in contributing to a broader behavior change program/initiative to motivate, support, and/or persuade the intended audience to participate in the program/initiative. Health education specialists need to determine and describe these intended outcomes to the planning team for their health campaign, based on all considerations previously detailed (NCI, 2008).

6.2.2 Write specific, measurable, achievable, realistic, and time-bound (SMART) communication objective(s).

Communication objectives are the specific actions that need to be undertaken to achieve the messaging goal (Chen et al., 2018. Objectives are statements that describe, in measurable terms, changes in health status, behavior, attitude, or knowledge that will occur as a result of the health communication campaign. These objectives are the small, specific factors that enable the goal to be met. As was presented in Sub-competency 2.2.4, objectives (including communication objectives) need to be SMART to help focus the objective and monitor progress toward it (Health Communication Capacity Collaborative, 2020). Examples of SMART communication objectives with behavioral factors addressed and example indicators are listed in Table 6.2:

Table 6.2
Examples of SMART communication objectives

Communication Objective	Behavioral Factors Addressed	Example Indicators
Within the next two months, all students at Elmhurst Elementary School will be able to describe the importance of washing hands with antibacterial soap to stop the spread of the flu.	Knowledge	Percentage of students who know about the importance of washing their hands with anti-bacterial soap.
Within the next four months, handwashing with antibacterial soap among students at Elmhurst Elementary School will have increased from 50% to 90%.	Behavior	Percentage of students washing their hands with antibacterial soap.
Within the next six months, all school health education/promotion specialists will counsel students on the importance of handwashing with antibacterial soap to prevent the flu.	Service provision	Number of school health education/promotion specialists trained to educate elementary students to practice handwashing in Greenville, NC.

Adapted from the SBCC for Emergency Preparedness Implementation Kit (Health Communication Capacity Collaborative, 2020)

The health education specialist should keep the following tips in mind when establishing SMART communication objectives:

- Be specific about the priority population and the behavior or health issue being addressed by the objective;
- Prioritize behaviors that will have the greatest impact in meeting health education objectives;
- Use only one action verb in each objective; and
- Typically, develop both short- and long- objectives.

6.2.3 Identify factors that facilitate and/or hinder the intended outcome of the communication.

In Sub-competency 6.1.4., the antecedents that motivate communication, including individual, interpersonal, and environmental or system-level factors, were outlined. Nevertheless, there are factors that can hinder the effectiveness and appropriateness of this communication. Drawing from communication theory (Barlund, 1970), there are four types of "noise" that can impede communication. These include: 1) physical factors related to the setting, equipment, and interactions that hinder the physical transmission of the communication; 2) physiological factors related to cognitive or emotional overload and the speaking style or hearing capabilities of the communicators; 3) psychological factors, including pre-conceived notions or beliefs (e.g., fatalism); and 4) semantic factors, which include the use of jargon in health education programming and interactions with members of a priority population. These examples are commonly referred to in offline communication, but Paige and colleagues (2018) outlined how these factors are uniquely conceptualized in hindering online communication.

Paige et al. (2018) revealed that there are a variety of techniques and considerations to help health education specialists overcome these hindrances to delivering health communication. Many of these are already outlined in Sub-competency 6.1.2., including the use of verbal and written health literacy universal precautions that are adapted to the cultural context of the priority audience. Another consideration for communication barriers is to take into account and continually promote health literacy or eHealth literacy, if online communication methods are applied. Individuals must have adequate skills to know what information they want and need, and must have the skills to adequately process and comprehend the information once it is obtained (Paige et al., 2018).

In considering factors that hinder or facilitate communication, it is important for health education specialists to remember that they are all technically communicators; health education is not a static, one-way delivery of information to a priority audience. Rather, a priority audience's response, whether it is in the form of feedback, information sharing, behavior change, or avoidance, is a form of communication. Health education specialists can use training on communications to their advantage to inform and adapt the content, delivery, and evaluation of health education programs for diverse communities.

Competency 6.3 Develop message(s) using communication theories and/or models.

To engage stakeholders in health and health education, it is often necessary for health education specialists to employ a variety of communication strategies, methods, and techniques. Health education specialists are often required to use behavioral theories to design communication-based interventions and determine the best channel through which to disseminate messages. Refer to Sub-competency 8.1.5 for a description of common behavior change theories and models. In the following section, the role of a health education specialist in developing, testing, and delivering health messages is pesented.

6.3.1 Use communications theory to develop or select communication message(s).

Consumers are increasingly seeking health information not only about disease treatment but also about disease prevention and health promotion. Consumer-focused health education specialists learn as much as possible about the target audience and influence behavior change by crafting messages in which consumer needs are addressed. Public perceptions about health-related messages are influenced by the following characteristics: ease of solution and immediate results, perceived susceptibility, and personal beliefs (NCI, 2008).

Health communication is used to inform and influence health-related decisions of the population of interest (NCI, 2008). A health communication campaign can be used to support a multicomponent approach to solving public health problems. Prior to campaign material distribution and promotion, health education specialists should remember to carefully define the market, segment the market, analyze the segments, and choose a target market with shared consumer preferences (CDC, 2007). Health education specialists are in a unique position to determine the format/type of materials to be developed by evaluating the nature and function of the message, as well as how it best fits with the channels selected.

Several behavior change theories and models (refer to Sub-competency 8.1.5 Use evidence-informed theories, models, and strategies) can be applied to health communication. Health communications should represent a social ecological perspective and foster multilevel strategies, such as tailored messages at the individual level, targeted messages at the group level, social marketing at the community level, media advocacy at the policy level, and mass media campaigns at the population level (NCI, 2005).

Communications alone likely are not enough to sustain behavior change related to health. Health education specialists can ask the question when choosing a theory: "How do communication processes and messages contribute to behavior change for the population of interest?" For example, communications can increase knowledge and awareness of an issue, influence perceptions and attitudes, debunk misconceptions, and potentially prompt action (NCI, 2005).

According to the Elaboration Likelihood Model, finding out how much the audience cares about an issue will help health education specialists craft effective messages (Parvanta & Bass, 2020). People who believe they are directly impacted by a topic will be more likely to pay attention to a message and want the details. (Petty et al., 2009). On the other hand, persons who are not engaged in a topic will need peripheral stimuli (e.g., images) to grab their attention.

No matter how much a person may care about a topic, everyone is limited in the amount of information that can be retained. Information Processing Theory (Rudd & Glanz, 1990) suggested that a health education specialist:

- include no more than 2-3 main messages.
- break information into small chunks that are simple and easy to understand.

In the **Social Marketing** model (CDC, 2007), health education specialists listen to the needs and wants of the consumer by looking at the marketing mix, traditionally consisting of the 4 "Ps:"

- **P**roduct: health behavior, program, or idea
- **P**rice: financial, physical, psychological, time
- **P**lace: how and where learning will take place
- **P**romotion: approach used to reach the audience

Resnick and Siegel (2013) added a fifth "P," Partners. This "P" refers to the importance of mobilizing resources by working with other organizations. Several other "P"s also should be considered when creating social marketing campaigns in the field of health education/promotion:

- **P**ublics: primary and secondary audiences involved in the program
- **P**olicy: creating the environmental supports to sustain behavior change
- **P**urse Strings: amount of money available at one's disposal for the campaign

(Sharma, 2017)

Selected Communications Theories

In addition to behavioral change theories presented in Chapter 8 (i.e., Theory of Planned Behavior, Social Cognitive Theory, Transtheoretical Model – Stages of Change, Health Belief Model, Community Organization Theory), there are several social science theories that can be useful for understanding the problem or situation for which the communication strategy is being used.

On the individual level, McGuire's (1984) **Communications for Persuasion** theory can be used to help define steps in which individuals proceed to engage in a desired behavior change. Below are the steps:

- Exposure to the message
- Attention to the message
- Interest in or personal relevance of the message
- Understanding the message
- Personalizing the behavior
- Accepting the change
- Remembering the message and continuing to agree with it
- Being able to think of the message
- Making decisions based on bringing the message to mind
- Behaving as decided
- Receiving positive reinforcement for behavior
- Accepting the behavior into one's life

Furthermore to these steps is to communicate the message in an effective manner, McGuire (1984) suggested five communication components that must work successfully:

1. Credibility of the message source
2. Overall message design
3. Message delivery channel
4. Intended audience
5. Intended behavior

These factors can assist health education specialists in ensuring the message will be received by the intended audience and are effective for achieving the desired outcomes of the messaging.

The **Consumer Information Processing Model** (CIP) (Bettman, 1979; Parvanta & Bass, 2020), although not developed specifically for health communication, is a useful model when applied in the field. Health education specialists use information as a tool to promote health and encourage healthy decisions. Information can decrease a person's anxiety over health issues, or depending on how much information and what type is given, it also can increase anxiety levels. Therefore, understanding how individuals process information regarding health can be useful in assisting health education specialists in being more effective in the type of information provided. CIP theory views the use of information as an intellectual process, with individual motivation driving how much information is sought out and used. The central assumptions of the model, include:

1. individuals are limited by the amount of information they can process, and
2. individuals divide information into usable "chunks," called heuristics, to use the information in a faster/ easier way.

Moreover, in the model, it is suggested that individuals will use health information more effectively if it is 1) available, 2) viewed as new and useful, and 3) is user-friendly and processable (NCI, 2008). In the model, some key concepts to consider when incorporating health information into messaging for intended audiences is provided.

At the interpersonal level, **Diffusion of Innovations Theory** (Rogers, 2003), provided an understanding of how new ideas, products, behaviors and social practices spread throughout communities. In the theory, a focus is posited on the innovation of the new idea, product, and/or practice, as well as the communication channels and social networks/systems within the intended population. Specifically, the likelihood of adoption of the innovation is directly related to its appeal; therefore, some of the most important characteristics to consider include the following:

- Relative advantage – Is the innovation better than what was there previously?
- Compatibility – How well does the innovation fit with the intended audience?
- Complexity – How easy is the innovation to adopt/use?
- Trialability – Can the innovation be tried out first?
- Observability – What is the visibility level of the results?

Communication channels in this theory involve a two-step flow of communication. Opinion leaders mediate the impact of the mass media regarding the innovation in a way that persuades adoption of the innovation via use of social networks (or interpersonal channels) (NCI, 2008). Specifically, there are five established adopter categories, with a majority of the population falling in the middle categories. These categories are as follows:

1. Innovators – individuals who are first to adopt/try the innovation
2. Early adopters – opinion leaders who embrace change opportunities
3. Early majority – individuals who adopt new ideas before the average/general population
4. Late majority – individuals who are skeptical of change, but will adopt after an innovation has been tried by the majority
5. Laggards – individuals who are very skeptical of change and are the hardest group to engage in innovation

Understanding the stages by which a person adopts an innovation can be used to accelerate the adoption of important health communication programs within intended audiences.

Another interpersonal theory that is applied to health communication is **Social Norms Theory** (Perkins & Berkowitz, 1986). In this theory, it is stated that behavior is influenced by individuals' incorrect perceptions of how other members in their social group behave and if thoughts on these beliefs are correct. Specifically, in the theory, it is posited that if individuals incorrectly perceive behaviors of peers to be different from their own, these misperceptions impact individual behavior (Borsari & Carey, 2003). Health communication programs that involve Social Norms Theory are focused on peer influences and the importance of normative beliefs on behavior. The communication campaign is centered around correcting the misperceptions as a proactive prevention approach focused on providing accurate information on the attitudes and behaviors targeted in the program. The program is centered on healthy attitudes and behaviors of the majority to increase those healthy norms throughout the intended audience(s).

Described in the **Extended Parallel Process Model** (EPPM) is how rational considerations (efficacy beliefs) and emotional reactions (fear of a health threat) combine to show how people determine behavioral decisions. In EPPM, the degree to which a person feels threatened (perceived severity + perceived susceptibility) by a health issue determines their motivation to act, while their confidence to effectively reduce or prevent the health threat determines what action they will take to address the threat (response efficacy + self-efficacy). When perceived threat is strong and response efficacy is high, EPPM reveals that self-protective behavior will occur. When perceived threat is strong, but perceived response efficacy is low, maladaptive denial or rejection of protective health behaviors is revealed in the model (Health Communication Capacity Collaborative, 2014).

Message framing is another core tenet of health communication presented in **Prospect Theory** (Kahneman & Tversky, 1979). The theory authors posit that individuals are risk-seeking when losses are made salient and risk-averse when potential gains are made evident. Framing involves developing messages which illustrate either positive or negative consequences of adopting or failing to adopt a particular behavior (Parvanta & Bass, 2020). Messages that are "gain-framed" show the benefits of a behavior, while messages that are "loss-framed" reveal the costs of not engaging in a behavior. Generally speaking, loss-framed messages are more effective in promoting disease detection. One example of a loss-framed (disease detection) message is: *If you do not get an annual mammogram, you are reducing your chances of detecting breast cancer in the early stages when cancer is more treatable.* Usually, gain-framed messages are more effective in promoting disease prevention. One example of a gain-framed (disease prevention) message is: *Applying sunscreen daily can significantly reduce your risk of skin cancer.*

Risk perception is a key predictor of health behaviors in many health communication models, such as the **Protection Motivation Theory** (Rogers & Prentice-Dunn, 1997). The decision of whether or not to engage in protective behavior is governed by two cognitive processes, i.e., threat appraisal and coping appraisal. Threat appraisal is the perceived vulnerability a person feels, which may warrant a response, while coping appraisal is response efficacy, self-efficacy, and perceived response-cost that govern whether or not an individual believes adopting the new protective behavior can lead to greater benefits, which predicts whether or not they will take action.

6.3.2 Develop persuasive communications (e.g., storytelling and program rationale).

Evidence-based and theoretically-driven approaches are used in health education programs to persuade members of a priority audience to take a prosocial action. Common persuasive techniques include, but are not limited to, advancing source credibility (e.g., recommendations from a likable, similar, and expert source), and leveraging features of cognitive and affective processes (e.g., emotional appeals, narrative frameworks).

Emotional appeals are commonly used to enhance the persuasive capacity of a health message (Harrington, 2016). These appeals are either negative (e.g., fear, disgust, guilt, anger) or positive (e.g., happiness, hope, humor). One of the most recently popular health communication campaigns in which emotional appeals are used is the Tips from Former Smokers® campaign. In this campaign, fear and disgust appeals alongside efficacy-building cognitive features are used to promote smoking prevention and cessation (CDC, 2019a). Emotional appeals rarely function in solidarity, as there is evidence that people read health information and experience what is called an "emotional flow" (i.e., emotional shifts), which has been shown to have more persuasive effects than a single emotion (Nabi & Green, 2015). Health education specialists must acknowledge the power of emotional appeals, including their combination and sequential flow, within their priority audience before launching an intervention or campaign.

Emotional appeals are often included in narratives. A **narrative** is a "cohesive and coherent story with an identifiable beginning, middle, and end that provides information about scene, characters, and conflict; raises unanswered questions or unresolved conflict; and provides resolution" (Hinyard & Kreuter, 2007; p. 777). Narratives are effective in promoting prosocial behavior change, but there is also evidence that these techniques are effectively used in policy change through advocacy and lobbying efforts (Fadlallah et al., 2019).

Health education specialists must consider the ethical implications when designing, implementing, and evaluating their programs that use persuasive techniques. For example, if a message is not sufficiently tested with members of a priority population, an alternative, unexpected emotion may be experienced. Additionally, fear appeals alongside high-efficacy messaging are highly effective in promoting attitude and behavior change (Tannenbaum et al., 2015; Witte & Allen, 2000), but a longstanding debate exists about the "dose" of fear that should be evoked by a message given a particular context and priority population before it becomes detrimental (Riley et al., 2017). To effectively and appropriately use persuasive communication techniques, health education specialists should rely on theory, peruse existing literature to assess their use in a given context (i.e., health, population, message delivery system setting), and engage multidisciplinary experts and members of the priority population. This comprehensive approach can help to proactively address and enhance the ethical use of these persuasive strategies. Other commonly used persuasive techniques to message design include adapted (targeted) and tailored messaging strategies, as described in the next section.

6.3.3 Tailor message(s) for the audience(s).

When it comes to health communication and promotion, one size does not fit all. Health education specialists must identify and understand the characteristics of the intended audience to communicate effectively. Health messages are either adapted (targeted) to patient populations or tailored to individuals within a priority audience. Adapting (or targeting) means making changes to health messages more suitable for a population of interest or an organization (Kreuter et al., 2000). Tailoring is a precise method of message customization, or the design of messages, to the characteristics of an individual, rather than a subgroup of a population (Noar et al., 2009). For example, targeted communication reaches a subgroup of a population with shared characteristics (e.g., Black women), whereas tailored information is intended to reach one specific individual within the subgroup of the population (Kreuter et al., 2003). See the following sections for examples of targeted and tailored messages. In both targeting and tailoring, the cultural practices and needs of the priority audience are taken into consideration and can be used to improve the effectiveness of a message or campaign.

Targeted Messages

Common reasons for adaptation include differences between the intended population and the audience for which the messages were designed, limited resources (e.g., money, time), resistance of implementers or priority population, or competing demands (Moore et al., 2013). Health education specialists may choose to adapt health communication materials so that they target the age, culture, or context of the population that is served. These changes may include substituting statistics for another racial population or adjusting instruction or activity to an age group (e.g., different knowledge game for youth versus older adults). Before adapting health messages, it is helpful to consider which elements to adapt, the reason for the change, and the extent to which the modification changes the original product. If health education specialists are choosing from packaged health education programs which existing messages and campaigns are integrated, caution should be applied when changing the core elements or key components that make the program effective (Castro et al., 2010).

Health education specialists should not change social influence or behavior change theory used to inform health communication or the channel or source used to deliver the message without advice from the priority population and content experts. Other types of adaptations that should be changed only with caution include changes to content (e.g., adding or substituting), the participants to be reached, cultural relevance (e.g., beliefs, customs, practices), dosage (e.g., number or length of materials/sessions), and logistics/procedures (e.g., time, location, deliverer) (Moore et al., 2013). If health education specialists have to conduct significant adaptations to the materials, they might consider following steps to guide them in this process (Castro et al., 2010). The steps are presented in Table 6.3.

Table 6.3
Steps for Adapting Materials or Programs

Gather information	Review the literature and/or community assessment data to understand the risk factors and health issue for that population.
Select the health communication materials	Select health communication tools and techniques based on your goals/objectives and the needs of the intended population.
Make changes	Modify health communication content (e.g., statistics, cultural aspects), logistics, or delivery based on information found in the needs assessment.
Preliminary test or review	Have experts or small group of similar to final intended audience to review materials and make any necessary modifications.
Pilot testing	Pilot test the adapted message or campaign and make refinements before launching with the intended population.

Note. Adapted from Castro et al., 2010

Tailored Messages

Message tailoring is a sophisticated communication technique that involves risk estimation (epidemiology), audience segmentation techniques (health communication), and behavior change theory (health education/psychology). Message tailoring is an increasingly popular and effective strategy for designing and implementing health communication interventions; tailoring cognitively prepares an individual to attend to and process a message, increasing the likelihood of the message's acceptance and desired behavior change (Hawkins et al., 2008). Tailored messages are intended to be used to address the mediating determinants of desired behavior change, including attitude, normative beliefs, and self-efficacy to perform the behavior.

Tailored message design includes personalization, feedback, and content matching (Hawkins et al., 2008; Jensen & Krakow, 2014; Noar et al., 2009; Noar & Van Stee, 2012). These strategies, which are generally used in combination and rarely alone, are presented in Table 6.4.

Table 6.4
Description of Message Tailoring Strategies

Tailoring Strategy	Description
Personalization	Enhancement of the relevance of a message by explicitly stating that the message was designed specifically for the consumer, i.e.,"you"
Identification	A personal identifier is used to refer to consumers and gain their attention, which could include their name, birthday, picture, or address. Information for identification is generally gathered from assessment profiles (e.g., pre-recorded healthcare records).
Customization	Information provided is used by the consumer and allows the consumer to determine what information can be used in the tailored intervention (e.g., In the survey assessment, the consumer is asked to report their age/birthday).
Contextualization	Provision of a context to the message that is relevant, salient, and meaningful to the consumer, which can include cultural identify, social identity, professional role, or even their socio-demographic characteristics they identify with most (e.g., gender)
Feedback	Sychosocial determinants of health are used to re-state information to the consumer.
Descriptive	Information about psychosocial determinants that the consumer reported in the initial assessment is used (e.g., "you said…").
Comparative	The psychosocial determinants of consumers are compared to others in their demographic or other group with whom they most identify (e.g., "compared with others…").
Evaluative	Provision of a value or judgment to a psychosocial determinant identified by the consumer (e.g., "You are thinking about quitting smoking in the next 30 days, which is a great way to better self-mange your COPD symptoms…").
Content Matching	Identify a theoretical behavior change approach in which key determinants of the behavior goal and characteristics of the priority audience are addressed (e.g., Stages of Change) or their psychographic preferences/abilities (e.g., information processing styles).

6.3.4 Employ media literacy skills (e.g., identifying credible sources and balancing multiple viewpoints).

As the public continues to rely more and more on technology to gather health information, health education specialists are becoming increasingly responsible for filtering out health-related misinformation in the media. Media literacy is defined as an individual's ability to access, analyze, evaluate, and create messages in a variety of forms (Livingstone, 2004). Health education specialists should employ media literacy skills to ensure that reliable media are delivered to audiences. As a general rule of thumb, health-related websites sponsored by the U.S. government (e.g., NIH, CDC), large health professional organizations (e.g., AMA), and academic institutions are typically reliable sources of information (National Institute on Aging [NIA], 2018).

The following checklist (NIA, 2018) can be used to ensure that online health information is trustworthy:

1. Is the sponsor/owner of the website a Federal agency, medical school, or large professional or nonprofit organization, or is it related to one of these?
2. If not sponsored by a Federal agency, medical school, or large professional or nonprofit organization, is the website written by a healthcare professional, or is one of these trustworthy sources for its health information referenced?
3. Why was the site created? Is the mission or goal of the website sponsor clear?
4. Can you see who works for the agency or organization and who authored the information? Is there a way to contact the sponsor of the website?
5. When was the information written or webpage last updated?
6. Is your privacy protected?
7. Does the website offer unbelievable solutions to your health problem(s)? Are quick, miracle cures promised?

Finding answers to these questions can help health education specialists steer clear of media resources that have underlying goals which are not clearly disclosed. To test the credibility of media sources, the CRAAP Test (California State Chico, n.d.) is often used. The acronym CRAAP stands for Currency, Relevance, Authority, Accuracy and Purpose.

Currency: the timeliness of the health information
- When was the health information published or posted?
- Has the health information been revised or updated?
- Is the information current or out-of-date for your health topic?

Relevance: the importance of the health information for your needs
- Does the health information answer your question?
- Who is the intended audience?
- Have you looked at a variety of sources before determining this reference is the one you will believe?

Authority: the source of the health information
- Are the author's credentials and organizational affiliations given?
- What are the author's qualifications to write on the health topic(s)?

- Does the URL reveal anything about the author or source?
  - ⊙ .com (commercial),
  - ⊙ .edu (educational),
  - ⊙ .gov (U.S. government),
  - ⊙ .org (nonprofit organization), or
  - ⊙ .net (network)

Accuracy: the reliability, truthfulness, and correctness of the health-related content
- Is the health information supported by evidence?
- Has the health information been reviewed by scientists in refereed journals?
- Can you verify any of the information in another source or from personal knowledge?

Purpose: the reason the health information exists
- Do the authors/sponsors make their intentions or purpose clear?
- Does the point of view of the author appear objective and impartial?
- Are there political, ideological, cultural, religious, institutional, or personal biases?

Adapted from: Evaluating Sources: The CRAAP Test (Benedictine University, 2019)

Competency 6.4 Select methods and technologies used to deliver message(s).

Health education specialists should make sure the intended audience, message, and channel align. For example, mass media (e.g., radio or television) can be good for raising awareness among general audience members; social media is good for delivering targeted messages that can be easily acted on and shared (Bensley et al., 2019); and one-on-one counseling can be good for teaching.

When choosing a delivery method, consider your message:
- Is it a sensitive or embarrassing topic?
- Is the message complex?
- Is it time sensitive?

Also consider your audience:
- Are they online (and if so, on a smart phone or computer)?
- Where do they go for health information?

6.4.1 Differentiate the strengths and weaknesses of various communication channels and technologies (e.g., mass media, community mobilization, counseling, peer communication, information/digital technology, and apps).

The health education specialist should consider the advanages and disadvantage of each potential health communication channel in planning health messages or for a health education campaign. In Table 6.5, various channels and some of their pros and cons are presented.

Table 6.5
Communication Channels and Activities: Pros and Cons

Type of Channel	Activities	Pros	Cons
Individual/Intrapersonal channel	• Print materials (brochure) • Videos • How-to booklets • Fact sheets	• Can be credible • Can supply messages in culturally sensitive format	• Can have limited intended audience reach • Can be difficult to link into inter personal channels
Interpersonal channels	• Hotline counseling • Patient counseling • List of questions for patients to ask health care providers • Points for discussions in private homes or within the family • Texting (automatic reminders systems and personalized messages)	• Permit two-way discussion • Can be motivational, influential, supportive • Most effective for teaching and helping/caring	• Can be expensive • Can be time consuming
Organizational channels	• Organizational meetings and conferences • Workplace campaigns • Newsletters • Educational programs (in-person, audiovisual, computerized, print) • In-house radio or video broadcasts • Add-ons to regular communication (e.g., messages handed out with paychecks or organi zation notices)	• May be familiar, trusted, and influential • May provide more motivation/support than media alone • Can offer shared experiences • Can reach larger intended audience in one place	• Can be time consuming to establish • May not provide personalized attention • Organizational constraints may require message approval • May lose control of message if adapted to fit organizational needs
Community channels	• Town hall meetings and other events • School campaigns • Faith-based organization campaigns • Educational programs • Speeches • Kiosks or displays in shopping malls, post offices, or other public venues	• May be familiar, trusted, and influential • Can reach larger intended audience in one place • Requires collaborative approach • Can evaluate knowledge change in some cases	• Can be time consuming to establish • Difficulties with establishing lead agency in collaborations can arise • Evaluating behavior change is difficult • No or limited one-on-one time with intended audience

Type of Channel	Activities	Pros	Cons
Mass media channels *Newspaper*	• Advertisements • Inserted sections on a health topic (paid) • Letters to the editor • Op-Ed pieces • Cartoons/comics • Newspaper inserts • Media kits	• Can reach broad intended audiences rapidly • Can convey health news more thoroughly than TV or radio and faster than magazines • Intended audience has opportunity to clip, reread, contemplate, and pass along material • Small circulation papers may take Public Service Announcements (PSA)	• Coverage demands a newsworthy item • Larger circulation papers may take only paid ads and inserts • Exposure usually limited to one day • Article placement requires contacts and may be time-consuming • Stories can be difficult to "pitch"
Mass media channels *Radio*	• Ads (paid or public service placement) • Radio • News • Public affairs/talk shows • Dramatic programming (entertainment education) • Audio news releases • Media kits • Music news releases/music videos	• Range of formats available to intended audiences with known listening preferences • Opportunity for direct intended audience involvement • Can distribute ad scripts that are flexible and inexpensive • Ads or programming can reach intended audience when they are most receptive • Paid ads can be relatively inexpensive	• Reaches smaller audiences than TV • Public service ads run infrequently and at low listening times • Many stations have limited formats that may not be conducive to health messages • Difficult for intended audiences to retain or pass on material
Mass media channels *Television*	• Ads (paid or public service placement) • News • Public affairs/talk shows • Dramatic programming (entertainment education) • Audio or video news releases • Media kits • Music news releases/music videos	• Largest audience reach • Visual combined with audio good for emotional appeals and demonstrating behaviors • Can reach low income intended audiences • Ads or programming can reach intended audience when most receptive • Ads allow message and its execution to be controlled	• Ads can be expensive • PSAs run infrequently and at low viewing times • Message might be difficult for audience to retain • Promotion can result in overwhelming demand
Mass media channels *Internet*	• Websites • E-mail lists • Chat rooms • Newsgroups • Ads (paid or public service placement) • Social networking sites	• Large reach • Can instantaneously update and disseminate information • Can control and tailor information • Can be interactive and visually appealing • Can use banner ads to direct intended audience to your program's website	• Can be expensive to design and maintain • Intended audiences may not have access to the Internet • Newsgroups and chat rooms may require monitoring • Can require maintenance over time

Type of Channel	Activities	Pros	Cons
Mass media channels *Social media*	• Facebook • Twitter • Blogs • LinkedIn • Podcasts	• Can have large reach • Can be interactive and visually appealing • Takes advantage of those comfortable with technology	• Requires training on how to use these tools • Can require larger commitment with timing to implement and evaluate

Note. Adapted from NCI, 2008.

Health communication is defined as the study and use of communication strategies to inform and influence decisions and behaviors to improve health (CDC, 2019c). A health communication campaign can be used to support a multi-component approach to solving public health problems. Prior to campaign material distribution and promotion, health education specialists should remember to carefully define the market, segment the market, analyze the segments, and choose a target market with shared consumer preferences (CDC, 2007). Health education specialists are in a unique position to determine the format/type of materials to be developed by evaluating the nature and function of the message, as well as how it best fits with the channels selected.

6.4.2 Select communication channels and current and emerging technologies that are most appropriate for the audience(s) and message(s).

After identifying and developing appropriate communication strategies, methods, and techniques, and selecting the appropriate channel(s), health education specialists must deliver messages to the intended audience. Message delivery requires constant evaluation and monitoring to ensure the message and channels for communication remain appropriate for the audience. As mentioned previously, there are a number of communication channels and various technologies that can be used to communicate to the intended audience(s). Health education specialists should fine tune their delivery to ensure intended audiences are being reached and use process evaluation to keep track of message and material delivery (e.g., quantities of materials distributed, number of special events held, number of website visits, or phone inquiries).

6.4.3 Develop communication aids, materials, or tools using appropriate multimedia (e.g., infographics, presentation software, brochures, and posters).

Health education specialists should develop communication aids, materials and tools including, but not limited to, an implementation guide, program procedural manual, project plan, or other materials to guide implementation. These "how-to" materials, tools, and aids will ensure the delivery team involved understands the program and can be used to create standards in case the program is replicated in the future (McKenzie et al., 2017). A literature review or environmental scan can be helpful in identifying existing protocols, plans, or other materials available. Existing materials that have been tested and proven successful should be considered as the review may save time and money when resources are limited. Refer to Sub-competency 8.1.5 for sources of evidence-based interventions. Another option to implementing a packaged program as is is to consider adapting or tailoring materials for the intended audience. New materials only should be created if funds and time are available, and nothing has been successfully used before with the audience. Any materials (new, adapted, or tailored) should be pilot tested before implementation. This testing will help health education specialists determine if changes are needed to ensure successful implementation. In Table 6.6, guides and resources for creating various communication aids and materials for further reference are provided.

Table 6.6
Resources for Developing Communication Aids and Materials

	Online Resources
Infographics	• Infographics: Healthcare Communication for the Digital Age https://www.ncbi.nlm.nih.gov/pmc/articles/PMC4920488/ • VENNGAGE: Infographics for Beginners: The Ultimate Guide https://venngage.com/blog/create-infographics • The 7 G.R.A.P.H.I.C. Principles of Public Health Infographic Design https://visualisinghealth.com/design-guidelines/
Brochures	• Data Visualization Checklist for formatting Graphs https://datavizchecklist.stephanieevergreen.com/ • Community Toolbox: Creating Brochures https://ctb.ku.edu/en/table-of-contents/participation/promoting-interest/brochures/main
Posters	• Designing Communications for a Poster Fair: Tips for Success http://www.personal.psu.edu/drs18/postershow/postershow.pdf • CDC: Gateway to Health Communication – Tools and Templates https://www.cdc.gov/healthcommunication/index.html • Community Toolbox: Creating Posters and Flyers https://ctb.ku.edu/en/table-of-contents/participation/promoting-interest/posters-flyers/main

6.4.4 Assess the suitability of new and/or existing communication aids, materials, or tools for audience(s) (e.g, the CDC Clear Communication Index and the Suitability Assessment Materials (SAM))

To determine if the health communication source is credible and reliable, health education specialists should be mindful of the following: purpose of the source, scientific methodology, qualifications of the author, standing of the publication or organization in the profession, and the quality of references and sources (Cottrell et al., 2018). Health education specialists need to be aware of the types of electronic health-related resources available and how to make decisions about when each is appropriate to use based on the information needed. Whether the resource is a bibliographic database or a Web-based information source, health education specialists need to analyze and evaluate the worthiness of the information retrieved, as some information on the Web is inaccurate, untruthful, or outdated. Health education specialists should look for websites hosted by reputable sources, consider biases reflected in the information, and determine if the information is outdated or misleading.

Accuracy. Evaluating the accuracy, quality, and significance of the information in relation to the needs of the priority audience is important. When assessing online information, the health education specialist should consider the following:
- Who is responsible for managing the site?
- What is the funding source for the site?
- What is the purpose of the site?
- Are evidence-based references cited?

- What are the credentials of the reviewers/editors that proof the accuracy of content?
- How is personal user information utilized and protected?

(NCI, 2015)

For electronic apps and devices, the health education specialist should ask the following:

- Are user needs addressed as described?
- Are the tools or resources easy to use to find the specific information you need?
- Does it work compatibly with other tools and resources you need to connect to (e.g., options to export data)?

(USDHHS, 2014a)

Critically evaluating the reliability of information is key for public health education, especially given the emergence of more Web content generated by end-users ("Web 2.0"). On blogs, comment fields, wikis, and online community boards, contributors may not clearly self-disclose identity, credentials, expertise, or distinguish opinion from fact. Interactive information sharing and personal experiences can enhance resource sharing as long as health education specialists can clarify how this information may complement evidence-based and accurate sources (Adams, 2012).

Relevance. In addition to knowing where to find and how to access health information, health education specialists must be able to evaluate the relevance, appropriateness, and effectiveness of materials for the priority population, group, or client. Resource materials for any program, such as handouts, brochures, fact sheets, talking points, and Frequently Asked Questions (FAQs), should be carefully reviewed to make sure they enhance message appeal.

Resources and materials should be selected based on the client/community's needs and the program objectives. When evaluating resources, the health education specialist should consider the following:

- Does the resource contain the information that the client/community wants to know?
- Does the material address needs and priorities identified in the community assessment?
- Is the information compatible with the community context and culture?
- Can the client/community understand the information contained in the resource?
- Is the format appropriate and the information culturally appropriate?
- Will the resource meet program objectives?
- What is the reading level of the materials?

(Doak et al., 2001; Doak et al., 2002)

When reviewing written resource materials, the health education specialist should consider the following questions:

- Does the material have audience appeal?
- Is it complete? Is there sufficient, too much, or too little information?
- Is it written in a logical, clearly developed, easy to follow format?
- Is the message supportive, positive, and personal?
- Does it attract and keep the reader's attention?
- Is the physical appearance (color, layout, print, illustrations) appropriate for the audience?
- Are the graphics simple, clear, and compatible with the text?
- Is the vocabulary appropriate for the audience? Are new terms defined, and has jargon been avoided?
- Is the reading level appropriate for the audience?

(Plomer & Bensley, 2009)

Health education resources and materials should be compiled and evaluated through a review process. An Educational Materials Review Form (Wurzbach, 2004) or a modified version may have health education specialists inventory the materials and determine which is most relevant and appropriate for your community group. The health education specialist can assess these aspects of the materials:

- Form
- Length
- Topic
- Mode of delivery
- Setting
- Intended audience

- Language
- Readability
- Scope of the material (national to local)
- Pretest or evaluated
- Availability
- Language

The CDC Clear Communication Index (CDC, 2019b) is a research-based tool to help the health education specialist develop and assess public health communication products and materials for diverse audiences (Baur & Prue, 2014). In The CDC Clear Communication Index, there are 4 open-ended introductory questions and 20 scored items that affect information clarity and audience comprehension. These items represent the most important characteristics that enhance and aid people's understanding of information. This evidence-based scoring rubric can be used to assess and improve the clarity of health education materials (Baur & Prue, 2014).

Through the Suitability Assessment of Materials (SAM) instrument, a systematic method to quickly, yet objectively, assess the suitability of health information materials for a particular audience (Practice Development, 2008) is offered. SAM is used to guide health education specialists to rate health information materials on factors that affect readability and comprehension. These factors include content, literacy demand, graphics, layout and type, learning stimulation and motivation, and cultural appropriateness. SAM results can be used to (1) determine how well the health education materials "fit" the target audience; (2) compare different health education materials and select those that are most suitable for the audience; and (3) guide the development of more culturally and linguistically appropriate health education materials.

Timeliness. Health education specialists also are tasked with evaluating if the information and resources are accurate, current, updated, and timely (NCI, 2014; Plomer & Bensley, 2009). Recommendations (e.g., how much an adult should exercise) may change over time. For example, fruit and vegetable intake changed from the Five-A-Day Campaign to More Matters (http://www.fruitsandveggiesmorematters.org/) based on enhanced USDA guidelines. Public health goals and objectives may change periodically over time; the Office of Disease Prevention and Health Promotion (US-DHHS, ODPHP, 2020) will be updating *Healthy People 2030* for the next iteration of emerging issues (https://health.gov/healthypeople). The evidence-base around what is effective in behavioral, policy, or environmental change is continually evolving as research and evaluation are used to fill the evidence gaps. Health education specialists should stay abreast of new evidence and updated findings in their areas of expertise.

As resource persons, health education specialists may need to share relevant information in a timely and rapid manner, especially when health issues are time sensitive, such as in crisis and emergency situations. The CDC Office of Public Health Preparedness and Response (OPHPR) hosts a website with tools for Crisis & Emergency Risk Communication (CERC) (https://emergency.cdc.gov/cerc/) (CDC, 2020). The CERC manual offers tools to help develop communication messages that are timely, correct, and credible.

The health education specialist should consider timeliness, whether a message is being delivered at the appropriate time given contextual circumstances and priorities. For example, if food insecurity is a top priority for a population, addressing chronic disease prevention may not be the top priority to address right away. The less urgent issue, however, still could be woven into a message in which the more pressing one is addressed. In this case, food insecurity could be addressed by initiatives to bring local healthy produce to increase access in food deserts, which, in turn, could contribute to chronic disease prevention via healthier options.

Evaluating Online Resources. While assessing resource materials from the Internet, health education specialists should consider elements such as the website purpose, domain name, appropriateness, readability, and affiliations. Then, they can gauge if those elements are applicable to those that need those resources. Considerations for evaluating the quality of online resources are summarized in the Table 6.7.

Table 6.7
Resources for Developing Communication Aids and Materials

Element	Application of Element
Website purpose	Intention of the site consistent with the institutional affiliation and author credentials (NCI, 2014)
Domain name	The URL ends in .org, .gov, or .edu. A website's domain name and extension may offer information about the credibility of the source. Those sites ending in .org (organization) or .gov (government) likely offer more unbiased information than those with a .com (commercial) extension.
Priority population	Content of the website is appropriate for the audience whether consumer, professional or both (Cottrell et al., 2014).
Website appropriateness	Review of sources and timeliness of information (NCI, 2014; Plomer & Bensley, 2009).
Website accuracy	Content of the site is backed by empirical research or facts and verified by expert opinion. References are available for statistics and information. (Eysenbach et al., 2002; Dreier et al., 2013)
Website's adequacy	Determine if website's research was conducted independently (Doyle et al., 2010)
Website's currency	Health information changes constantly; data updated regularly (National Library of Medicine, 2009)
Readability	Reading level of the content of the website is acceptable to audience (Dreier et al., 2013)
Reputable affiliations	Type of organizations sponsoring the website; Materials being published consistent with the agency's mission
Author/administrative names	Qualified people writing the information posted (professional credentials) (NCI, 2014)
Author contact information	A mailing address, telephone, fax or E-mail information available on the site (Cottrell et al., 2014)

6.4.5 Pilot test message(s) and communication aids, materials, or tools.

Conducting a pilot test (using focus groups, interviews, questionnaires, readability tests) of draft materials is important to make sure they are understandable and relevant (Plomer & Bensley, 2009). The pilot testing methods should fit the program's budget and timeline. Include individuals who share similar characteristics as the intended audience such as gatekeepers, opinion leaders, and community influences as test segments where appropriate. Pilot testing can be used to assess comprehension and recall, determine personal relevance, and evaluate controversial elements, but health education specialists need to consider the time it takes to revise the communication message based on the findings of the pilot test (NCI, 2008).

In the CDCynergy Lite Social Marketing Edition, steps for piloting and revising materials are outlined as follows:

1. Test creative concepts with intended audiences to see if the ideas resonate.
2. Pretest specific messages with intended audiences to ensure that they hear what you want them to hear.
3. Pretest products and materials with intended audiences to ensure that your products and materials elicit the intended response and produce the desired actions.
4. Choose pretest settings – the places where you hope to provide your service(s) or expose your audience to messages.
5. Pretest product distribution plans.
(CDC, 2014b).

Pilot testing involves evaluative research techniques, such as using focus groups, conducting interviews, or even survey research, to formatively evaluate the effectiveness of the communication materials and overall program. For example, pilot testing a program on a small scale before full implementation includes collecting formative evaluation data on all aspects of the small scale program for the purpose of program improvement. Focus groups are often used at this stage to identify any unknown issues and/or concerns, in addition to gauge reactions to potential benefits, actions, or concepts established during the planning phases of the communication program (NCI, 2008).

Health education specialists can pilot test their delivery methods (e.g., Web, e-mail, social media, or print) in addition to message testing. The results from the pilot test will allow for the identification of any potential issues before full implementation.

6.4.6 Revise communication aids, materials, or tools based on pilot results.

Health education specialists can think of message creation and testing as an iterative process; after piloting test messages, health education specialists can revise them to incorporate audience feedback. This participatory process can enhance the effectiveness and reach of health education messages. After modifications, the communication message should be tested again.

Pilot testing and modification should be integrated into the overall timeline to ensure that products, services, and communication materials will be ready for program launch. The creation of materials, including the pretesting process, can be time-consuming (Plomer & Bensley, 2009). Feedback received, however, is necessary to improve message efficacy.

Health education specialists responsible for revising health education communication materials based on the feedback acquired from the pilot must take into consideration the following:

- The nature of the message (e.g., style, sensitivity, complexity)
- The function of the message (e.g., calling attention to an issue or teaching a new skill)
- Goals and objectives of the message
- Activities and channels to reach (e.g., senior centers, schools, universities, churches, health clinics)
- Additional effort and implications by modifying the message
- Costs and accountability
- Budget and/or in-kind resources from other sources

(CDC, 2007; NCI, 2008)

Depending on the extent of revisions, costs may range from minimal to extensive. To minimize cost, program planners should share revised messages with the priority population to ensure changes are appropriate. Also, results from pilot testing will help program planners identify new, old, or a combination of new and old channels through which revised messages will be disseminated.

Regardless of the channel used to disseminate revised messages, health education specialists must be scientifically accurate, consistent, clear, credible, and relevant to the intended audience (Kreps et al., 2019: NCI, 2008). Key primary cultural factors should be taken into account when revising messages. These factors for consideration include race, ethnicity, language, nationality, and religion (Schiavo, 2014). In addition to these factors, other secondary cultural factors should be taken into consideration, such as age, gender, educational level, occupation, and income level (NCI, 2008). Program planners must stay in touch with the norms, perceptions, and views of their priority populations. Therefore, through the use of a participatory approach, it is necessary to periodically revise messages to enhance their effectiveness and reach to priority populations.

Competency 6.5 Deliver the message(s) effectively using the identified media and strategies.

Health education specialists should identify appropriate media outlets, media activities, and strategies for effectively communicating health education information to intended audience(s). Effective delivery of communication messages requires using the identified media outlets to provide messages that are clear and timely, maintain visibility, and are targeted to the segmented audience. Characteristics of effective communication related to message delivery include the following:

- Availability: The message content is delivered in a way/place where the intended audience can easily access the message. Placement of content will vary, depending on the audience, purpose, and message complexity. Delivery will range from social networks to radio, TV ads, public kiosks, and even to a variety of social media channels.
- Reach: The message content is available to the largest number of people in the intended audience(s).
- Repetition: The content is delivered multiple times in a repeated fashion to reinforce the impact with the intended audience.

Effective communication strategies involve a multi-pronged approach, coupled with policy changes, health behavior interventions, etc. (US Dept of Health and Human Services: Health Resources and Services Administration (HRSA), 2019).

6.5.1 Deliver presentation(s) tailored to the audience(s).

The health education specialist should select a presentation style that is appropriate for the intended audience(s), paying close attention to the norms and expectations of the audience. The preferences of the audience(s) will be used to inform a health education specialist on whether an emotional or rational approach would be more effective. Moreover, it is important to pretest the tone of the presentation (i.e., serious or funny) to ensure no audience member is offended by the manner in which the content is delivered.

Audience research, or research about the make-up of the audience, will assist in creating relevant presentation materials. The health education specialist should incorporate the experiences of the audience into the presentation. This use of the audience's experiences will allow for the inclusion of new information, along with familiar context, which will likely result in increased audience engagement in the presentation. The presentation message should be linked to audience's levels of readiness to change, so as to start where they are in the process. To that end, a realistic outcome of the tailored presentation could be to raise awareness for potential considerations of behavior change (NCI, 2008).

Priority populations. Health education specialists present health information to priority populations or communities across different settings. Moreover, it is important to consider communication objectives and best strategies for the presentation of the data. Some examples of ways to communicate to the public are presentations, discussions, lectures, demonstrations, printed educational materials, or posters. For statistical health data, it may be more effective to present graphical data instead of tabulations of numbers in tables for the lay audience. Also helpful is to ask people knowledgeable about the population for the presentation style that would be best received by the audience. Remember that simplicity of health messages is best to increase the understanding of the information. While certain methods are acceptable to one group or culture, they might be less acceptable to others. Therefore, it is important to match the methods to the content and audience needs. In addition, if time permits, health education specialists could pilot strategies with small audiences to receive feedback and evaluation of the best methods of presentation.

Key stakeholders. Key stakeholders are individuals who are interested in the health information for a particular health campaign. They may be community, business, religious, health agency, or other leaders. Health education specialists should communicate with stakeholders regularly to increase the utilization of the health-related information. The presentation methods could include an oral presentation, a one or two page executive summary, a short report, graphs or tables of data, or an oral presentation with a PowerPoint.

Health education specialists should consider whether the presentation will be formal (i.e., at an organized function), semiformal, or informal. Some steps for conducting effective presentations are as follows:
1. Prepare for the presentation.
2. Understand the presentation setting.
3. Open the presentation.
4. Use effective skills in delivering the presentation .
5. End the presentation.
6. Respond to the audience's questions.
(Wagenschutz & Rivas, 2009)

6.5.2 Use public speaking skills.

Health education specialists need to review the essentials of public speaking and practice these skills to effectively present health information to the intended audience(s). To be a successful orator of health information, there are three key areas to emphasize: 1) delivery, 2) structure, and 3) style. How the audience takes and uses the message provided is as much about how the presentation is delivered as the content in the message. Use the following skills when presenting health information:

Delivery. If the delivery of the presentation is poor, the important content may be overlooked by the audience. To deliver the presentation in a more effective way, think about the fluency of the presentation. Provide a steady flow of the presentation, with correct pronunciation of words, and practice multiple times before giving the presentation to the audience. Delivery also can be impacted by pace, power, and pitch. Use these three skills to emphasize points, engage audience members, and allow time for audience members to digest important information. The best way to ensure these skills are used to improve delivery is to practice.

Structure. As a health education specialist, it is assumed that credible information is being presented to the audience. To ensure the audience understands the essence of the presentation, however, it is important to structure it in a logical sequence. Provide an introduction that is captivating and brief, followed by the content of the presentation, and close with a conclusion with a summarized "take-home" message.

Style. Use a style in which enthusiasm, audience engagement, and purpose are incorporated. Consider posture and poise when standing in front of the audience, and project your confidence in a reassuring way. Maintain eye contact with the audience, and avoid reading presentations slides or notes directly to them. Preparation and practice are key in providing a natural delivery of a presentation (White, 2010).

6.5.3 Use facilitation skills with large and/or small groups.

Facilitation is a neutral process that allows health education specialists to help manage the work that needs to be done among the group by minimizing any problems that arise. For groups to be productive and overcome any challenges of collaboration, health education specialists can apply facilitation skills to support more efficient and effective group dynamics. Based on resources provided by the International Association of Facilitators, the tasks of a facilitator are summarized as follows:

- Developing group meeting agenda(s),
- Preparing tools and methods/techniques before meeting,
- Supporting the process of group collaboration throughout the entire process,
- Encouraging participation,
- Facilitating group interaction, and
- Evaluating the overall process.

(Kofschoten et al., 2012).

The health education specialist should keep in mind that facilitation involves three basic principles: 1) a facilitator is present to guide the process, not to give opinions, but to garner the opinions of those in the group, 2) facilitation should be about how people participate, and 3) facilitators should remain neutral in the discussion(s). Tips on successful facilitation of a large or small group includes things like:

- ensuring all participants feel comfortable.
- using a structure that allows all opinions to be heard (e.g., Nominal Group Process).
- making sure participants feel good about their contributions to the meeting.
- ensuring the participants believe the ideas and decisions being made are theirs and not the facilitator's.

(University of Kansas, 2019k).

Health education specialists should plan the facilitation process by focusing on the climate/environment of the meeting, logistics and room arrangements, and by setting ground rules for participants. The environment of the meeting can set the tone; therefore, ensure the space is accessible, comfortable, and deemed a "safe space" to hold the meeting. Having chairs in a circle is suggested, if possible, to encourage equality and inclusiveness. Decisions on logistics regarding things such as refreshments (Will they be available? Who will bring them? How to set them up?), microphones and audio/visual equipment (Do you need a microphone? Can the equipment be set up in advance?), and even the sign-in sheet (Do you have one? Is there a table to place it?) need to be determined prior to the meeting. Common ground rules for facilitation of meetings include the following:

- One person speaks at a time.
- Indicate that you have something to say by raising your hand.
- Listen to others.
- Do not attack or mock people for their comments.
- Stay on-time with the agenda items.
- Respect all participants.

To set the ground rules, start the meeting by indicating that some "rules" will be set to ensure the meeting goes smoothly. Ask for suggestions on what those rules should entail, and, if no one speaks up, begin with suggesting a rule or two to get participants thinking. This process usually gets people talking (University of Kansas, 2019l). Once the meeting begins, there are basic steps health education specialists can use as a guide to ensure the meeting is organized:

1. Start the meeting on-time.
2. Welcome the participants.
3. Make introductions in a manner that increases comfort level of participants (e.g., consider icebreakers).
4. Review the agenda and make the ground rules.
5. Encourage participation.
6. Stick to the agenda.
7. Avoid detailed decision-making.
8. Seek commitments.
9. Bring closure to every agenda item.
10. Respond each participant.
11. Be flexible.
12. Summarize meeting "take-home points" and next steps for follow-up.
13. Thank all participants.
14. Close the meeting.

(University of Kansas, 2019l)

Facilitators should maximize their role by considering the following tips:
- Be aware of the body language of participants (Are they bored? Look confused?).
- Always check back with the group to answer questions before proceeding.
- Summarize and pause throughout to ensure engagement.
- Be aware of your own behavior (Are you standing too close to people? Are you making appropriate eye contact with participants?).
- Use appropriate words/speech to prevent offending or alienating participants.

(University of Kansas, 2019k)

6.5.4 Use current and emerging communication tools and trends (e.g., social media).

Health education specialists should determine the best tool and delivery mechanisms for communication messages based on audience preferences. They can assess current and emerging tools for appropriateness of use with the intended audience. Message delivery requires continual monitoring. Health education specialists should fine tune their delivery to ensure intended audiences are being reached and use process evaluation to keep track of message and material delivery (e.g., quantities of materials distributed, number of special events held, number of website visits, or phone inquiries). Specifically, social media sites have become popular avenues for exchanging health communication and information via an online format. The value of social media includes the ability for health organizations to create ongoing conversations with the intended audiences. Examples of current and emerging communication tools include Twitter, Facebook, LinkedIn, Instagram, and even Pinterest listed in Table 6.8.

Table 6.8
Types of Social Media

Social medium		Description	Uses in health promotion
Facebook		Site for people or organizations to connect and share with family, friends, or public online	Post events for health promotion or messages to engage public in health
Twitter		Site to connect people and allow people to share their thoughts with a big audience (character limits in content of the tweets)	Tweet a short message about a health month (i.e., Getting a mammogram in October) or link to a website
LinkedIn		Online networking site for professionals and groups	Post health education event from your agency's page
Instagram		Online network based primarily on sharing of photos	Post infographics on COVID-19 preventive behaviors (e.g., social distance –stand 6 ft apart, wash hands, cough into elbow); post educational fliers
Pinterest		Social network where people can find ideas for their interests and hobbies	Post healthy recipes for nutrition, images for exercises for physical activity, etc.
YouTube		Repository of videos	Post educational videos (e.g., how to wash hands correctly using soap and for 20 seconds)

Other digital media options for communicating health messaging effectively exist and include blogs, image sharing, mobile devices, and podcasts. The Centers for Disease Control and Prevention (CDC, 2014a) has developed social media tools, guidelines, and best practices for health education specialists to use to determine how to maximize social media for reaching the intended audience(s) in the communication program.

6.5.5 Deliver oral and written communication that aligns with professional standards of grammar, punctuation, and style.

Health education specialists use writing and oral dialogue to communicate about a myriad of health issues to community members, other professionals, funders, stakeholders, and policymakers from various cultural backgrounds. To communicate effectively and in a professional manner, health education specialists should ensure all communication aligns with professional standards of grammar, punctuation and style. Proper style and correct grammar are important elements for being taken seriously in communication efforts. All writing should be assessed for complexity of sentence structure, sentence length, grammar, tone, vocabulary and voice (Stamatakis et al., 2010). The American Psychological Association (APA) supports APA Style writing and formatting as a foundation for effective scholarly communication (APA, 2019). APA Style provides a simple set of style guidelines that assist in writings to present ideas in a clear and concise manner. For general guides to editorial style, both Elements of Style (Strunke & A-Morelli, 2018) and the Chicago Manual of Style (University of Chicago Press, 2017) are good resources. Similarly, oral communication should be aligned with these grammatical styles, and it is important to practice this communication prior to delivery to the intended audience(s).

Being digital media proficient means being able to meet priority populations and impact change within virtual environments in which they live, work, and play. Six types of social media platforms are commonly used in health education/promotion: 1) social networking (e.g., Facebook), 2) blog comments and forums, 3) microblogging (e.g., Twitter), 4) media sharing (e.g., Instagram), 5) book marketing, and 6) social news (Bensley et al., 2019). Many challenges abound to effectively using these social media platforms within health education/promotion campaigns. Many challenges are directly attributable to the nature of social media itself, where health education specialists cannot fully control what, when, and how health information is shared.

6.5.6 Use digital media to engage audience(s) (e.g., social media management tools and platforms).

While challenges are to be expected, audience engagement can be maximized on social media through managing misinformation, reducing agency barriers to use, measuring actual reach and impact, and keeping up with new trends. To effectively engage audiences, there are several steps that can be followed to help develop a strategic approach to social media use: 1) understand how the priority population uses social media; 2) identify evidence-based social media strategies; 3) select appropriate communication times and channels; and 4) determine which particular types of social media apps will engage the audience (Bensley et al., 2019). Facebook is among the most widely used social media sites among adults in the U.S., with approximately 7 in 10 adults (69%) reporting use of Facebook. Facebook use is relatively common across a range of age groups, with 68% of those ages 50 to 64 and nearly half of those 65 and older saying they use the popular profile-based social media website. Younger populations are more likely to use Twitter and Snapchat. Instagram and Snapchat are used by 67% and 62% of 18- to 29-year-olds, respectively). A majority of Facebook, Snapchat, and Instagram users visit these sites daily) Pinterest use is three times higher in women than men. Around half of college graduates and those who live in high-income households use LinkedIn, compared with 10% or fewer of those who have not attended some college or those in lower-income households. WhatsApp continues to be popular among Hispanic populations, with 42% using the messaging app, compared with 24% of African Americans and 13% of whites. (Perrin & Andersen, 2019).

Competency 6.6 Evaluate communication.

Evaluating the effectiveness of the communication messages to assess how well efforts met the identified communication objectives is important. In addition, evaluation allows health education specialists know what to change or improve to make communication efforts more effective. Specifically, understanding how the communication used met the objectives is important for the following reasons:

- Justifying the need for communication messaging/program to stakeholders
- Providing evidence of communication success
- Increasing organizational understanding and support of the communication efforts
- Encouraging collaborations and partnerships with other organizations

(NCI, 2008)

In thinking about evaluating communication, there are questions to be answered to ensure the evaluation methods used give the information needed (NCI, 2008). The questions include:

1. What are the communication objectives? What should the intended audience do or how should they think as a result of the message, and how does this differ from baseline? How are these differences measured?
2. How do you expect change to happen with the use of this communication? Will change happen slowly or rapidly? What are measureable steps or outcomes that are likely to occur along the way?
3. How long will the communication program last? What kind of changes are likely to occur during this timeframe (e.g., awareness, attitude, behavior, policy changes)? What changes are reasonable to expect during this time?
4. What outcome evaluation methods are appropriate for capturing expected change? How will long-term change be measured?

Overall monitoring of the communication approach(es) includes evaluating all activities, staff, and budgets, while also involving problem solving, measuring intended audience changes and satisfaction, and revising plans and operations, as needed (NCI, 2008).

Evaluation can and needs to occur on many different levels, including evaluation of communication strategies, methods, or techniques. Evaluation can include several surveillance and monitoring of campaign efforts. For example, since 2002, evaluation of the statewide Strategic Tobacco Retail Effort Campaign (California Department of Public Health, 2002), a campaign that was designed to look strategically at tobacco retail licensing to minors, has consisted of several surveillance and evaluation efforts. These efforts included tobacco purchase surveys, point of marketing surveys, law enforcement surveys, surveillance studies, media tracking, opinion polls, and ordinance tracking, among others.

6.6.1 Conduct process and impact evaluations of communications.

Health education specialists should conduct process evaluation periodically to assess whether:
- activities are being implemented as planned (e.g.,at scheduled times).
- the intended audience(s) are being reached and are satisfied with the communication outreach.
- if certain materials are more effective than others.
- if certain components or aspects of the program need to be improved or altered.
- if your expenditures are within budget.

Use appropriate data collection techniques to assess aspects of communication strategies. Problems often can be corrected promptly if they are identified through process evaluation. Process evaluation steps take place during implementation phases of communication. Process evaluation allows health education specialists to know whether the messages are being delivered appropriately, effectively, and efficiently. Specifically, use process evaluation to assess the following:
- Program quality and overall functioning
- Partner involvement
- Outreach and promotion effectiveness
- Media response
- Participation of the intended audience(s)
- Schedule adherence
- Expenditures and adherence to budget
- Contractor activities:
  - Are seasoned professionals engaged in the work?
  - Are deadlines being met?
  - Is there enough time being devoted to the project?
  - Is the relationship working well?
  - Are tasks completed and deliverables within the terms in the contract?

(NCI, 2008)

According to the National Cancer Institute (NCI, 2008), the following are examples of ways to gather vital information for process evaluation:
- Use tracking forms for all activities.
- Monitor all requests for information from the intended audience(s).
- Gather regular status reports from partners, contractors and any staff working on the communication project.
- Meet in person or by phone with partners regularly.
- Track media impressions.
- Track traffic to project social media sites and websites.

Evaluating the impact of the delivered messages will provide evidence of success that health education specialists need to demonstrate and improve effectiveness. Three common measures for health communication include change in a) awareness, b) knowledge, c) comprehension, d) attitude, and e) behavior. Using communication/behavior theories (refer to Sub Competency 6.3.1 Use communications theory to develop or select communication message(s)) can assist health education specialists in assessing effective communication messages. For example, evaluation of the five communication components in the Communications for Persuasion theory will allow health education specialists to understand if the message(s) are reaching the intended audience(s) and how effective they are for the desired outcomes of the messaging. Moreover, health education specialists can ask in an evaluation, "What do we want people to think or do as a result of the communication intervention?" (e.g., get a flu shot or wear a bike helmet).

After determining the evaluation questions, health education specialists should define the data they want to collect. Next, they need to decide on the data collection methods (e.g., survey, media tracking (impressions vs. reach), social media engagement (likes, comments, shares). Finally, they need to collect and analyze the data. Health education specialists should plan to disseminate the evaluation report to others in the field who can learn from the findings.

6.6.2 ■ Conduct outcome evaluations of communications.

Outcome evaluation shows how well the communication approaches worked with the intended audience(s). This process allows for the evaluation of the overall effectiveness of the communication plan. Important to consider is which outcome evaluation methods capture the scope of the change that is likely to happen, based on the communication strategies used. The following are steps to use when conducting outcome evaluation:

- Figure out what information the evaluation must provide.
- Determine why type of evaluation data to collect.
- Decide on the appropriate data collection techniques/methods.
- Create and pretest all data collection tools.
- Collect data.
- Aggregate and process data.
- Analyze data.
- Write an evaluation report with relevant findings.
- Disseminate relevant findings to all stakeholders.

(NCI, 2008)

The simplest evaluation design is a pre (before) and post (after) measurement. This evaluation design, however, does not account for the influence of external factors. A health education specialist's goal in evaluating a communication effort is to get the most reliable and accurate information possible, given:

- the specific evaluation questions.
- nature of the communication initiative.
- availability and willingness of participants.
- time and resource constraints.

(University of Kansas, 2014m)

A well-designed evaluation will help to determine the effectiveness of the communication approach, and subsequently, the results can be used to inform future initiatives to help the public learn more regarding how to communicate effectively about health information. Outcome evaluation is large and does take time to design and analyze; however, if planned well, the evaluation can occur in tandem with a well-planned program. Report results in the context of what health communication programs are expected to accomplish, knowing that results will vary depending on the issue and intended audience(s) (NCI, 2008).

6.6.3 ▲ Assess reach and dose of communication using tools (e.g., data mining software, social media analytics and website analytics,).

Evaluating the impact, including the reach (number of people exposed to the communication message) and the dose (how frequently the communication message is delivered) will provide the evidence of success that health education specialists need to demonstrate and improve effectiveness. Three common measures for health communication include change in a) knowledge, b) attitude, and c) behavior. Tools such as website analytics, social media analytics, and data mining software can assist health education specialists in assessing the reach and dose of communication messages. website analytics is the collection and reporting of data that is gathered via a website. The website data can be used to determine the success or failure of the goals of the communication program. For example, the click-stream, scroll-tracking, and heat maps of the website data can provide insights into how many users were exposed to the communication (USDHHS,2019c). Social media analytics "is concerned with developing and evaluating informatics tools and frameworks to collect, monitor, analyze, summarize, and visualize social media data, usually driven by specific requirements from a [population of interest]" (Zeng et al., 2010, p. 14). These analytics help in extracting useful patterns of active users to assess the reach and dose of social media communication messages. Moreover, using data mining software, such as R-language, an open source tool for statistical computing, or another statistical software package (e.g., Statistical Package for the Social Sciences (SPSS)) to analyze data produced from social media analytics or website analytics to look for valid and potentially useful patterns can provide insights into how the communication program worked to reach the intended group(s) (R Core Team, 2017).

To measure the dose and reach, first, health education specialists should define the data they want to collect. Next, they need to decide on the data collection methods (e.g., survey). Finally, they need to collect and analyze the data. Health education specialists should plan to disseminate the evaluation report to others in the field who can learn from the findings. Common metrics to evaluate the impact of delivered messages are in Table 6.9.

Table 6.9
Communication Outcomes

Communication Indicator	Definition
Reach	Number of people exposed to the message
Dose	How frequent the message exposure occurred within the intended audience)
Recall	How well people remember seeing or hearing the message
Traffic	Number of unique visitors or hits to a web or other social media site
User Engagement	User interactions with social media (e.g., number of "likes" or "retweets")
Impressions	Mentions in the media

Communication Indicator	Definition
Changes in attitudes or beliefs	Person has new thoughts about disease, health or healthy action (e.g., number of people who believe the flu shot will help protect them from the flu)
Changes in behavior	Person takes action (e.g., number of people getting the flu shot)

Specific indicators for communication tracking with social media. Common key performance indicators (KPIs) and metrics for communication strategies delivered via social media (e.g., posts, tweets, and post 'likes') should be tracked during the communication program/campaign (Neiger, et al., 2012). A metric is a single variable; whereas, KPIs are unique metrics for assessing the engagement and influence of the social media campaign with the targeted audience (Sterne, 2010). In Table 6.10, KPIs for social media and metrics to consider for evaluation are described.

Table 6.10
KPIs for Social Media and Metrics for Evaluation (Neiger et al., 2012)

Key Performance Indicator	Metrics to be monitored
Exposure – *Number of times content is viewed on social media site*	Number of comments, Number of reviews; Number of ratings; Clickthroughs; Views on a video; Total visits on site
Reach – *Number of people in contact with the social media site*	Number of friend/page 'likes;' Number of people providing comments; Number of friends; Growth rate of friends & subscribers
Engagement – *Number of people who indicate agreement with the content posted or shared and/or who share posted content to influence others*	Likes on posts; Frequency of favorites; Likes or dislikes on videos; Comments on posts; Comment rate; Frequency of new discussions; Downloads; Uploads; Frequency of content shares

Chapter 7
Area of Responsibility VII: Leadership and Management

KEY: No symbol - entry level; ▲ - advanced 1; ■ - advanced 2

7.1. Coordinate relationships with partners and stakeholders (e.g., individuals, teams, coalitions, and committees).

7.1.1   Identify potential partners and stakeholders.

7.1.2   Assess the capacity of potential partners and stakeholders.

7.1.3   Involve partners and stakeholders throughout the health education and promotion process in meaningful and sustainable ways.

7.1.4 ▲ Execute formal and informal agreements with partners and stakeholders.

7.1.5   Evaluate relationships with partners and stakeholders on an ongoing basis to make appropriate modifications.

7.2. Prepare others to provide health education and promotion.

7.2.1   Develop culturally responsive content.

7.2.2   Recruit individuals needed in implementation.

7.2.3 ▲ Assess training needs.

7.2.4 ▲ Plan training, including technical assistance and support.

7.2.5 ▲ Implement training.

7.2.6 ▲ Evaluate training as appropriate throughout the process.

7.3. Manage human resources.

7.3.1 ▲ Facilitate understanding and sensitivity for various cultures, values, and traditions.

7.3.2 ▲ Facilitate positive organizational culture and climate.

7.3.3 ▲ Develop job descriptions to meet staffing needs.

7.3.4 ▲ Recruit qualified staff (including paraprofessionals) and volunteers.

7.3.5 ▲ Evaluate performance of staff and volunteers formally and informally.

7.3.6 ▲ Provide professional development and training for staff and volunteers.

7.3.7 ▲ Facilitate the engagement and retention of staff and volunteers.

7.3.8 ▲ Apply team building and conflict resolution techniques as appropriate.

7.4. Manage fiduciary and material resources.

7.4.1 ▲ Evaluate internal and external financial needs and funding sources.

7.4.2 ▲ Develop financial budgets and plans.

7.4.3 ▲ Monitor budget performance.

7.4.4 ■ Justify value of health education and promotion using economic (e.g., cost-benefit, return-on-investment, and value-on-investment) and/or other analyses.

7.4.5 ▲ Write grants and funding proposals.

7.4.6 ■ Conduct reviews of funding and grant proposals.

7.4.7 ▲ Monitor performance and/or compliance of funding recipients.

7.4.8 ▲ Maintain up-to-date technology infrastructure.

7.4.9 ▲ Manage current and future facilities and resources (e.g., space and equipment).

7.5. Conduct strategic planning with appropriate stakeholders.

7.5.1 ▲ Facilitate the development of strategic and/or improvement plans using systems thinking to promote the mission, vision, and goal statements for health education and promotion.

7.5.2 ▲ Gain organizational acceptance for strategic and/or improvement plans.

7.5.3 ▲ Implement the strategic plan, incorporating status updates and making refinements as appropriate.

The Role. A great deal of leadership, administration, management and coordination is needed to bring a health education/promotion program to fruition. Depending on the specific work setting, some entry-level health education specialists may be called upon to lead and manage programs, but most often these are the responsibilities of health education specialists at more advanced levels of practice. It takes good leadership and management skills to recruit partners and stakeholders who will participate in the program, but more importantly to assess their capacity and involve them in the process in meaningful ways. The effective health education specialist must be able to manage human resources and fiscal resources as well as physical resources. A good leader/manager establishes a long-range vision for the program and can work with others to develop, implement and evaluate a strategic plan. Leadership skills are not only needed in health education program development, but also within the profession. It is important that good leaders step forward to chair committees and accept positions as officers and board members. There are many health organizations, foundations, and state and national professional associations that need good leadership (NCHEC, 2020).

Setting: The following text is presented to describe how Leadership and Management is used in different practice settings (NCHEC, 2020).

Community Setting: Health education specialists in a community setting, especially those working at an advanced-level, may be responsible for managing and administering health education/promotion programs and/or organizations. Such work includes gaining acceptance for programs, utilizing evidence-based approaches, and managing the financial, technological, and human resources associated with programs. These tasks require health education specialists to create and monitor a program budget, hire and evaluate personnel, and work with both internal and external partners, as well as stakeholders, to ensure a program's success. In addition, health education specialists are responsible for managing the relationships with program partners and other stakeholders. This includes accepting cultural differences, utilizing conflict resolution skills, and ensuring that dissenting opinions are heard. In addition, health education specialists use their leadership and management skills to influence policy and advocate for positive health practices.

School (K-12) Setting: Health education specialists in K-12 schools may serve as program managers, or team leaders to promote health education in their school and throughout the school district. They may have a leadership role in developing content to be addressed at each grade level in the curriculum, supervise instruction and measure learning outcomes. Health education specialists may also manage budgetary issues for the school health program and work with school leaders/stakeholders to obtain acceptance and support for health education.

Health Care Setting: Health education specialists who are employed in health care settings may hold managerial and/or leadership positions. Usually these are health education specialists who hold advanced degrees and/or have significant experience in the field. In these roles, they supervise staff and volunteers and manage professional development and continuing education programs for staff and volunteers. In addition, they may plan and implement programs that contribute to institutional maintenance of accreditation and/or compliance with government regulations. In addition, they must provide guidance and technical assistance to staff, volunteers, and health care partners. To be effective leaders, they must understand and practice ethical leadership and encourage an ethical environment and a fair and inclusive culture that promotes integrity, accountability, equality, and respect. Thus, it is essential for health education specialists at this level to have the ability to facilitate and sustain partnerships and collaborations with a variety of medical and allied health professionals, aides, volunteers, patients, families, and stakeholders in their particular health care settings. They also might participate in interdisciplinary efforts to establish advisory and consultation services to stakeholders. Health education specialists serving as managers and leaders are well positioned to ensure cultural sensitivity, diversity and inclusion by engaging a diverse group of stakeholders in every stage of program planning.

College/University Setting: Health education specialists in the college/university setting may be involved in a variety of administrative responsibilities, including coordinating professional preparation programs and chairing academic departments. In this role, health education specialists must provide program leadership, develop and/or manage program budgets, hire and supervise faculty members and staff, and be responsible for the annual evaluations of those employed in the department. They also must align their professional preparation program goals with the goals and mission of school/college and university. In addition, health education specialists may coordinate and supervise student internships, provide leadership in course and program development and student organizations, and chair or facilitate committees and task forces. In this setting, health education specialists might be responsible for teaching competencies related to leadership and management to health education students.

Worksite/Business Setting: Health education specialists may lead or be part of a team for health education and health promotion efforts. Health education specialists may hire, supervise, provide support, and/or evaluate the performance of staff, contracted staff, vendors, and/or "wellness champion" volunteers who deliver programs virtually and/or at the worksite. Health education specialists in this setting may take the lead to develop and advocate for annual budgets and other resources that support the planning, implementation, and evaluation of worksite programs and services and policy initiatives.

College/University Health Promotion Services Setting: Health education specialists in this setting serve as leaders to provide health education and promotion services, programs, and resources for the campus community and its members. In this role they manage resources associated with programs and interventions and must demonstrate leadership through strategic planning, organizational change, and daily operations associated with health promotion services on campus. This includes utilizing management skills such as hiring, training, evaluating, and retaining professional and student staff, developing stakeholder and partner relationships, and securing and managing financial, technological, and other resources.

Key Terms

Coalitions are groups of individuals in an alliance who represent various organizations from within the community and comprised of individuals who agree to work together toward a common goal (McKenzie et al., 2017).

Goals are broad statements of intent that provide directions related to where the organization's or program's efforts should be directed (McKenzie et al., 2017).

Ecological approaches involve various dimensions, (e.g., physical, social, and cultural) to affect behavior change. Five levels of influence on health behavior are considered in the ecological model: intrapersonal (individual), interpersonal (group), institutional, community, and public policy (Cottrell et al., 2018).

Leadership is the activity of guiding a group of people or an organization by establishing a clear vision; sharing that vision with others so that they will follow willingly; providing the information, knowledge, and methods to realize that vision; and coordinating and balancing the conflicting interests of all stakeholders (Rowitz, 2018).

Leadership development is expansion of a person's capacity to be effective in leadership roles and processes such as communication, ability to motivate others, and management (Rowitz, 2018).

Management-leadership continuum is the range of styles and actions used by managers and leaders (Rowitz, 2018).

Mission statements are concrete, outcome-oriented statements that provide information about the overarching goals of an organization in a broad context (University of Wisconsin, 2010).

Negotiation is the utilization of a third party to aid people in conflict resolution (Rowitz, 2018).

Organizational Development (OD) is a term that encompasses strategies and interventions that are focused on building capacities and well-being within groups and organizations to achieve maximum effectiveness and efficiency. Organization development includes team building, organizational design, fostering strong and ethical organizational cultures, intergroup relations, group problem solving, and managing organizational change (Robbins Judge, & Millett, 2015).

Strategic planning is an organizational management activity that is used to set priorities, focus energy and resources, strengthen operations, ensure that employees and other stakeholders are working toward common goals, establish agreement around intended outcomes/results, and assess and adjust the organization's direction in response to a changing environment (Rowitz, 2018).

Teamwork is cooperative or coordinated effort on the part of a group of persons acting together in the interests of a common cause (Rowitz, 2018).

Competency 7.1 Coordinate relationships with partners and stakeholders (e.g., individuals, teams, coalitions, and committees).

Identifying partners who are knowledgeable and committed to the effort, forming viable coalitions, and working with the community to identify and/or validate issues that are important to the community members is critical in gaining and maintaining program support. Furthermore, establishing clear relationships between the program's goals and the assets, capacities, and values of the community are critical (Butterfoss, 2007).

Because many health challenges experienced by individuals and communities are associated with multiple risks and causations, the ecological systems approach is one of the most effective models for leveraging the complexity of managing relationships with partners and other stakeholders (Healey & Lesneski, 2011). Therefore, multilevel, multisectorial, and multidisciplinary partnerships are necessary for health education specialists to be competent in creating, sustaining, monitoring, and managing partnerships, coalitions, and collaborations (Butterfoss, 2007; Schiavo, 2014).

7.1.1 Identify potential partners and stakeholders.

Stakeholders are important for a health education programming in sharing their expertise and input into health promotion processes (McKenzie et al., 2017). The priority population consists of the entire population if an intervention is being implemented for the total community. The audience for an intervention or program includes individuals who are part of the at-risk population. Participants are individuals who receive the intervention or participate in the program. The participants' roles are important, because they affect program evaluation (Issel & Wells, 2018). Other stakeholders can provide insights into the work of partnerships through having expertise in health topics and/or the priority population, being gatekeepers in for specific communities or having previous experience working with the community.

Health education specialists need support from community leaders and groups, including the following:
- Local elected officials
- Clergy
- Influential members of the community
- Community-based organizations and civic associations
- Local departments of health or related agencies
- Social service organizations
- Print journalists and broadcast media representatives

Decision makers such as business leaders and school administrations in the community are able to provide financial, organizational, and/or administrative support to the program planning process.

A comprehensive plan for health promotion also includes the identification of individuals in the community to be part of the planning committee. A planning committee may consist of the following:
- Representatives from all segments of the priority population
- Active community members
- Influential members of the community
- Representatives of the sponsoring agency
- School district faculty and staff
- Local government representatives
- Law enforcement
- Local health department representatives
- Business owners and managers
- Stakeholders
- Effective leaders

(Hodges & Videto, 2011; McKenzie et al., 2017)

A number of ways to identify stakeholders exist. Often, the use of more than one strategy will yield the best results. The strategies to find stakeholders include the following:

Brainstorm. Get together with people in the organization, officials, and others already involved in or informed about the effort, and start calling out categories and names to gather potential stakeholders. Part of the point of brainstorming is to come out with anything that comes to mind, even if it seems silly. On reflection, the silly ideas can turn out to be among the best, so be as far-ranging as the group can. After 10 or 15 minutes of brainstorming, stop and discuss each suggestion, perhaps identifying each as a primary, secondary, and/or key stakeholder.

Collect categories and names from informants in the community (if they are not available to be part of a brainstorming session), particularly members of a population or residents of a geographic area of concern.

Consult with organizations that either are or have been involved in similar efforts or whose members have worked with the population or in the area of concern.

Get more ideas from stakeholders as you identify the ideas.
If appropriate, **advertise**. The health education specialist can use some combination of the media through various community service arrangements such as community meetings, community and organizational newsletters, social media, targeted e-mails, announcements by leaders at meetings and religious gatherings, and word of mouth to get the word out (University of Kansas, 2019n).

7.1.2 Assess the capacity of potential partners and stakeholders.

When developing partnerships, leaders must assess the appropriateness of potential partners to assist in health promotion efforts. As part of the assessment, an examination of the potential partner's history, capabilities, resources, and vision/mission needs to be undertaken to determine if that potential partner is a good fit for the partnership (Healey & Zimmerman, 2010).

The United Nations Development Programme (UNDP) Capacity Assessment Framework has three dimensions including 1) points of entry, 2) core issues, and 3) functional and technical capacities.
- Points of entry: Within the UNDP framework, capacity resides on different levels (e.g., the enabling environment, the organizational, and the individual). Each of these levels can be the point of entry for a capacity assessment. The UNDP Capacity Assessment Framework is specifically tailored to the enabling environment and the organizational level.
- Core issues: These are the four capacity issues that UNDP's empirical evidence suggests to be the most commonly encountered across sectors and levels of capacity: 1) institutional arrangements, 2) leadership, 3) knowledge, and 4) accountability. Not every assessment needs to cover all four, but a capacity assessment team should at least consider all of them as team members define the scope of an assessment. The assessments can be amended based on the needs of the client and the situation.
- Functional and technical capacities: Functional capacities are necessary for creating and managing policies, legislations, strategies, and program. In the UNDP framework, the following functional

capacities are key: 1) engage stakeholders, 2) assess a situation and define a vision and mandate, 3) formulate policies and strategies, 4) budget, manage and implement, and 5) evaluate. Various technical capacities also may need to be assessed, depending on the situation (UNDP, 2008).

Frameworks, such as the social determinants of health and the ecological systems model, can serve as invaluable tools for identifying partners who can provide the leverage and insight necessary to address community needs (Healey & Lesneski, 2011). Several factors that can contribute to the success of these partnerships include: (a) determining the needs, capacity, and resources of the organizations as early as possible, (b) raising awareness of policy requirements and regulations that are critical to the mutual interests and goals of the potential partners, and (c) developing alliances through positive relationships with constituency groups (Schiavo, 2014).

One important indicator of capacity is influence. Influence can be interpreted in several ways:
- An individual or group can wield official power in some way, as a government official or agency.
- As an administrator, board member, or funder, an individual or group has some power over the organization conducting the effort.
- Another influencer could be a "community leader," such as a college president, hospital CEO, clergy member, bank president. These people are often "listened to" as a result of their positions in the community and may hold one or more actual or honorary positions that give them even more influence, e.g., chair of the United Way campaign, officer of one or more corporate or nonprofit boards.
- Key stakeholders are often connected to large networks and thus can both reach and sway many community members. Such connections can be through work, family, long generations or years of residency, membership in many clubs and organizations, or former official status.
- Great influence can be exercised by people (or, occasionally, organizations) who are simply respected in the community for their intelligence, integrity, concern for others and the common good, and objectivity.
- Some people and organizations exercise influence through economics. The largest employer in a community can exert considerable control over its workforce, for example, or even over the community as a whole, using a combination of threats and rewards.

(University of Kansas, 2019o)

In this role of involving partners, health education specialists' responsibilities may include conducting assessments, selecting appropriate evidence-based strategies and interventions, and using assessment information to adapt the selected interventions to respond to the priority population's or organization's needs.

7.1.3 Involve partners and stakeholders throughout the health education and promotion process in meaningful and sustainable ways.

Coalitions, partnerships, committees, subcommittees, advisory boards, consortia, and other organizational structures can be used to facilitate intra- and inter-organizational cooperation to meet the needs of the program and achieve mutual goals (University of Kansas, 2019f). After identifying partners with mutual and/or supporting interests, the following are critical for health education specialists to establish viable working relationships:
- Develop trust and credibility.
- Arrange a meeting with leaders from various organizations who have the ability to make decisions.

- Have the leaders identify where coordination is required or beneficial and where various resources can be utilized.
- Identify common interests.
- Develop memorandums of agreement or understanding (MOUs) after trust and other issues have been resolved.

(Fallon & Zgodzinski, 2011)

Guidelines for public health leaders working at the community level include the following:

- Build trust.
- Form coalitions.
- Develop partnerships.
- Teach community groups about the core public health functions.
- Do community building with partners.
- See the community as a system.
- Encourage coalitions or partnerships to continue after a public health crisis has been resolved.
- Use the media to promote best practices in public health.
- Push a prevention agenda.
- Understand the connections between public health at a global level and public health at a local community level and their connections.

(Rowitz, 2018)

Constituency relations through bidirectional communication are important to the viability of an organization in which cooperation is valued (Schiavo, 2014). Whether partnerships are translated into organizational structures, such as internal/external advisory boards, committees, coalitions, or collaboratives, effective communication is critical for identifying and addressing program resource needs. Furthermore, community concerns and needs should be addressed in ways that are consistent with the values and expectations of their constituencies (Schiavo, 2014; Shi & Johnson, 2013).

Understanding group dynamics and focusing on team building to develop support is necessary for a successful program (Johnson & Johnson, 2012). Planning groups, such as consortia and planning boards, help to increase community and stakeholder involvement to enhance the strategic plan. A group leader can be selected, appointed, or may emerge naturally; therefore, a standardized process for leadership selection should be stated at formation of the planning committee or team. The person in the leadership position may change as the task or stage changes (Issel & Wells, 2018).

Communication with internal and external stakeholders is essential, and, optimally, the process includes a feedback loop through which intentions, ideas, and information can be exchanged (Longest, 2011). This information can be used as a part of process evaluations as a way to guide and inform the actions of a program, project, or organization. The structures through which feedback can be elicited can include coalitions, coordinating councils, committees, and other partnering organizations. Specific vehicles for sending, eliciting, and capturing the feedback include face-to-face meetings, phone calls, Web-based conferences, e-mails, memoranda, policy statements, reports, and letters (Longest, 2011).

Effective leadership skills, including team building, conflict resolution, and the ability to communicate effectively, are key to facilitating discussions with and among partners and other stakeholders. As such, advanced-level health education specialists may play a key role as facilitators of community dialogues by conducting assessments, translating technical information, and undertaking other processes that enhance community participation within the broader context of programs and operations.

7.1.4 ▲ Execute formal and informal agreements with partners and stakeholders.

Health education specialists should consider formalizing relationships with partners through shared agreements, memoranda of understanding (MOUs), and/or subcontracts to solidify participation commitments. Common elements of a MOU are introduction and identification of key partners, purpose, roles, and responsibilities of all parties, other provisions and administration (i.e., who signs the MOU, as well as any modification and/or termination). A MOU is not an enforceable or legal document (unless it indicates an exchange of money), but it is a means of facilitating interagency cooperation. Cooperative agreements with other agencies and organizations are critical to having effective relationships and partnerships. These relationships are best achieved by having clear and documented goals, objectives, and expected outcomes. Another strategy for securing partners is for health education specialists to form a coalition or partnership among committed individuals and organizations.

7.1.5 Evaluate relationships with partners and stakeholders on an ongoing basis to make appropriate modifications.

Just as health education programs are evaluated, partnerships and collaborations should be evaluated to determine their effectiveness. A plan should be established to evaluate partnership or collaboration activities before these activities begin. A determination needs to be made about what will be measured, when measurements will occur, and who will do the measurements. Healey and Zimmerman (2010) and Butterfoss (2007) provided the following as a guide for evaluating partnerships and collaborations:

- Develop an evaluation plan.
- Evaluate progress toward goal and objective achievement.
- Record and track data based on established timeline.
- Report the results.
- Determine the levels of goal, objective, and other achievements.
- Use the findings for program improvement.
- Prepare evaluation reports.
- Broadly share achievements as a mechanism for partnership promotion.

A successful program is often indicative of successful relationships. Therefore, establishing clear mission statements, goals, and agreed-upon outcomes are essential first steps for monitoring relationships with internal and external stakeholders (Longest, 2011; Shi & Johnson, 2013).

A social network analysis tool that can be used to measure and monitor relationships between and among people and organizations is The Program to Analyze, Record, and Track Networks to Enhance Relationships (PARTNER). As a tool, this program can be used to collect data and monitor the extent to which partnerships are engaged, resources are effectively/efficiently used, and the benefits are being attained (Shi & Johnson, 2013). The Community Engagement Continuum is another tool that can be used to guide and monitor the evaluation of relationships among partners and other stakeholders through (a) outreach, (b) consultation, (c) involvement, (d) collaboration, and (e) shared leaderships (http://www.atsdr.cdc.gov/communityengagement/pdf/PCE_Report_508_FINAL.pdf) (Clinical and Translational Science Award Consortium, 2011; Shi & Johnson, 2013).

Partnership evaluation may include: 1) processes that maintain the partnership infrastructure and function; 2) programs or activities that accomplish targeted activities of the partnership's goals; and 3) changes in health status or the community. In Table 7.1 the following are some examples of each of these areas and elements to measure in the evaluation (Butterfoss, 2007).

Table 7.1
Partnership topics and measures

Topic	Evaluation Elements
Partnership infrastructure and function	• Level of participation • Benefits/costs of participation • Level of collaboration • General functioning • Satisfaction • Leadership • Perceived effectiveness
Partnership programs and activities	• Implementation • New program, services or activities • New or modified policies or practices
Changes in health status or the community	• Health status or behavior change • System change • Community capacity

Additional tools for evaluations include surveys, questionnaires, checklists, key informant interviews, focus groups, and community conversations. Most important for health education specialists, however, is to establish feedback loops, so that adjustments can be made when needed to improve the program (Johnson & Breckon, 2007).

After partnerships have been evaluated, health education specialists have to decide if the partnership should be sustained. Health education specialists can make informed decisions regarding the utility of continued partnerships by weighing the results of the evaluation against resources used or saved in the partnership, as well as a reevaluation of the mission and goals of each organization.

Competency 7.2 Prepare others to provide health education and promotion.

Health education specialists should have the skills and abilities to analyze, prioritize, deliver, and evaluate training provided to interested groups. In this capacity, health education specialists will utilize their skills to develop a variety of training experiences that can be used to address issues ranging from, for example, improving self-efficacy regarding diabetes management, conflict resolution skills among youth, car seat safety for children, or teambuilding to strategic planning in the workplace. Regardless of the area around which training is intended, health education specialists play an important role in delivering such training and should have the necessary skills to lead training sessions. The Council on Linkage between Academia and Public Health Practice (2012) has a short resource for training, called *Guide to Improving and Measuring the Impact of Training.*

7.2.1 Develop culturally responsive content.

Culturally and linguistically competent health education specialists value diversity, develop the capacity for self-assessment, raise awareness of dynamics inherent when cultures interact, use organizational processes to institutionalize cultural knowledge, and strive to develop individual and organizational adaptations to diversity (Institute of Medicine, 2002). Delivering programs in a culturally sensitive manner requires conscientious attention by program planners and may mean providing an environment in which people from diverse backgrounds feel comfortable discussing culturally derived health beliefs and sharing cultural practices.

In delivering health information, health education specialists should use words and examples in the audience's primary language to ensure information is understandable (USDHHS, 2009). **Plain language** (also called plain writing or plain English) is communication that the audience can understand the first time they read or hear it. In the Plain Writing Act of 2010, plain language is defined as writing that is clear, concise, well-organized, and follows other best practices appropriate to the subject or field and intended audience. (USDHHS, 2009).

Literacy level, preferred language, and preferred media sources should be considered when delivering interventions. Health education specialists should use design techniques for low-literacy audiences for interventions not offered in other languages to improve reception of the instruction, including oral delivery (Doak et al., 2002; Plain Language and Information Network, 2019). When an audience is culturally diverse, matching the source as closely to the audience in key demographics is important to message credibility. Where languages other than English are spoken, health education specialists must take care to ensure accurate translations or develop interventions with that culture in mind to put the behavior into the proper cultural context.

7.2.2 Recruit individuals needed in implementation.

The recruitment of volunteers and staff is essential to the successful achievement of goals and objectives. Individuals filling positions within an organization can come from within the organization or from outside of the organization if they have the required knowledge and skills (Fallon & Zgodzinski, 2011). Recruiting individuals who successfully can fill positions within organizations consists of a process of planning, implementation, and evaluation. During the process, the following questions must be answered (Hernandez & Conner, 2009):
- Planning Phase
  - Why is a position required?
  - What are the qualifications required of the individual(s) needed to fill the position(s)?
  - When are the services of these individuals required?
  - Who will be responsible for recruiting for the position?

- Implementation Phase
  - ⊙ Where will potential volunteers/staff be recruited?
  - ⊙ Who in the organization will attract potential individuals to fill the positions?
  - ⊙ Who will be the appropriate individuals to fill the positions?
- Evaluation Phase
  - ⊙ Does the strategy result in the selection of appropriate personnel?

Health education specialists should think about three aspects of training when selecting individuals to deliver the program. First, the characteristics of the individual(s) who will conduct the training are critical to its success. Personal characteristics to look for in instructors include a desire to teach, the ability to communicate, skill at getting people to participate, and being "learner-oriented" (Kirkpatrick & Kirkpatrick, 2016). Second, participants for training sessions should be considered future intervention deliverers. By considering what is required for successful intervention delivery, health education specialists can identify some intervention specific characteristics of participants. Examples of questions that can be asked include:

- Are specialized technology skills needed, such as working knowledge of distance learning, webinars, or blogs? Are other skills required?
- Does the intervention require multiple sessions? What does that mean about the availability of the person delivering it? Are multiple persons acceptable or should one facilitator be used throughout?
- Does the audience require a person fluent in their language?
- Would the intervention strategy benefit from a particular sort of experience helpful in using the intervention, such as experience in peer leading?

Health education specialists must take care to select individuals with skills that match those needed for the program delivery. Additionally, those individuals who implement training should know the intended audience.

Health education specialists should understand the organizational context where the intervention will be delivered. An intervention poorly supported or unsupported by an organization may not be delivered properly or at all, thereby making it useless regardless of its apparent efficacy. The following considerations about implementation not only assist health education specialists in selecting individuals to train, but also in setting the stage for successful delivery and later maintenance of the intervention (Livet, Courser, & Wansderman., 2008).

- Will the individual delivering the intervention have the support of management or decision-makers?
- Has the organization had any experience using the particular intervention strategy?
- Is the strategy in line with the philosophy and mission of the organization?
- Does the organizational site(s) have the prerequisites for using the strategy? Prerequisites include the essential characteristics needed in a delivery site, such as sufficient personnel, bilingual, or bicultural staff, access to meeting space, proven relationship with the intended audience, and proven fiscal responsibility. These prerequisites will vary by intervention. Health education specialists can determine these from the intervention strategy, audience targeted, and setting of the intervention.

7.2.3 ▲ Assess training needs.

Trainings are delivered to individuals or groups to increase the knowledge, skills, or proficiency in a topic area to improve job performance. Health education specialists may get requests for training from a variety of different organizations or for in-service training. Requests for training should be collected and assessed by the health education specialist to determine if they fit the needs of the organization and produce positive outcomes for participants.

A training needs assessment is conducted to identify the gap between the actual and desired performance in organizations (Sleezer et al., 2014). Health education specialists should involve key staff from the organization, planning committee, and other stakeholders to inform the assessment process. The four recommended steps in conducting a training needs assessment are:

1. planning.
2. methods.
3. training logistics.
4. evaluation.

(University of Kansas, 2019p)

In determining training needs, health education specialists must consider intervention characteristics and requirements, the skills, knowledge, and experience of individuals involved in implementation, and the setting for the training. Health education specialists should understand the critical knowledge and skills necessary for implementing an intervention successfully. Before delivering training, health education specialists should conduct a needs assessment to help them plan the training and ensure individual needs are met (Northwest Center for Public Health Practice, 2020). A training needs assessment should reveal what the desired learning outcome is, the characteristics of the participants (e.g., age, abilities such as hearing loss or visual difficulties, intellectual abilities, language), the learning context, and the content and training expertise. Health education specialists should not overlook the logistics for training when identifying training needs.

In the identification of needs, health education specialists can learn about the organizational context, perform a gap analysis, and set objectives for the assessment. Next, health education specialists can establish criteria for the needs assessment design and evaluate the advantages and disadvantages of methods. The criteria for choosing data collection methods may be dependent on time, staffing, preference of the leaders of the organization, number of stakeholders, workplace disruptions, complexity of training issues, the validity and reliability of methods, and the training audience members themselves. Data are then collected through a variety of methods, including interviews, surveys, document reviews (e.g., individual development plans, procedures, organizational plans, reports, or audits), proficiency tests, performance appraisals, training evaluations, job descriptions, or observations (Sleezer et al., 2014). An individual development plan is a tool to create and track progress toward goals related to job performance. The individual development plan can be used for annual performance reviews or for training purposes. Regarding timeliness, it is important to conduct the assessment at least three to four weeks before the training to allow for adequate time to review the data and plan for training content. Some examples of training assessment questions are:

- Topics for training:
  - ⊙ What training have you received to prepare you for your job?
  - ⊙ What additional training topics and skills would help you do your job better?
  - ⊙ What are the most difficult aspects of your job that could be improved with more training?
  - ⊙ What skills, knowledge, or behaviors do you think your participants/employees need to receive or improve upon to do their jobs better?

- Previous training:
  - ⊙ What trainings have been offered in the past?
  - ⊙ What types of training topics have you received?
  - ⊙ What kinds of training do you personally deliver?
- Training logistics:
  - ⊙ How do you want to receive training (e.g., in person, webinar, conference)?
  - ⊙ What are barriers to the training efforts?
  - ⊙ What helps you get to trainings? What types of incentives would encourage you to attend?

In the data analysis step, health education specialists conduct qualitative and/or quantitative analyses and determine some potential solutions or recommendations for training. Finally, health education specialists can disseminate needs assessment findings by writing a report or making oral presentations. The data and implications can be shared with the organization members and other stakeholders to determine the next steps. Information collected through past training efforts, training needs assessments with the intended audience, training records, performance evaluations, and other organizational data will provide the basis for developing training goals and objectives (Sleezer et al., 2014).

7.2.4 ▲ Plan training, including technical assistance and support.

Health education specialists plan for the training and offer technical assistance and support after the training. Refer to Sub-competency 3.1.4 for more information about how to establish a training protocol. Once it has been determined that trainings need to be conducted, health education specialists may have to prioritize the multiple requests for training. Health education specialists can use different criteria to assist in making decisions on which trainings should occur first. Then, health education specialists can schedule and plan for high priority requests. Some considerations in prioritizing requests include the following:
- Urgency of the need for education
- Objectives of the training
- Potential impact on the organization or community
- Projected return on investment
- Training design needs
- Size of the audience and/or training
- Costs of the training
- Importance of the requester
- Projected workload associated with the training

(Lawson, 2008; Sleezer et al., 2014)

Health education specialists should select priority populations for the training. Some considerations for identifying these populations include which individuals will benefit most from the training or has unmet needs for knowledge and skills, which individuals are the primary stakeholders, and which groups may have the greatest impact on the organization after receiving the training (Lawson, 2008). Past and current training needs assessment data and discussions with the stakeholders for the training can be used to inform the selection of priority training populations. In addition, administrative factors may be taken into consideration as well, including time, budget, and staff capacity.

Effective training programs should follow these major steps:

1. Determine training needs.
2. Set objectives.
3. Determine subject content to accomplish the objectives.
4. Select participants.
5. Determine the best schedule.
6. Select appropriate facilities.
7. Select appropriate instructors.
8. Select and prepare audiovisual aids.
9. Coordinate the program.
10. Evaluate the program.
(Kirkpatrick & Kirkpatrick, 2016)

The training needs assessment or other formative research can help health education specialists with steps one to six. Health education specialists can determine if it is appropriate to deliver training or if other content experts need to be recruited to best present the training content. Then, health education specialists should prepare the training curriculum based on training objectives and using appropriate strategies from learning theories to make learning successful.

The trainer should take into consideration the following:
- Priority audience
- Where training will be held
- Goals and objectives of the initiative/intervention
- Planned activities for the program
- Materials needed

Agencies and organizations, such as the CDC, publicize programs and interventions in which best practices are used on their websites and may be use in training efforts. Where no list can be considered comprehensive or exhaustive, the CDC provides a starting point for health education specialists under their various divisions. Recognized programs on these CDC websites are grounded in a variety of Areas of Responsibility for health education specialists.

Health education specialists should be media literate, meaning that they should have a basic knowledge about publication layout and design, the creation, processing, and editing of images whether printed or video, and website design to be able to create websites and evaluate the quality of health-related websites. These skills are especially important when reaching Limited English Proficiency audiences or low health literate audiences (Plain Language and Information Network, 2019; United States Department of Justice, 2014).

Instructional technology is a vital tool for reaching the intended audience and achieving program objectives. For example, the computer can be used to prepare visual aids, access the Internet for instructional resources, or conduct a virtual meeting. Teleconferencing technology allows participants in different locations to attend discussions and lectures. Scanners and digital cameras can be used in the creation of print media and multimedia presentations (Fodor et al., 2010). Asynchronous training is a type of distance learning in which training occurs outside of real time where the instructor and the learners communicate at different times; conversely, synchronous training is a type of distance learning in which training occurs in real time and the instructor and the learners communicate at the same time (McKenzie et al., 2017).

Training resources are often provided for professional development through workshops or conferences from local, regional, or national professional associations. Professional organizations also may offer annual meetings, workshops, distance learning, and webinars (i.e., presentations delivered through the Internet) about health promotion issues. Health education specialists can locate training resources that fulfill continuing education requirements for CHES®/MCHES® credentialed individuals through the NCHEC website located at http://www.nchec.org/.

Health education or public health-related training may be offered by local health departments, colleges, or universities, local or regional professional associations, extension services, area health education centers (AHECs), or through national professional associations. Some of these organizations or governmental agencies also may offer online training courses. See the following:

- The Community Tool Box has practical information and skills for health education and is created and maintained by the Work Group on Health Promotion and Community Development at the University of Kansas (http://ctb.ku.edu/en/).
- The Public Health Foundation has a learning resource center that has high quality training and health promotion materials (http://www.phf.org/). The Foundation offers Training Finder Real-time Affiliate Integrated Network (TRAIN), a Web-based learning management clearinghouse of distance and on-site training for local, state, or national arenas (https://www.train.org/main/welcome). Materials are in a variety of formats, including print, computer-based, and video.
- The Society for Public Health Education (SOPHE) has the Center for Online Resources & Education (CORE) in which print materials and e-learning on multiple topics are offered (https://www.sophe.org/professional-development/core-elearning/).
- The National Associations of County & City Health Officials (NACCHO) has a Workforce Resource Center that offers training resources (http://www.naccho.org/topics/workforce/workforce-resource-center.cfm).
- The Health Resources and Services Administration funds a Public Health Training Centers Network with regional centers that provide online and in-person training content to build workforce capacity for students and professionals (https://bhw.hrsa.gov/grants/publichealth/regionalcenters).

Support and technical assistance may be required if other people or organizations help implement the plan. Health education specialists must know (or be able to assess) the program needs and capacities, be able to engage people, and build trusting relationships to provide quality, effective, and efficient technical assistance. These qualities are critical for health education specialists who do not live or work in geographic locations that receive technical assistance. Challenges to providing technical assistance may include inadequate funding, managing the volume of technical assistance requests, and a person's or organization's readiness to receive technical assistance (West et al., 2012).

7.2.5 ▲ Implement training.

Health education specialists must consider the best way to instruct an intended audience while also considering available funds and expertise-levels of the individuals providing the training. Depending on cost, content, and instructional expertise required, a variety of methods should be used, such as on-the-job training, one-on-one training, in-person group work, and distance learning techniques (e.g., video conferences, computer-based training, Internet, or conference calls). A health education specialist should oversee the implementation of the training.

The implementation plan should involve the following:
- Administrative details
- Promotion of the training
- Recruitment of the audience
- Schedules and venue selection
- Training objectives, curriculum, and supporting materials
- Assignment of the trainers
- Evaluation procedures and instruments
- Budget

(Council on Linkages, 2014)

Although one individual or group may take the lead in a training event, several individuals or groups could be involved in the marketing and arrangements related to the training event (McKenzie et al., 2017). Training may involve a variety of strategies based on its goals and audience. Some common strategies such as teaching and peer education strategies are presented in Table 7.2. Audiovisual materials, multimedia, and printed educational materials often support the instruction.

Table 7.2
Examples of Teaching Strategies

Teaching strategies	Lecture Brainstorming Case studies Coaching Group or cooperative learning Debates Demonstrations Discussion Drills Guest speakers Panel Peer teaching Simulations and games Role playing Problem solving
Audio visual materials	Charts, pictures, posters Computer Video/DVD Television Projector

Printed educational materials	Handouts and worksheets Pamphlets Study guides Text and reference books Workbooks
Computer-based	Internet Distance learning Social media Video conferencing
Training simulations	Training on equipment Training simulators Computer simulation Gaming

Note. Adapted from McKenzie et al., 2017

7.2.6 ▲ Evaluate training as appropriate throughout the process.

Evaluation is critical to understand the factors that influence training and to make decisions to improve training. To acquire the best results from the training provided to individuals, health education specialists should evaluate the training process and content (University of Kansas, 2019m). An evaluation of training can occur at the individual level, individual training workshop level, or at the curriculum level.

Kirkpatrick and Kirkpatrick (2016) developed a four-level model to evaluate training that is widely used. The levels are as follows:

- Level 1: Reaction
- Level 2: Learning
- Level 3: Behavior
- Level 4: Results

Level 1 (Reaction) participant satisfaction is measured through evaluations wherein a Likert scale (e.g., a scale of items used to assess agreement or disagreement) and/or open-ended questions are used. These evaluations are administered at the end of a learning activity (e.g., workshop, seminar, course) and can be detailed, comprehensive, and cover both individual sessions and daily activities. Participants' feedback on each session should be simple and should vary in format to address the main points covered in the course. An open-ended question in which qualitative feedback is requested can be helpful in planning future training activities.

Participants, as well as the individual trainer or facilitator, should evaluate the following course components: venue, organization, quality of presentation, and quality of participants' participation. The training presentations should be evaluated based on elements such as meeting stated objectives, clarity of presentation, interest in presentation, and responsiveness to participant's questions and concerns.

Sample questions may include the following:
- What will you do differently as a result of this training?
- What was the most or least useful aspect of the session?
- Were the trainees' opinions valued and how?
- What went well or did not go well in the session?

Examples of Likert scale items are as follows:
- My learning was enhanced by the variety of teaching techniques used by the facilitator.
- Immediately, I will be able to apply what I learned.
- I was comfortable with the pace of the workshop.
- I found the room setup comfortable.

Such questions should be standardized so that the aggregation of results from multiple offerings can provide more reliable direction for training refinement.

In Level 2 (Learning), health education specialists measure the amount of knowledge gained as a result of the learning activity. In most skills-based or competency-based training, there is an associated need for enhancement of knowledge related to the skills being developed. One way to evaluate knowledge gains is through the administration of pre- and post-tests. These tests may include true/false, multiple-choice questions, case-based scenarios, written essays, oral review, self-assessment of knowledge, or direct observations. A before and after self-assessment rating by participants may be useful to address their perceived competency in performing the skills described in the behavioral objectives of the course. Skills evaluations may take place through direct observation by an expert observer or by written self-assessment.

Level 3 (Behavior) evaluations are used to measure the extent to which behavior change occurs. This evaluation is conducted sometime after the training when there has been enough time for behavior to change. Surveys and interviews often are used to measure behavior changes.

Level 4 (Results) is most often used in workforce programs to measure the longer-range results that occurred due to participation in a training session (e.g., reduced turnover or improved work quality). In this level, health education specialists can have difficulty showing that changes are directly due to a training workshop or program.

Conducting an evaluation will help prove the worth of the training programs. Formative and summative evaluations may be helpful to describe the impact of training. Formative evaluation involves evaluation activities to generate information that will guide improvements for a program or health promotion efforts. Summative evaluation includes activities taken to create a judgment on the performance of the program, including whether specific goals and objectives were met (McKenzie et al., 2017). In terms of training, formative evaluation could help get rapid reactions or input to make midcourse corrections or changes while training is being delivered, while summative evaluation will be focused on assessing if the training goals and specific objectives were obtained. Refer to Competency 4.1 for more information about formative and summative evaluation.

Kirkpatrick and Kirkpatrick (2016) recommended three primary reasons that training programs must be evaluated: (a) to justify the existence of the training and its contribution to the organization or participants, (b) to determine whether to continue the training program, and (c) to collect information on how to improve the training. Four levels of training and what they measure are presented in Table 7.3. Evaluation should start at level one and move sequentially through the other levels.

Table 7.3
Levels of Training

Level	Description	Tools
Level 1 – Reaction	Participants' feelings about the training	Surveys Feedback forms
Level 2 – Learning	Extent to which participants change attitudes, improve knowledge or competencies, and/or increase skills because of the training	Survey before and after the intervention
Level 3 – Behavior	Extent to which participants are employing the skills on the job	Interviews and observations over time
Level 4 – Results	Effects on the organization because of the training	Archival review of documents for the indicators of success

Note. Adapted from Kirkpatrick and Kirkpatrick, 2016

Quantitative and qualitative methods can be employed by the health education specialist to evaluate training at all levels. Common quantitative methods for training evaluation may be surveys or self-assessments; qualitative methods may be interviews, focus groups, or observations of training participants. For Level 1, the health education specialist could have ratings on a Likert scale or open-ended questions about the training in terms of meeting its objective, presentation content, presenter(s), and the training logistics. For Level 2, the trainer could have participants rate changes in their attitudes, complete knowledge, or Competency items, or rate knowledge or skills changed as a result of the training. For Level 3 and 4, the trainer could follow up at times after the training to have participants describe or rate their use of the acquired knowledge or skills, or the trainer could review organization documents for changes in the performance of the staff in attendance or the organization as a result of the training.

As expected, it is important to review the results of training evaluation to inform the development of future trainings. Sharing the results with key stakeholders and having discussions about the interpretation of the data and the actions to be taken as a result of the evaluations promotes the use of evaluation data. Training evaluation results could be summarized into the following formats:

- A short report with narrative and tables
- An executive summary of key findings (fewer than five pages)
- Graphs in an evaluation document, short summary in print or via social media (e.g., Facebook)
- PowerPoint file
- A short newsletter article

Sharing the evaluation findings can help the health education specialist with discussions about keeping presenters and logistics the same or making changes based on the comments or ratings (e.g., reactions, satisfaction). Ideas or suggestions for how to improve acquisition of knowledge and skills also could be implemented in future training. Making refinements ensures that for future trainings, health education specialists use the feedback given in evaluations.

Competency 7.3 Manage human resources.

The management of human resources is integral to working with any health agency, association, or organization. Health education specialists need to be aware of the division of work to be accomplished within the context of designated roles and functions. Entry-level health education specialists may be responsible for building, leading, and sustaining teams or work groups within and/or among organizations. Advanced-level health education specialists are likely to be placed in the unique position of developing job descriptions, selecting staff for program or organizational roles and functions, forming teams, and guiding other leaders. Both the entry- and advanced-level health education specialists may be responsible for facilitating and supporting the work of people both internal and external to their direct line of operations. For example, human resources responsibilities may include managing coalitions, facilitating community-based initiatives, and forming or sustaining interagency collaborations. Effectively managing human resources requires familiarity with participatory forms of leadership with diverse work styles, respecting the talents of group members, and incorporating the strengths of team members to achieve organizational and programmatic mission are considered.

7.3.1 ▲ Facilitate understanding and sensitivity for various cultures, values, and traditions.

Culturally and linguistically competent health education specialists value diversity, develop the capacity for self-assessment, raise awareness of dynamics inherent when cultures interact, use organizational processes to institutionalize cultural knowledge, and strive to develop individual and organizational adaptations to diversity (Institute of Medicine, 2002). Delivering programs in a culturally sensitive manner requires conscientious attention by program planners. This process may mean providing an environment in which people from diverse backgrounds feel comfortable discussing culturally derived health beliefs and sharing cultural practices.

There are four levels to these cultural concepts:
- **"Cultural knowledge"** means that the health education specialist knows about some cultural characteristics, history, attitudes, values, and behaviors of a cultural group.
- **"Cultural awareness"** is being open to modifying cultural beliefs or attitudes.
- **"Cultural sensitivity"** is acknowledging differences exist between cultural groups and not making judgments on the differences (better or worse, right or wrong).
- **"Cultural competence"** is having the capacity of bringing into an organization many different behaviors, attitudes, and policies and work effectively in cross-cultural settings to produce better health or community outcomes.

(University of Kansas, 2019q)

7.3.2 ▲ Facilitate positive organizational culture and climate.

Health education specialists often may find themselves in situations in which they are required to facilitate needed organizational cultural changes. In this role, health education specialists may be an organization's staff member (i.e., internal change agent) or work in a consulting capacity (i.e., external change agent). To be successful change agents, health education specialists must develop strategies to reinforce or change organizational culture to achieve health education goals.

Culture is the patterned ways of thought and behavior that are used to characterize a social group and are learned through socialization processes. Social groups include organizational groups and groups of individuals within organizations. Health education specialists need to be aware of an organization's culture, because culture impacts how individuals who make up the organization will respond to health education/promotion efforts and programs. When considering the implementation of a health education/promotion program, an analysis or assessment, also referred to as cultural audit and health cultural audit, should be conducted to gain an understanding of the assumptions, values, and other factors that may impact program implementation. Various Web-based resources, including checklists, exist and are available to aid in the accomplishment of this task (McKenzie et al., 2017).

Health education specialists must consider organizational culture in their efforts, as well as develop and implement effective strategies to manage or change it, as appropriate. Rowitz (2018), Johnson and Breckon (2007), and others present various methods or strategies that may be utilized to reinforce or change organizational culture.

Rowitz (2018) presented a systems approach to organizational change that includes various stages linked to the development of a strategic plan, business plan, work plan, and evaluation plan. The stages include:

- values clarification,
- mission and vision construction or revision,
- goals and objectives identification,
- action plan development,
- action plan implementation, and
- evaluation.

There are evolutionary and revolutionary approaches to organizational change. The revolutionary approach is often utilized when there is new leadership, during a crisis, or when an organization may fail if things are not done differently; the evolutionary approach is often used when there is stable leadership and long-range program planning and execution is an option (Johnson & Breckon, 2007).

7.3.3 ▲ Develop job descriptions to meet staffing needs.

To have successful programs, managers must select appropriate individuals to fill positions within an organization/program. A number of instruments are available to aid managers in the evaluation of staff and volunteer qualifications. Instruments commonly used by health organizations include tests, interviews, reference checks, job simulation, work sampling, credentialing, licensing, application forms, resumes, and assessment centers (DeCenzo et al., 2016). Each of the methods or instruments that are available for use has strengths and weaknesses. Therefore, each method should be carefully examined to determine which is most appropriate for the category of personnel being sought for a particular position as well as the organization seeking to fill a position.

Job descriptions include information on the duties of a job and the attributes of the individual who is filling the job should possess. The content and style of job descriptions may vary, but they typically include the following elements:

1. Date of development
2. Job status – exempt/nonexempt

3. Title
4. Identification – position number/code, department
5. Position objectives
6. Supervisor's position
7. Summary of responsibilities
8. Education, experience, licensure, and other requirements
9. Essential functions of the position
10. Disclaimers
11. Signatures or appropriate individuals

(DeCenzo et al., 2016)

7.3.4 ▲ Recruit qualified staff (including paraprofessionals) and volunteers.

The recruitment of volunteers and staff is essential to the successful achievement of goals and objectives. Individuals filling positions within an organization can come from within the organization or from outside of the organization if they have the required knowledge and skills (Fertman & Allensworth, 2016). Recruiting individuals who will successfully fill positions within organizations consists of a process of planning, implementation, and evaluation.

In examining potential staff, health education specialists should consider qualifications of the individuals, past experience, specialized skills, and training (e.g., degrees, certification). Some of the questions that the health education specialist should answer are the following:

- What kind of people do you want as staff members?
- What can you afford?
- What will the hiring process look like? (University of Kansas, 2019r).

7.3.5 ▲ Evaluate performance of staff and volunteers formally and informally.

Evaluating the performance of staff and volunteers is an essential aspect of management and provides organizational leadership with important information. The benefits of performance evaluations include the following:

- Reinforcing open communication and rapport-building
- Provision of two-way performance feedback
- Recognition or motivating employees
- Opportunity to reinforce and note personnel feedback and decisions
- Goal-setting for the next review period in the context of organizational needs

(Armstrong, 2010)

There are various methods for conducting performance appraisals which include the following:

- Critical incidents, which are focused on key behaviors related to accomplishing the job
- Checklist, which includes a list of behaviors
- Graphic rating scale in which an individual is assessed on a scale based on a list of factors such as job knowledge, cooperation, and attendance
- Forced-choice, which requires the rater to choose between two or more statements

- Behaviorally anchored rating scales in which critical incident and graphic rating scales are combined
- Group ordered ranking, which requires employees to be placed in a classification (e.g., top ten percent of an organization's health education specialists)
- Individual ranking, which requires employees be ranked from highest performers to lowest performers
- Paired comparison, which involves an employee trait being selected and all employees in a group be compared based on that trait

(DeCenzo et al., 2016)

Program managers must understand the method or methods chosen by their organization and evaluate their staff accordingly. In addition to being aware of the evaluation process, program managers need to be aware of distorted evaluations/appraisals. Distortions can occur in the following forms: (a) leniency errors, (b) halo errors, (c) similarity errors, (d) low appraisal motivation, (e) central tendency, (f) inflationary pressures, and (g) using something other than actual job performance to provide the evaluation (DeCenzo et al., 2016).

Maintaining and improving the abilities of staff should be an ongoing effort, and it should be an important part of a manager's job. To accomplish the maintenance and improvement of staff, abilities assessments are necessary. Information for completing assessments and determining needs may be gathered from employee and manager questionnaires and interviews, focus groups, and exit interviews (Sleezer et al., 2014). In addition, the self-assessment in the beginning and the practice questions in this publication can be used to identify health education Areas of Responsibility that require further training. The gathered information should be used to determine professional development needs.

7.3.6 ▲ Provide professional development and training for staff and volunteers.

Employee and volunteer training and development as well as career development are among the myriad of tasks that health education specialists must manage. Training and development are important tasks because they:

- may provide employees with essential knowledge and skills.
- improve employee performance and learning culture of an organization.
- increase sense of usefulness and belonging to an organization.
- help an organization achieve its strategic objectives.
- offer opportunities for employees.
- can serve as a mechanism for the orientation of new employees.

(Saks et al., 2010)

Employee/volunteer training is focused on assisting the individuals with acquiring or improving knowledge, skills, attitudes, and/or behaviors necessary to perform in their current position. Staff development is designed to assist the organization and the employee with preparing for future needs within the organization. Strategies to accomplish this task may include job rotations, acting as an assistant to the individual filling the position, committee assignments, lectures/seminars, and simulations (DeCenzo et al., 2016). Career development is designed to assist employees with advancement in their careers, but it is focused on the long-term career effectiveness and success of an individual versus the more immediate/intermediate effectiveness, which is the focus of training and development programs (DeCenzo, Robbins, & Verhulst, 2016).

Fallon and Zgodzinski (2011) provided the following as methods for employee training and development: (a) new employee orientation, (b) training to correct performance issues, (c) training within departments, (d) cross-training for efficiency, (e) on-the-job training, and (f) mentorship. Health education specialists should join professional associations and organizations, attend meetings and conferences, and read the latest periodicals sponsored or endorsed by those organizations to ensure they stay abreast of information and developments in the field.

7.3.7 ▲ Facilitate the engagement and retention of staff and volunteers.

The retention of good staff members is linked to making work a positive experience and motivating employees (Rowitz, 2018). Knowledge, skills, and abilities enhancement are factors in motivating employees and making work a positive experience, and these factors should be included in any retention strategy. Methods for motivating employees include: (a) coaching and mentoring, (b) rewards and recognition, (c) training and conference opportunities, (d) career opportunities, (e) employee benefits, and (f) good communications (Rowitz, 2018).

7.3.8 ▲ Apply team building and conflict resolution techniques as appropriate.

Teams of individuals or groups from different departments or organizations may be brought together to accomplish specific goals and objectives. For the individuals and groups to work together effectively, activities to enhance members' trust and openness may have to be undertaken. Activities to help build individuals and groups into effective teams involve the following:

- Goal setting
- Interpersonal relationship development
- Role and responsibility clarification
- Process analysis

Organizations can be affected by intra- or inter-personal, intra- or inter-group, and inter-organizational conflict. Effective leadership includes negotiating, mediating, planning proactively, designing programs, and communicating effectively to prevent or minimize its effect on the organization's climate and performance (Hellriegel & Slocum, 2013).

Conflict resolution is used to direct individuals and organizations to see the similarities and differences that exist between them and then is used to lead them to focus on reducing or eliminating differences to accomplish goals and objectives. Rowitz (2013) presented an eight-step process for conflict resolution that can be applied in most situations:

1. Create an atmosphere that is effective for goal or objective accomplishment.
2. Clarify the perceptions of all parties involved.
3. Focus on the needs of the individuals and organizations as separate entities, as well as the needs of collective individuals and organizations.
4. Build shared positive power.
5. Work toward and with a future orientation, but learn from past activities.
6. Create options.
7. Develop goals, objectives, and activities that can be accomplished.
8. Make sure there are benefits for all involved parties.

Negotiation between two or more individuals or organizations may be part of the conflict resolution process. Among the models for negotiation, a 14-step model developed by Schoenfield and Schoenfield (1991) incorporates many of the strategies from other models (Rowitz, 2013). The steps of this model include:

Pre-negotiation:
1. Information gathering
2. Goal determination
3. Issues identification
4. Analysis
5. Assessment of strengths and weaknesses
6. Estimation of the parties' positions
7. Consideration of outcomes that present wins for both/all parties

Negotiation:
8. Setting the opening position
9. Setting the bottom line
10. Selection of strategies
11. Concession consideration
12. Agenda determination
13. Timing analysis
14. Selection of communication modes

Competency 7.4 Manage fiduciary and material resources.

Health education specialists often need to secure and manage fiscal resources. Health education specialists work in many different settings often requiring skills such as completing funding searches, writing and submitting grants, budgeting, and managing resources.

7.4.1 ▲ Evaluate internal and external financial needs and funding sources.

An important part of the financial plan is evaluating the financial needs and resources necessary to reach the goals set forth by the health education specialists' organization. This evaluation may include reviewing:
- a list of all items and needs of the project.
- the amount of money required to sustain each item.
- current resources.
- required resources.
- potential matching money by other funding organizations or individuals.
  ⊙ Amount of money that will be requested from each organization, individual, or funding source
  ⊙ How the funds will be requested, by whom, and when

(University of Kansas, 2019s)

Health education specialists, especially at advanced-levels, may have the responsibility of securing resources for program activities. Resources may be procured through participant fees, third-party support, cost sharing, organizational sponsorship, grants, gifts, and a combination of the various sources (McKenzie et al., 2017). In each source, there may be different rules for obtaining and using funds. Therefore, health education specialists must understand the policies, rules, and laws that govern these processes.

Health education specialists also must be aware of possible sources of funding to support their initiatives. Some funding sources can be found internally (e.g., general organizational funds, specific program/intervention funds, and cost sharing from other departments). Potential external sources may include foundations, governmental agencies, corporations, local businesses, and civic organizations.

In addition to consulting with colleagues and mentors about opportunities, health education specialists also can access many electronic resources to help identify external funding sources:

1. **Searchable funding databases.** For example, the Grants.gov website (http://www.grants.gov/web/ grants/home.html) managed by the United States Department of Health and Human Services is a place where different grant programs across federal grant-making agencies are centralized.
2. **Searchable foundation directories.** For example, the Foundation Directory online (https://fconline. foundationcenter.org/) provides access to over 150,000 foundations and corporate donors.
3. **Alerts from potential funders.** For instance, health education specialists can sign up for electronic funding alerts from the Robert Wood Johnson Foundation (https://www.rwjf.org/en/how-we-work/ grants-explorer/funding-opportunities.html).

7.4.2 ▲ Develop financial budgets and plans.

A broad plan for financial sustainability can be used to help organizations or initiatives reach both short- and long-term goals. Similar to other planning documents, the financial plan should include specific objectives, strategies, and action steps. Components of the plan may include a review of the current operating budget, plans for expansion, fundraising goals, and a timeline of action steps. Health education specialists should check with those stakeholders who oversee their organization (e.g., Board of Directors) to confirm which components may be required for their plan.

Ideally, a team should be assembled to lead financial plan development (e.g., a standing financial committee or a temporary working group). The group should make time to circulate an initial draft of the plan to stakeholders such as funders, clients, and staff members. The stakeholders' comments can help guide revision of the financial plan before implementation (University of Kansas, 2019t).

With the broader financial plan of the organization in mind, health education specialists and program managers will need to prepare specific budgets. In a budget, a plan is shown for how funds will be used.
(Fallon & Zgodzinski, 2011).

In Fallon and Zgodzinski (2011), five components of a complete budget are outlined:
- **Statistics budget:** includes items that can be accurately predicted (e.g., service utilization and staffing levels)

- **Expense budget:** includes a calculation of the total expenses needed to do business (e.g., staff wages and office space)
- **Revenue budget:** includes a prediction of the amount of income that will be generated through various streams and sources (e.g., grants and donations)
- **Cash budget:** includes a summary of the anticipated cash receipts and payments for an agency
- **Capital budget:** includes a plan for purchasing or upgrading long-term assets with significant purchase prices (e.g., property and technology infrastructure)

Chenoweth (2011) delineated key factors that should be considered when preparing budgets. Preparers should be aware of how others in the organization view the project/program. Also, the health education specialist should be aware of whether recent programs/projects and budgets have been successful. Health education specialists should be aware of available program analysis outcomes and utilize input from all staff members when making any decisions about the budget. Finally, health education specialists should be flexible and keep everything regarding any actual or potential budget changes in perspective.

Health education specialists should finalize the development of the budget based on the approval request from the finance department. The complexity of the actual budget document will vary from organization to organization and is dependent on factors such as the size of the budget, amount of funders (and their requirements), and the breadth of programs or services. Regardless of the complexity of the budget, it should include the following components:

1. Projected expenses: This section should be broken down into specific categories (e.g., salaries).
2. Projected income: This section should be broken down by sources (e.g., fundraising).
3. The interaction of expenses and income: This section explicitly states which funding sources will fund each program activity or item.
4. Adjustments: As the fiscal year progresses, estimates will be updated or replaced by actual costs to keep the budget as accurate as possible.
   (University of Kansas, 2019u)

7.4.3 ▲ Monitor budget performance.

In conjunction with securing fiscal resources and developing budgets, health education specialists are often responsible for continual management of the budget. Ongoing monitoring is essential, because fiscal viability is related to program evaluation performance and overall well-being of the organization, program, or project (Longest, 2011). The primary method for using a budget as a monitoring tool is tracking the budget variance . The budget variance is defined as the difference between the projected and actual expenditures (Issel & Wells, 2018).

According to Issel and Wells (2018), program managers should review the budget variance on an ongoing and regular basis, typically monthly. One reason that it is important for organizations to maintain updated and accurate budgets is so that they can communicate to funders exactly how their investment is being used (University of Kansas, 2019u).

Reports related to project/program budgets are typically prepared and distributed to funding agencies and other key stakeholders on a monthly, quarterly, and/or annual basis. Routinely, reports include information related to fiscal activity during the time period for which it was prepared, as well as total income and expenditures for the budget year (McKenzie et al., 2017). Budget reports serve several purposes. Internally, program managers and other organizational leaders utilize accurate and updated budget information to make appropriate decisions about organizational operations. External stakeholders, such as funding agencies, may use the information to assess program feasibility and to assure fiscal and programmatic accountability.

Financial planning should be an ongoing process. A group should be convened to develop a financial plan. This group should be involved with monitoring and reviewing/revising of the plan. Procedures should be put in place that not only allow for monitoring but also communicate the findings of each review to relevant stakeholders (e.g., staff, board of directors, funders).

7.4.4 ■ Justify value of health education and promotion using economic (e.g., cost-benefit, return-on-investment, and value-on-investment) and/or other analyses.

Several types of analyses are available that can be completed to evaluate the costs of health programs. The selection of analysis methods is based on whether one or more programs are being compared and whether program outcomes are being assessed in addition to cost (Issel & Wells, 2018). The primary types of analyses are as follows:

- **Cost description:** The simplest form of economic analysis and is appropriate when only one program is being considered. Cost description merely presents the expenses related to the delivery of a program.
- **Cost analysis:** When a health education specialist examines cost description expenses by more specific factors (e.g., time periods), it becomes a cost analysis.
- **Cost minimization:** This analysis is used to determine the most effective ways to deliver the program at the lowest cost.
- **Cost comparison:** This analysis is used to compare the costs to deliver two or more programs. Not taken into account, however, are the programs outcomes or impacts.
- **Cost effectiveness:** In this analysis, the health education specialist compares the costs of two programs alongside one type of impact that is identically measured in both programs.
- **Cost benefit:** In this analysis, the health education specialist compares the costs of two programs; however, the health education specialist does not need to measure the same program impact nor the same health problem. Instead, larger societal impacts are considered.
- **Cost utility:** This analysis is the most complex and is used to measure the impact of health programs in terms of the prospective participants' inclination for the health outcome.

Accessing, using, and understanding information to justify programs and identify the capacities, assets, and needs of a community/constituency and/or program require proficiency in conducting targeted searches for information.

Evidence to substantiate the status of or extent to which an issue exists can be accessed through: primary (e.g., surveys, interviews) and secondary data sources (e.g., national, regional, and local databases (e.g., clearinghouses, registries and surveillance data). Geographic information systems (GIS) and data mapping can be used to aggregate information from many sources to create a visual representation of the evidence to justify or support a program (Shi & Johnson, 2013).

7.4.5 ▲ Write grants and funding proposals.

Funding sustainability may be the primary responsibility of advanced-level health education specialists, which means that they must be forward thinking with a broad knowledge of fundraising and other methods of securing fiscal resources. When searching for external funding, health education specialists will come across announcements for Requests for Proposals (RFPs) or Requests for Applications (RFAs). These requests come from agencies that invite organizations to submit proposals. Miner and Miner (2013) recommended that organizations keep three issues in mind when reviewing an RFP to determine if it is a good match:

- Relevance: Do we want to do this?
- Feasibility: Can we do this?
- Probability: Will we be competitive?

If an organization decides to pursue an RFP or RFA, then the health education specialists involved should review the instructions carefully and follow them exactly to have their proposal considered. The instructions provide guidance regarding topics such as the following:

- Letter of intent (if required)
- Deadlines
- Formatting and page limits
- Checklists of required components
- Section scoring
- Grant requirements for funded grantees (e.g., reporting requirements)

(University of Kansas, 2019v)

Grant proposals typically contain, at a minimum, the following elements:

- Cover letter: an introductory acknowledgement page in which the program to which the proposal is being submitted and an overview of the proposal are identified.
- Abstract or executive summary: a synopsis of the entire proposal
- Table of contents: the basic layout of the submission
- Proposal narrative broken down into key sections:
  - ⊙ Introduction/background: a description of the problem, its magnitude, and the purpose of the funding request
  - ⊙ Significance of the proposed project: a justification for the request (e.g., literature, data, evidence, and information about the issue for which funds are requested), and information about the requesting organization's experience with the issue
  - ⊙ Proposed program description: goals, objectives, priority population, activities that are to be performed, expected outcomes, an evaluation plan, and a timeline for when the objectives and activities are to be accomplished
  - ⊙ Dissemination plan: detailed strategy to circulate project results (e.g., through peer-reviewed publications and professional conferences)
  - ⊙ Sustainability plan: detailed strategy to continue some or all of the project activities beyond the grant period
  - ⊙ Resources: facilities, equipment, supplies, personnel, etc.

⊙ Key Personnel: resumes and job descriptions of personnel associated with the program
⊙ Budget and budget narrative: Include all expenditures for the project: (e.g., salaries, employee benefits, travel, equipment, materials/supplies, consultants, contracts). The "description should be used to justify every line item in the budget and describe (a) the specific item, (b) the item's relevance to the project, and (c) the basis of cost calculations for that item.
● References: list of cited sources
● Appendices: supportive secondary information (e.g., letters of support and consortia agreements)
(Miner & Ball, 2019; University of Kansas, 2019v)

7.4.6 ■ Conduct reviews of funding and grant proposals.

Health education specialists are often called upon to provide service to the field by serving as a reviewer of grant proposals. This opportunity offers many benefits to participating health education specialists including having the opportunity to improve their own grant writing by reviewing/evaluating those written by others and obtaining firsthand knowledge about the funder and their priorities (University of Northern Iowa, n.d.).

The review process can vary by funder. For instance, some agencies may ask reviewers to review the proposals independently and communicate their recommendations directly to the funding agency coordinator. Other agencies may convene a review panel where recommendations will be discussed as a group. In general, reviewers are asked to evaluate proposals based on specific criteria (e.g., how closely the proposal aligns with the RFP instructions, the strength of the budget justification, inclusion of clear and evidence-based research/evaluation methods).

7.4.7 ▲ Monitor performance and/or compliance of funding recipients.

The methods utilized for performance monitoring or evaluation may be based on absolute standards, relative standards, or outcomes (DeCenzo et al., 2016). The absolute standards methods is based on comparison. These include techniques such as critical incident, checklist, graphic rating scale, forced choice, and behaviorally anchored rating scale appraisals. Relative standards methods consist of comparing an individual to other individuals, and these include methods such as group order ranking, individual ranking, and paired comparisons. Outcomes methods, or management by objectives (MBO), are based on the achievement of established objectives or outcomes (DeCenzo, Robbins, et al.,).

The following are steps in an appraisal process: 1) establish performance standards, 2) communicate expectations, 3) measure actual performance, 4) compare actual performance with established standards, 5) discuss the appraisal or findings with employee (funding recipient), and 6) initiate corrective action, if necessary (DeCenzo, Robbins, et al.,). Other individuals present different steps, but the underlying process is basically the same: establish and communicate standards, monitor performance based on established standards, and communicate and correct failures to perform to established standards.

7.4.8 ▲ Maintain up-to-date technology infrastructure.

Technology can be used to assist the project team in managing program data and collaboration efforts. In addition, it can be used to assist with the collection, storage, and retrieval of data collected from program participants. For example, electronic surveys can be used to enroll participants in an intervention and collect demographic data and responses that can be accessed later for follow-up and/or evaluation. Program planners also can use database software like Microsoft Access to develop a participant tracking system and run queries on a variety of variables (Bull, 2011).

Health education specialists should keep up with emerging technology that holds promise for intervention development. Because technology can be trendy and fleeting, it is important to be selective about the methods incorporated into programs. There are several ways to research potential technologies:

- Review guidance from trusted public health agencies: For example, the CDC has released several guides that are used to acknowledge the value of social media and present discussion strategies for effectively integrating the technology into health communication programs.
- Review the evidence presented in peer-reviewed literature: For example, in 2014, the *Journal of Medical Internet Research* published an e-collection focused on "Web-based and Mobile Health Interventions" (http://www.jmir.org/themes/50).
- Review national trends regarding technology use: For example, the Pew Research Internet Project (http://www.pewresearch.org) regularly publishes data on the demographics of social media users and which platforms are most popular.

7.4.9 ▲ Manage current and future facilities and resources (e.g., space and equipment).

Good managers ensure resources are utilized efficiently and effectively. They calibrate these resources to the organization's needs and use projections of future needs in securing additional resources. Health education specialists who serve as managers should determine funding mechanisms to use for different resource procurement desires and find the necessary resources to fulfill them. Managers are also responsible for the systems that account for income and expenditures, billing, payroll, and other critical administrative work of an organization. They carefully monitor budgets, ensuring that expenditures do not outpace income and providing for a profit margin cushion. They also can meet with their organization's finance staff to track expenditures and budget reports.

Competency 7.5 Conduct strategic planning with appropriate stakeholders.

There are various definitions and principles of "leadership" that are applicable to the practice of health education. Fallon and Zgodzinski (2011) defined leadership as the skills needed to incorporate local rules and policies to allow an organization to be successful in a particular setting. Johnson and Breckon (2007) defined it more in terms of influence, where leaders aims to achieve goals and objectives by influencing people in the organization. Healy and Lesneski (2011) indicate that the ability of an individual to influence others to accomplish a predetermined goal is a tenet of leadership. A combination of these various definitions and tenets provides a good perspective of leadership and offers a framework for health education specialists.

Health education specialists are called upon to exercise leadership within a variety of contexts, situations, and environments to address health-related behaviors and systems change within and throughout groups, organizations, and communities. Health education specialists design strategies, lead projects, make decisions, and communicate program inputs and outcomes to ensure programs are administered effectively and efficiently (Longest, 2011). Although advanced-level health education specialists perform more administrative functions than entry-level, all health education specialists are expected to exemplify the ideals of organizational leadership and conduct themselves in accordance with The Code of Ethics for Health Educators (CNHEO, 2019).

7.5.1 ▲ Facilitate the development of strategic and/or improvement plans using systems thinking to promote the mission, vision, and goal statements for health education and promotion.

Health education specialists can contribute to the achievement of organizational missions and visions in several ways. They can provide technical assistance, advocacy, strategic planning, and aid in building and supporting teams that plan and implement interventions or strategies. Each task or set of tasks is associated with specific knowledge, skills, and abilities.

Health education specialists often may find themselves in situations in which they are required to facilitate needed organizational cultural changes. In this role, the health education specialist may be an organization's staff member (i.e., internal change agent) or work in a consulting capacity (i.e., external change agent). To be successful change agents, health education specialists must develop strategies to reinforce or change organizational culture to achieve health education goals.

Strategic planning should assist the administrative process by analyzing availability of resources in an organization, as well as barriers to implementation of the organizational mission .Strategic planning is a process that encompasses individual, group, community, environment, policy, and other systems-level factors that support or impinge upon the successful implementation of an organizational mission. The strategic planning process captures the course of managing the constant change that affects almost any organization. The term strategic planning is often misused to refer to a specific document: the strategic plan. A strategic plan document is a product of the strategic planning process. The document serves as a road map that can be referred to over time to serve as reminder, check assumptions, and measure progress (Kreuter et al., 2003).

Kreuter et al. (2003) specified tools and actions that may be used to implement a comprehensive strategic planning process using the first three questions, with Longest (2004) adding a fourth question that makes the connection between program performance, evaluation, fiscal viability, and the overall well-being of the organization, program, or project. The four questions are as follows:

- *What is the current status of the organization?*
  The answer to this question provides a baseline measure of where the organization stands at the current time. An internal assessment generally is focused on the strengths and weaknesses of the organization. In an external assessment, the health education specialist looks at the opportunities and threats outside the organization. One useful tool in assessing the baseline is a stakeholder analysis. This analysis takes into account the following considerations:
      - ⊙ Who are the key stakeholders for the organization?
      - ⊙ What do they think of the organization's performance?
      - ⊙ What criteria do they use in judging the organization's performance?

- *What is the desired direction of the organization?*
  The answer to this question provides a measure of organizational direction. The strategic direction of an

organization should consist of short- and long-term timeframes, such as one year and four to five years or more into the future. This strategic plan is designed to capture where the organization should be at the end of the time frame in a perfect world without real world constraints.

- *What steps are necessary to move the organization towards the desired future?*
  - ⊙ The answer to this question is used to identify specific steps which the organization could take to get to its perfect world ideal, which are described in the following questions. The questions address topics such as:
  - ⊙ What resources are required (e.g., money, people, skills, and training)?
  - ⊙ What alternative routes exist if some or all of these resources are not available?
  - ⊙ What kinds of new or reinforced collaborations may be required?
  - ⊙ Who will be responsible for implementation of the steps, and when will they be implemented?

- *What progress is being made?*
  Each of the preceding questions has various dimensions, such as funding levels, staff skill sets, new programs, collaborative relationships, and the use of resources tied to effective outcomes. The nature and complexity of maintaining quality while monitoring costs, requires attention to fiscal and human resources, program standards, desired outcomes, and planning with the end in mind. When tracked over time, each of the factors offers insights into how programs are managed, as well as their performance, strengths, weaknesses, and areas for improvement.

Kreuter et al. (2003) presented a ten step strategic planning process. Refer to Table 7.4.

Table 7.4
Ten Strategic Planning Steps

Step	Activities Performed
1. Initiate and agree on a planning process	• Identify key decision-makers. • Determine who should be involved.
2. Clarify organizational mandates	• List mandates and sources of mandates. • Determine implications of mandates. • Determine if mandates should be changed.
3a. Identify and understand stakeholders	• Identify internal and external stakeholders. • Determine criteria stakeholders use to judge performance. • Determine how stakeholders would rate performance.
3b. Develop/refine mission statement and values	• Clarify organizational purpose. • Respond to key stakeholders. • Define philosophy/core values. • Identify distinct/unique contributions. • List current values and additional values to guide conduct in the future.

Step	Activities Performed
4. Assess the environment	• List internal strengths and weaknesses. • List external opportunities and threats. • Identify options for building on strengths and opportunities, and minimizing weaknesses and threats.
5. Identify/frame strategic issues	• Identify challenges that require immediate action, monitoring, or action in the near future. • Identify consequences of not addressing issues.
6. Formulate tactics to manage strategic issues	• Determine strategies, barriers, and actions. • Develop a draft strategic plan.
7. Review and adopt the plan	• Include key internal and external stakeholders.
8. Establish an effective organizational vision for the future	• Describe the "vision of success" based on the mission statement, values, and strategies.
9. Develop an implementation process	• List existing programs and services. • Set priorities. • Determine actions, results, and milestones. • Decide who is responsible. • Assign dates and resources.
10. Reassess the process	• Identify strengths and weaknesses. • Suggest modifications. • Decide what should be maintained, revised, or terminated.

Rowitz (2018) outlined J. M. Bryson's 10-step strategic planning model and linked it to public health's core functions, organizational practices, essential services, and system activities. The model steps with public health core function linkages include the following:

1. Initiation and agreement on a planning process, which is linked to policy development
2. Identification and clarification of mandates, which is linked to policy development and assurance
3. Mission and values clarification, which is linked to policy development
4. Organization strength, weakness, opportunity, and threat (SWOT) analysis, which is linked to assessment
5. Organization strategic issues identification, which is linked to policy development as assessment
6. Strategy formulation for addressing identified issues, which is linked to policy development
7. Strategic plan(s) review and adoption, which is linked to policy development
8. Vision establishment, which is linked to policy development
9. Implementation process development, which is linked to assurance
10. Strategy and planning reassessment, which is linked to assessment, policy development, and assurance

7.5.2 ▲ Gain organizational acceptance for strategic and/or improvement plans.

Health education specialists must consider organizational culture in their efforts, as well as develop and implement effective strategies to manage or change it, as appropriate. Rowitz (2018), Johnson and Breckon (2007), and others presented various methods or strategies that may be utilized to reinforce or change organizational culture.

Rowitz (2018) presented a systems approach to organizational change that includes various stages linked to the development of a strategic plan, business plan, work plan, and evaluation plan. The stages include the following:

- Values clarification
- Mission and vision construction or revision
- Goals and objectives identification
- Action plan development
- Action plan implementation
- Evaluation

Evolutionary and revolutionary approaches to organizational change exist. The revolutionary approach is often used when there is new leadership, during a crisis or when an organization may fail if things are not done differently; the evolutionary approach is often used when there is stable leadership and long-range program planning and execution is an option (Johnson & Breckon, 2007).

7.5.3 ▲ Implement the strategic plan, incorporating status updates, and making refinements as appropriate.

Implementation of the strategic planning process is the ninth step of the processes presented by Kreuter et al. (2003) and Rowitz (2018). The implementation process involves:

1. listing programs and services,
2. setting priorities,
3. determining actions, results, and milestones,
4. deciding who will be responsible for specific tasks,
5. assigning dates for the completion of tasks, and
6. assigning resources.

Specific implementation processes presented by others may be different but should lead to similar results.

The tenth step of the strategic planning processes presented by Rowitz (2018) involves monitoring or reassessing/revisiting strategies, as well as making changes as appropriate. The process includes identifying strengths and weaknesses, making suggestions for modifications, and making decisions about what should be maintained, revised, or discontinued. Specific monitoring processes presented by others may be different but should lead to similar results.

Consumers of health education and public health services should receive the highest quality of services possible. Various techniques exist that may be used to ensure high quality services for implementation including, but not limited to, the following: Continuous Quality Improvement (CQI), Total Quality Management (TQM), and Six Sigma (Rowitz, 2018). CQI is a performance management approach in which program and service effectiveness is monitored with a focus on positive results over times. TQM is focused on customer satisfaction through continuous improvements of organization processes. Six Sigma is a management approach that is focused on objectives and data collection, as well as analysis as mechanisms for reducing or eliminating errors (Rowitz, 201). Each technique has positive and negative factors and should be examined in detail before an organization selects a specific one to use as a mechanism for quality assurance/process improvement.

Chapter 8
Area of Responsibility VIII: Ethics and Professionalism
KEY: No symbol - entry level; ▲ - advanced 1; ■ - advanced 2

8.1   Practice in accordance with established ethical principles.

8.1.1   Apply professional codes of ethics and ethical principles throughout assessment, planning, implementation, evaluation and research, communication, consulting, and advocacy processes.

8.1.2 ▲   Demonstrate ethical leadership, management, and behavior.

8.1.3   Comply with legal standards and regulatory guidelines in assessment, planning, implementation, evaluation and research, advocacy, management, communication, and reporting processes.

8.1.4   Promote health equity.

8.1.5   Use evidence-informed theories, models, and strategies.

8.1.6   Apply principles of cultural humility, inclusion, and diversity in all aspects of practice (e.g., Culturally and Linguistically Appropriate Services (CLAS) standards and culturally responsive pedagogy).

8.2.   Serve as an authoritative resource on health education and promotion.

8.2.1 ▲   Evaluate personnel and organizational capacity to provide consultation.

8.2.2 ▲   Provide expert consultation, assistance, and guidance to individuals, groups, and organizations.

8.3.3 ■   Conduct peer reviews (e.g., manuscripts, abstracts, proposals, and tenure folios).

8.3.   Engage in professional development to maintain and/or enhance proficiency.

8.3.1   Participate in professional associations, coalitions, and networks (e.g., serving on committees, attending conferences, and providing leadership).

8.3.2   Participate in continuing education opportunities to maintain or enhance continuing competence.

8.3.3   Develop a career advancement plan.

8.3.4   Build relationships with other professionals within and outside the profession.

8.3.5 ■   Serve as a mentor.

8.4.   Promote the health education profession to stakeholders, the public, and others.

8.4.1   Explain the major responsibilities, contributions, and value of the health education specialist.

8.4.2   Explain the role of professional organizations and the benefits of participating in them.

8.4.3   Advocate for professional development for health education specialists.

8.4.4   Educate others about the history of the profession, its current status, and its implications for professional practice.

8.4.5   Explain the role and benefits of credentialing (e.g., individual and program).

8.4.6 ▲   Develop presentations and publications that contribute to the profession.

8.4.7 ▲   Engage in service to advance the profession.

Area of Responsibility VIII

The Role. Ethics refers to the moral principles generally accepted as the proper way to conduct one's self while working as a health education specialist. There is an official Code of Ethics for the Health Education Profession (Coalition of National Health Education Organizations, 2020; Cottrell, et.al., 2018). Professionalism relates to the accepted conduct, aims or qualities that characterize someone working in the health education profession. Examples of professionalism include practicing in accord with accepted standards, participating in continuing education, belonging to professional associations, serving on committees, attending conferences and providing leadership to the profession. Ethical behavior and professionalism are expected when assessing needs, planning programs, implementing programs, managing programs, evaluating programs and conducting research. Acting in an ethical and professional manner is always expected of health education specialists and doing so helps establish one's reputation within the community and profession. It can take years to build one's reputation within the profession, but one unethical action or unprofessional interaction can destroy that reputation.

Setting: The following text is presented to describe how ethics and professionalism is used in different practice settings (NCHEC, 2020).

Community Setting: Health education specialists must follow the Health Education Code of Ethics which defines ethical behavior within the profession. In a community setting, health education specialists work to promote equitable partnerships with communities to address issues of health and maintain professional partnerships with other community stakeholders in order to effectively serve the community. This includes practicing cultural humility and treating colleagues, community partners, and priority populations with dignity at all times. Health education specialists working with numerous entities such as public health departments, community-based organizations, local voluntary health organizations, churches, civic organizations, neighborhood associations, and other nonprofits must maintain the highest of ethical and professional standards. Individual as well as agency reputations are based on ethical behavior. Health education specialists are also responsible for continual professional growth and development to remain up to date on current research, health trends, and emerging technology in order to better serve their priority populations. Professional association membership is important to stay up to date, network with other health education professionals and demonstrate commitment to the profession (NCHEC, 2020).

School (K-12) Setting: According to the Code of Ethics for the Health Education Profession, "The health education profession is dedicated to excellence in the practice of promoting individual, family, group, organizational and community health" (CNHEO, 2020). This must be done within the Health Education Code of Ethics. When a conflict arises among individuals, groups, organizations, agencies or institutions, health education specialists must consider all issues and give priority to those that promote wellness and quality of living through principles of self-determination and freedom of choice for the individual. Health educators in the K-12 setting promote integrity in the delivery of health education. They respect the rights, dignity, confidentiality and worth of all people by adapting strategies and methods to meet the needs of diverse populations and communities. The health education specialist must demonstrate professionalism at all times staying up to date with best practices in the field and joining and supporting professional associations.

Health Care Setting: Health education specialists are expected to lead by example and demonstrate professional behavior and appropriate demeanor while on duty as they are representatives of the profession. It is the responsibility of all health education specialists to follow the 6 ethical principles outlined in the Health Education Code of Ethics guidelines as referenced in Apppendix A.

It is expected that they also follow policies and regulations regarding workplace conduct and demeanor as warranted by their employers. Health education specialists working in health care settings may have access to highly confidential and personal health information. Therefore, they must be familiar with the Health Information Portability and Accountability Act (HIPAA) and abide by the principles of patient confidentiality. Health education specialists are expected to have cultural sensitivity and competency awareness skills, and advocate for diversity and inclusion. They must evaluate their own unconscious biases and demonstrate no bias to colleagues, clients, and the community they serve. Health education specialist professionals are accountable for their actions, decisions, and the impact of their practice. It is incumbent on all health education specialists to seek professional development opportunities for themselves so as to remain current in the field and provide professional development opportunities for any others they may supervise.

College/University Setting: Ethical behavior in all health education settings is guided by the Code of Ethics for the Health Education Profession. The Code of Ethics applies to the college/university health education specialist when teaching, advising students, conducting and disseminating research (via presentations and publications) and service. Traits related to responsible practice include honesty, equity and fairness, cultural humility, preparation for practice and ongoing reflection. Professionalism involves behaving in a manner consistent with best practices and ethical behavior, staying up to date in the field, and taking the responsibility to further the health education profession. One's personal reputation and the reputation of the health education profession is dependent on ethical and professional behavior.

Worksite/Business Setting: Health education specialists' behavior is guided by the Health Education Professional Code of Ethics. In addition, there may be additional ethical guidelines related to the business function(s) of the worksite, the health education specialists' role in the organization, and/or statutory guidelines. For example, a health education specialist may have fiduciary responsibilities if they are part of the decision-making process related to the employer's health plan and medical benefits. There may also be vendor contractual obligations that govern aspects of a health education specialist's behavior. Every worksite has a unique culture and a set of either formal and/or informal standards of professional behavior that guide health education specialists. It is expected that the health education specialist will demonstrate professional behavior at all times within the cultural norms of the setting. The health education specialist will remain current and updated on the latest trends and initiatives in the field.

College/University Health Promotion Services Setting: Health education specialists in this setting adhere to the Health Education Professional Code of Ethics and professionalism as outlined by a variety of health and higher education professional organizations. Within this setting, health education specialists must practice cultural humility, inclusion, respect, and promote equity when working with diverse and changing priority populations of colleagues, employees, and students. They must adhere to ethical protocols and procedures, ensure privacy of data and files, and comply with federal laws and regulations. To do so they must engage in a variety of professional development opportunities and should participate in one or more professional associations.

Key Terms

Adaptation is making changes to health education messages, materials, or programs to make them more suitable for a population of interest (Moore et al., 2013).

Cultural competence is a person's ability to understand and respect attitudes and values of various cultures and to address these differences in planning, implementing, and evaluating health education and promotion programs (Brown et al., 2012).

Cultural humility is an ongoing process of self-exploration for health education specialists in which they honor the beliefs, customs, culture, and values of the people with whom they work in communities (National Council on Aging, 2019).

Health disparities are differences in the incidence, prevalence, mortality, and/or burden of disease that exist among specific population groups (United States Department of Health and Human Services (USDHHS), 2011).

Online database refers to any systematically organized information accessible on the Internet, which may be used by health education specialists to obtain health knowledge and/or resources for the health education process. An online database may include text documents, citations, abstracts, images, audios, videos, and/or Web links (McKenzie et al., 2017).

Policies are sets of rules and objectives to guide activities (Doyle et al., 2019).

Professional Development Plan (**PDP**) is a career document in which short-term, mid-term, and long-term goals and objectives for a professional person are outlined (Indeed, 2020).

Social determinants of health (**SDOH**) are factors that could lead to health inequities and influence an individual's or community's health. SDOH barriers to health include race or ethnic status, gender, mental health, disabilities, or location (USDHHS, 2019a).

Technical Assistance is a dynamic, capacity-building process for designing or improving the quality, effectiveness, and efficiency of specific programs, research, services, products, or systems (West et al., 2012).

A theory is a set of interrelated concepts and definitions that present a systematic view of events and is used to describe a relationship among variables to explain or predict events (Glanz et al., 2015).

Workforce Development Plan (**WDP**) is the same as PDP; however, this plan is used for teams or organizations in an agency or system.

Competency 8.1 Practice in accordance with established ethical principles.

Ethics are principles or rules, which provide guidance for behaviors that may be classified as right or wrong (DeCenzo et al., 2016). Ethics are often delineated in Codes of Ethics, which various organizations and professions utilize to govern its members. (Health education specialists are expected to behave ethically and according to the Unified Code of Ethics approved by the CNHEO (2020)). Ethical dilemmas consist of issues with two sides and involves a judgment of right or wrong. Health education specialists are confronted with such dilemmas every day. The CNHEO Code of Ethics is not only used to set the standards for the health education specialist, but also tells the public what to expect from the practitioner (Cottrell et al., 2018).

Ethics permeate all aspects of the health education specialists' various roles. Practicing within the boundaries of the profession's ethical standards is imperative. Because health education specialists are an important factor in behavioral development, professionals are expected to stay current in their knowledge of health-related content, as well as effective interventions and strategies (Plomer & Bensley, 2009). The community also should be considered if the program is focused on the community as a setting, target, resource, or agent. Health education specialists may wish to use a community advisory board or something similar to obtain community feedback and support.

Professional ethics are used to guide health education specialists in the performance of their duties. The complete Code of Ethics is provided in Appendix A.

The Code of Ethics for the Health Education Profession (CNHEO, 2020) includes the following articles:

1. Responsibility to the Public
2. Responsibility to the Profession
3. Responsibility to Employers
4. Responsibility in the Delivery of Health Education/Promotion
5. Responsibility in Research and Evaluation
6. Responsibility in Professional Preparation and Continuing Education

8.1.1 Apply professional codes of ethics and ethical principles throughout assessment, planning, implementation, evaluation and research, communication, consulting, and advocacy processes.

Ethical Principles in Assessment
At the outset, it is important for health education specialists to consider ethical principles to guide the decision-making process of an assessment. While engaging the population, stakeholders, and partners, health education specialists may encounter conflicting priorities on the methods selected for program planning, data collected, and findings of the needs assessment. Issel and Wells (2018) provided an overview of six frequently used ethical frameworks that can be applied to planning programs, which includes needs assessment:

- Autonomy – personal right to self-determination and choice
- Criticality – the worst-off benefit the most
- Egalitarian – all persons of equal value; minimize disparities
- Needs-based – equal opportunity to meet own needs, such as healthy life
- Resource sensitive – resources are scarce
- Utilitarian – the greatest good for the greatest number; the end justifies the means

Ethical Principles in Intervention or Program Planning and Implementation

Health education specialists should maintain a high standard of conduct at all times and ensure the ethical behavior of everyone involved with implementation (CNHEO, 2020). They must use their knowledge and experience to fulfill their responsibilities to the public, profession, and employers in the delivery of health education. Ethical practices in program planning may include using the most recent data or best evidence-based practices or theories to adopt or create health interventions or policy change. For example, Section 4, Responsibility in the Delivery of Health Education, holds that health education specialists should be sensitive to cultural diversity and be informed of the latest science of theory and practice (CNHEO, 2020). During implementation of health programs, health education specialists are responsible to the public, the health education profession, and employers both when delivering health education and in research and evaluation. They should undertake activities for which they are competent and apply rules of conflicts of interest when sharing their work. Process check-ins, project management meetings, and other regular monitoring should be used to ensure compliance with the Health Education Code of Ethics.

Ethical Principles in the Evaluation and Research

Professionals in the health education profession are dedicated to practicing and promoting individual, family, organizational, and community health. Therefore, it is necessary to conduct evaluation with human subjects central to the investigations. An institutional review board (IRB) for universities or community agencies should be consulted to review research and/or evaluation protocols to help identify and avoid any possible and unforeseen risks to which participants may be subject. Members of an IRB support the worth, dignity, potential, and uniqueness of all people and are responsible for upholding the integrity and ethics of the profession. Respect for autonomy, promotion of social justice, active promotion of good, and avoidance of harm is the responsibility of each health education specialist (CNHEO, 2020).

In the protection of human subjects, a standard for ethics is established, and details can be found in the Belmont Report (National Commission for the Protection of Human Subjects of Biomedical and Behavioral Research, 1979). In this report, the basic ethical principles and guidelines for the protection of human subjects of research is summarized. Not all health education specialists will conduct research, but all health education specialists should recognize the fundamental concepts for human subjects' protection: respect for persons, beneficence, and justice.

- Respect for persons: People have the right to make choices about participation in research and some people may not have the ability to self-determine participation in research and should be protected (e.g., children, prisoners).
- Beneficence: Research staff should do no harm and should maximize the benefits of the research and reduce any possible harms to participants.
- Justice: Address fairness in distribution of the benefits of the research and selection into research projects (National Commission for the Protection of Human Subjects of Biomedical and Behavioral Research, 1979).

Consequently, health education specialists should complete all required training as it relates to their work (e.g. ,privacy or security, good clinical practice).

When planning and conducting research or evaluation, health education specialists do so in accordance with federal and state laws and regulations, organizational and institutional policies, and professional standards. The CNHEO provides health education specialists who are engaged in research or evaluation guidelines for ethical behavior in Section 5 of the Code of Ethics for the Health Education Profession. Outlined in Section 5 are health education specialists' responsibility in research and evaluation (CNHEO, 2020). See Sections A-F of the CNHEO Section 5 as follows:

A. Health Education Specialists ensure that participation in research is voluntary and based upon the informed consent of participants. They follow research designs and protocols approved by relevant institutional review committees and/or boards.

B. Health education specialists respect and protect the privacy, rights and dignity of research participants and honor commitments made to those participants.

C. Health education specialists treat all information obtained from participants as confidential unless otherwise required by law and inform research participants of the disclosure requirements and procedures.

D. Health education specialists take credit, including authorship, only for work they have performed and give appropriate authorship, co-authorship, credit, or acknowledgement for the contributions of others.

E. Health education specialists report the results of their research and evaluation objectively, accurately, and in a timely manner.

F. Health education specialists promote and disseminate the results of their research through appropriate formats while fostering the translation of research into practice.

(CNHEO, 2020)

G. Health education specialists conducting research or evaluation sometimes will be required to obtain informed consent. Informed consent is designed to allow participants to choose what will or will not happen to them, and the informed consent is signed by participants to indicate their choice. Informed consent includes the following information:
  - Nature and purpose of the program
  - Any inherent risks or dangers associated with participation in the program
  - Any possible discomfort that may be experienced from participation in the program
  - Expected benefits of participation
  - Alternative programs or procedures in which the same results would be accomplished
  - Option of discontinuing participation at any time

(Dake & Jordan, 2016)

With the enactment of the HIPPA (Health Insurance Portability and Accountability Act of 1996), the importance of standards and use of participant or patient information was stressed (Cottrell et al., 2018). HIPPA is legislation in which rules around data privacy, integrity, and availability are offered. A HIPPA section is often included in an informed consent or consent form that allows researchers and health education specialists to use participant data in research. HIPAA statements include what types of personal identifiers or personal health information (PHI) is collected, how it is protected, and who has access to the data. PHI can include demographics, medical history or diagnoses, test results, medical records, or insurance status.

The health education specialist will encounter ethical considerations to apply to the research process. Research misconduct can include activities that compromise the integrity of research or evaluation findings. Common types of research misconduct include the following:
  - **Plagiarism:** using other people's words, thoughts, or results without offering them credit through appropriate citations
  - **Fabrication:** making up results and reporting them
  - **Falsification:** changing or omitting data or manipulating results or processes so that research is not truthfully presented (National Institutes of Health (NIH), 2012).

The planning stage of data analysis is also the appropriate time to determine the level of significance that will be applied when testing the research hypotheses. By convention, a significance value of 0.05 is used in health education/promotion research (Sharma & Petosa, 2014). More stringent or relaxed significance values may be applied, however, depending on the scope of the project. Significance values must be decided a priori, or before implementation of the research, so that ethical guidelines of research are followed. Adjusting significance values post hoc, or after the fact, can be considered a violation of research ethics. Additional ethical issues that are best determined during the planning stage concern authorship and least publishable units. Prior to initiating the research process, it behooves the research team to determine how authorship will be granted, as well as the order of authorship on subsequent publications. Failing to address these issues at the outset of the research project can lead to ethical dilemmas. Specifying how to present the findings of the research is another issue that should be determined during the initial stages of research planning. Researchers must carefully consider if they will publish in least publishable units, or the minimal amount of information that can generate a peer-reviewed publication. This type of publishing occurs when data are published incrementally as opposed to simultaneously. There are instances in which this practice may be beneficial; however, "salami publishing," as it is frequently called, can fragment the literature and compromise the legitimacy of significance testing (Karlsson & Beaufils, 2013).

Ethical Principles in Consultation

Consultants must have a set of principles wherein ethical behaviors are defined and their actions toward those behaviors are guided. Ethical practice may be based on deciding what is right and wrong, then performing the right behavior. Therefore, health education specialists must practice integrity in the conduct of health education consulting.

Some important ethical guidelines to consider when working with organizations follow:
- Do no harm to your client. Health education specialists should, in their actions and work with other organizations, protect clients and other stakeholders from harm.
- Keep client information private or confidential unless the client or law requests otherwise.
- Avoid conflicts of interest. For example, health education specialists should not represent two opposing interests at one time.
- Do not act in the official capacity as an advocate for the client.
- Do not go beyond your own expertise or qualifications. Health education specialists should know their level of competence with various health education skills and perform actions that match their own education, training, or professional experiences (i.e., not exceeding those boundaries of competence).
- Respect others. Consultants should respect the opinions, values, and beliefs of others different from their own.
- Ensure that all participation in research and data collection is voluntary and includes informed consent.
- Represent accurately potential services and outcomes to their employers.
- Maintain competence in their field of practice.
(American Psychological Association, 2019)

Ethical Principles in Advocacy
Health education specialists should be aware of advocacy policies and procedures for the setting in which they work. For example, nonprofit agencies can perform lobbying as long as lobbying activities meet the federal guidelines and do not exceed a certain percentage of the nonprofits activities. Lobbying is any attempt to influence specific legislation according to federal law (Internal Revenue Service (IRS), 2019). Federal, state, and organizational laws and policies affect health education specialists' ability to participate in certain types of advocacy efforts while "on" organizational time.

Health education specialists should comply with state and federal law, as well as the organizational policy regarding such activities. Formal organizational policy, as well as departmental or individual management policy, may apply. In the Code of Ethics for the Health Education Profession (CNHEO, 2020), it is stated that health education specialists have a responsibility to promote, maintain, and improve individual, family, and community health. The Health Education Code of Ethics includes articles reminding health education specialists to always consider actions and social policies that support and facilitate the best balance of benefits over harm for all affected parties. Outside of their daily role, health education specialists can strengthen advocacy efforts as members of a professional organization in which advocacy exists and may lobby for issues of interest. Health education specialists also can use the organization's name in support of an issue if that organization has an established position on the issue and approves such use. An individual acting as a private citizen can participate in any level of advocacy or lobbying. Care must be taken not to use any resources (e.g., time, computers, phones, letterhead) that belong to an employer when acting as a private citizen. Health education specialists may have to declare views belonging to themselves and not the organization from which they are employed.

Finally, the health education specialist could attend workshops and participate in trainings on ethics to stay mindful to commit ethical practices. The CDC has links to ethical training materials at https://www.naccho.org/programs/public-health-infrastructure/ethics. This CDC website includes a link to an online course called, Good Decision Making in Real Time: Public Health Ethics Training for Local Health Departments. This training includes proposed public health ethical behaviors from the 2002 Public Health Leadership Society.

8.1.2 ▲ Demonstrate ethical leadership, management, and behavior.

Health education specialists must follow guidelines and legal standards for their organization and in their professional practice. They should always review state or local laws, rules, and regulations related to their practice. These standards are often given in employee orientation or onboarding and employee/manager handbooks. In addition, if health education specialists conduct research or oversee projects under grant funding, they should review those funding announcements or solicitations, award notices, and/or other guidance documents.

Ethical Principles in Management

Health education specialists have an obligation to manage fiscal resources in an ethical manner. The demonstration of ethics relative to fiscal management, however, is a complex process that encompasses considerations that are more expansive than the legality of specific actions. Part of managing fiscal resources in an ethical manner is being able to understand which programs offer the best value. Health education specialists have an obligation to apply and utilize findings from these various types of analyses to make informed, responsible, and timely programmatic decisions.

According to Bull (2011), there are several unique ethical issues related to technology-based health promotion:
- ***Beneficence:*** Program planners need to justify why the chosen technology modality is best for participants (not the health promoter).
- ***Transparency:*** Informed consent processes and information provided by both participants and health promoters must be clear and accurate.

- **Equity:** Given health disparities data, special attention should be paid to whom has access to the technological modality.
- **Confidentiality:** Data security protocols must be employed to protect private participant data.
- **Special populations:** Additional standards to verify participant identity must be employed and regulations for protecting special populations must be followed if participants are members of included categories such as pregnant women.

Health education specialists also should consider the Health Information Technology for Economic and Clinical Health (HITECH) Act when managing technology resources (USDHHS, 2014a). Through HITECH, it is proposed that the meaningful use of interoperable electronic health records throughout the United States health care delivery system should be a critical national goal. In the HITECH Act, the privacy and security concerns associated with the electronic transmission of health information are addressed (USDHHS, 2014a).

8.1.3 Comply with legal standards and regulatory guidelines in assessment, planning, implementation, evaluation and research, advocacy, management, communication, and reporting processes.

Health education specialists must comply with all laws and regulations that apply to the profession in the context in which they practice. The laws and regulations may be at the federal, state, or local level, and they may be in a broad range of categories and specific to a setting (e.g., laws related to employment practices or laws related to business operations). For example, health education specialists within a health care setting must be familiar with the policies related to confidentiality, compliance, data security, and government regulations related to institutional accreditation. Further, health education specialists in school settings may have responsibilities that include the implementation of obesity prevention activities, which may have federal, state, and local regulations related to food services, student exposure to nutrition education, and time allocations for physical activities to which they must consider and adhered.

Institutions, such as universities and hospitals, wherein research that includes human subjects is conducted, are required to establish an Institutional Review Board (IRB). The IRB functions to protect human subjects involved in research (Neutens & Rubinson, 2014). Because evaluations may have similar ethical considerations as research projects, an IRB review and approval are often desired or required prior to data collection (McKenzie et al., 2017. An IRB is at times referred to as an independent ethics committee or a committee that has been formally designated to approve, monitor, and review biomedical and behavioral research involving humans. This type of monitoring and oversight is designed to protect the rights and welfare of the research participants. An IRB performs critical oversight functions for research conducted on human subjects that are scientific, ethical, and regulatory.

Health education specialists should pay special attention to legal issues that will affect data sharing with regard to Health Insurance Portability and Accountability Act (HIPAA) laws (PL 104-102), informed consent, and commitments to confidentiality (McKenzie et al., 2017). In the HIPAA Privacy Rule, conditions are established regarding when protected health information may be used for research or program evaluation. Under the Privacy Rule, health education specialists or researchers are permitted information for research with individual authorization or for limited circumstances without individual authorization (McKenzie et al., 2017).

Legal Standards for Assessment and Planning

All health professionals wrestle with legal standards, and health education specialists are no exception. Liability insurance to cover the cost of any physical or psychological risks to program participants is highly recommended. Some steps to reduce the risk of legal liability include the following:

- Ensure that all informed consent procedures are implemented.
- Maintain the privacy of participants' personal health information (i.e., HIPPA).
- Choose currently certified instructors to teach classes.
- Provide written guidelines for emergency medical procedures for participants.
- Ask program participants to be cleared by health professionals before modifying their diet or engaging in strenuous exercise.
- Make sure classrooms and other facilities comply with building codes and are regularly maintained.

(adapted from McKenzie et al., 2017)

Legal Standards for Implementation

In some funding announcements, restrictions are placed regarding how funds can be used (e.g., cannot be used for research, patient, or clinical care, cannot substitute for existing funds, or cannot cover pre-award costs). Examples of some administrative requirements, laws, and regulations that may apply include the following:

- The Paperwork Reduction Act of 1995 and information collection review helps reduce the paperwork burden and maximize information collection (USDHHS, 2014a).
- According to Section 508 of the Rehabilitation Act, federal agencies are required to make websites, electronic materials, and other information technology accessible to people with disabilities (United States General Services Administration, 2018).
- The Plain Writing Act of 2010 has stipulations that federal agencies to use language that the general public can understand (Plain Language Action and Information Network, 2019.). Plain language is now expected for websites, print and other electronic materials, social media, and other materials (i.e., not just the informed consent).
- Cost sharing or matching funds (e.g., in-kind funds) may be required to leverage funds.
- Anti-lobbying, smoke free worksites, and nutrition policies may be put in place.
- Accounting system, security clearance, data release/sharing, and reporting requirements should be considered.

Health education specialists might discuss questions with a supervisor, organization leadership, legal counsel, and/or the funding organization to determine what legal standards apply to implementation.

Negligence is the failure to act in a careful or reasonable manner. Negligence may result from omission (not doing something that should have been done) or commission (doing something that should not have done). To reduce the likelihood of legal improprieties:

- be aware of legal liabilities.
- use only professionals or experts in the area being presented (When appropriate, they should be licensed, certified, or in other ways credentialed.).

- when appropriate, require medical clearance for participation.
- instruct staff not to practice outside their area of expertise.
- follow building codes and regulations.

(Anspaugh et al., 2006)

Health education specialists should seek help from their supervisor, organization leadership or legal counsel, or partners when needed. They should ask questions and make adjustments early on rather than have to stop a program or intervention midcourse.

Legal Standards for Advocacy

Health education specialists should be aware and comply with legal standards related to advocacy efforts. Government employees cannot advocate because it may appear that federal or state government agency has biases. Health educators or researchers may offer education, offer data, or provide information to local community organizing or formal advocacy efforts but may not be able to advocate themselves. Those who work for nonprofits that have 501c3 status must abide by rules to ensure that they comply with IRS regulations (Fertman & Allensworth, 2016). Personal advocacy as a private citizen is acceptable as long as it is not happening with health education specialists' work e-mails, phone number, or on their company letterhead.

Legal Standards for Management

Federal, state, and local laws, regulations, and policies govern human resources, and it is essential that program managers be familiar with them. Laws, regulations, and policies are updated periodically, and state and local laws, regulations, and policies vary. This variance makes periodic review and familiarization essential. Major federal laws, regulations, and policies that apply to human resource management include, but are not limited to, the following:

- Statutes Prohibiting Discrimination in Employment
  - *Civil Rights Act of 1964/1991*
  - *Age Discrimination in Employment Act (1967)*
  - *American with Disabilities Act (1990)*
  - *Rehabilitation Act (1973)*
  - *Pregnancy Discrimination Act (1978)*
  - *Fair Credit Reporting and Disclosure Act (1970)*
  - *Immigration Reform and Control Act (1986)*
- Employment Rights
  - *Family Medical Leave Act (1993)*
- Employee Benefits and Compensation
  - *Fair Labor Standards Act (1938)*
  - *Employee Retirement Income Security Act (1974)*
  - *Consolidated Omnibus Budget Reconciliation Act (COBRA) (1986)*
  - *Federal Unemployment Compensation Act (1939)*
  - *Equal Pay Act (1963)*
  - *Lily Ledbetter Fair Pay Act (2009)*

- Other Federal Laws
  - ⊙ *Social Security Act (1935)*
  - ⊙ *National Labor Relations Act (1935)*
  - ⊙ *Labor-Management Relations Act (1947)*
  - ⊙ *Occupational Safety and Health Act (1970)*
  - ⊙ *Health Insurance Portability and Accountability Act (HIPAA)(1996)*
  - ⊙ *Employee Polygraph Protection Act (1988)*
  - ⊙ *Pension Protection Act (1987)*
  - ⊙ *Drug Free Workplace Act (1988)*
  - ⊙ *Genetic Information Nondiscrimination Act (2008)*
  - ⊙ *Sarbanes-Oxley Act (2002)*
  - ⊙ *Privacy Act (1974)*
  - ⊙ *Uniformed Services Employment and Reemployment Act (1994)*
  - ⊙ *The Affordable Care Act (2010)*

(DeCenzo, et al., 2016); Fallon & Zgodzinski, 2011)

Managers may have to respond to issues that may not be clearly defined as right or wrong, legal or illegal including the following:

- Electronic surveillance of employees (e.g., monitoring Internet usage, telephone usage, and e-mail)
- Monitoring employees' access to records and documents (e.g., employees looking at electronic records on clients about whom they may not need to know information in the direct performance of their job)
- Monitoring employees personal behaviors that may not be directly related to job performance (.e.g., smoking or tobacco usage)

(DeCenzo, Robbins, & Verhulst, 2016).

8.1.4 Promote health equity.

Health equity is defined in *Healthy People 2030* as achievement of the highest level of health for everyone (USDHHS, 2019a). Health inequities are differences in health due to social, economic, and/or environmental disadvantage or injustices. Factors that could lead to health inequities and influence an individual's or community's health are called social determinants of health (SDOH). SDOH can be barriers to health and include race or ethnic status, gender, mental health, disabilities, or location (USDHHS, 2019b). These factors can lead to differences in the incidence, prevalence, mortality, and burden of disease among specific groups or **health disparities** (USDHHS, 2019c).

Health People 2030 has sections that are organized by these social determinants of health into 5 key categories in its framework (See Table 8.1 that follows.). Refer to Competency 1.3.1 for more information on social determinants of health. Individuals who are minority and have lower incomes typically are more likely to be uninsured, face barriers to accessing care, and have higher incidence rates of diseases compared to whites and those having higher incomes (Kaiser Family Foundation, 2018). Almost always, those with higher education have lower incidence of some diseases and better health outcomes than those with lower education attainment.

Table 8.1
Types of SDOH and Examples

SDOH	Indicators
Economic Stability	Employment Poverty Food Insecurity Housing Instability
Education	Early Childhood Education and Development Enrollment in Higher Education High School Graduation Language and Literacy
Social and Community Context	Civic Participation Social Cohesion Discrimination Incarceration
Neighborhood and Built Environment	Access to Foods that Support Healthy Eating Patterns Quality of Housing Environmental Conditions Crime and Violence
Health and Health Care	Health Literacy/Numeracy Access to Health Care Access to Primary Care

United States Department of Health and Human Services (2019b)

Changing health inequities is challenging but it requires many sectors of the community to work with public health. The following are some suggested strategies to be used to address these inequities.

- ***Collection of data.*** Collating or collection of social determinants of health data helps health education specialists to understand, investigate, and spread awareness about the causes of inequities. This data collection could include secondary data that are stratified on SDOH indicators and primary data collected through participatory methods (e.g., focus groups, community forums) from those experiencing inequities and primary data collection.
- ***Advocacy.*** Educate or help advocate for support for a specific action or policy in communities. This advocacy could ensure the creation of policies, regulations, or rules that can impact the behaviors and environmental conditions of all who reside in the community.
- ***Health in all policies.*** Personnel in local, state, and federal agencies should identify multi-sectorial opportunities for advancing equity in all areas of social, economic, and health policies within their communities. Examples of these policies are increasing access to healthy foods, reliable transportation, having safe housing, quality education, availability of green spaces, and opportunities for economic development.

- *Comprehensive approaches.* To be impactful, it is better to have a set of strategies and often at many levels (e.g.., individual, community, policy). Intervening at multiple levels can increase reach of the program or intervention.
- *Addressing root causes of health disparities.* Identifying housing, education attainment, environments, and access or transportation and so on can be useful to address upstream issues leading to health disparities.
- *Specific initiatives.* Community-wide or population approaches may be foundational but, sometimes, specific programming to reach a group or place that is underserved is important (e.g., National School Lunch program to offer free/reduced lunches, support or initiatives for food outlets to open in food deserts, direct funds to low-resource communities where physical activity opportunities are needed).
(CDC, 2013b; Fertman & Allensworth, 2016)

CDC (2010) offers a health equity checklist (Table 8.2) in health promotion initiatives to develop interventions or strategies, which are aimed to reduce health inequities.

Table 8.2
Health Equity Checklist

Steps	Activity
Identify	○ Identify protective factors and health equities in a community and geographic region through community assessment, secondary data, and environmental surveys.
Engage	○ Include representation of populations affected by health issues. ○ Engage the representatives in your leadership team or partnerships.
Analyze	○ Select or design and implement interventions or strategies in which inequities are addressed.
Review	○ Monitor and evaluate so that efforts to reduce health inequalities are successful. ○ Conduct appropriate sub-analyses of data to assess differences in outcomes for populations due to your strategies or interventions.

Evidence-based Interventions for Health Equity

The Community Guide Taskforce recommends interventions to address health equity. These interventions have evidence that they are effective and address social determinants such as education and housing that can help people achieve health and well-being (Community Guide to Preventive Services, 2019).

Table 8.3 describes evidenced-based health equity interventions.

Table 8.3
Evidence-based Health Equity Interventions

Type	Evidence-based Intervention	Description
Education Programs/Policies	Center-based Early Childhood Education programs	Providing programs to improve the cognitive or social development of children ages 3 or 4 years
	Full-day Kindergarten programs	Offering kindergarten programs that are 5 days a week and last 5 to 6 hours per day
	High School completion program	Offering programs that increase the chance that students receive a high school or a general educational development (GED) diploma in school-based or community settings
	School-based health centers	Providing primary health care on-site (school-based) or off-site (school-linked). The services could include mental health care, social services, health education and dentistry.
Housing Programs/Policies	Tenant assistance programs	Offering vouchers or direct cash assistance for low-income families to afford more housing options

https://www.thecommunityguide.org/content/task-force-findings-health-equity

8.1.5 Use evidence-informed theories, models, and strategies.

Theories are the pillar of every well-planned intervention. Although abstract in nature, theories provide a guide for what to expect about human behavior. A theory is "a set of interrelated concepts, definitions and propositions that present a systematic view of events or situations by specifying relations among variables, in order to explain and predict the events or situations" (Glanz et al., 2015, p. 26). Models or theories can be used to help program planners understand a health issue in a specific context.

Theories are useful during the various stages of planning, implementing, and evaluating interventions. Health education specialists can use theories to shape answers to the questions of why, what, and how. In other words, they can use theories to guide the search for why people are not following public health and medical advice or not caring for themselves in healthy ways. Theories can be used to help pinpoint what health education specialists need to know before developing and organizing an intervention program.

Theories and models are used to:
- identify targets for change in health promotion effort,
- select strategies for implementation based on known influences on behavior and design interventions, and
- specify potential outcomes to be monitored, measured or compared in a program evaluation for an intervention (Glanz et al., 2015).

Additionally, most theories and models have constructs that can help health education specialists measure change in a program, strategy, or policy implementation. Considering the role of theory, specifically based on how the constructs can be applied in practice, can help health education specialists understand the behavior change at the community, interpersonal or individual level.

Applying theories and/or models in assessment

Given the complexity of health education and promotion practice, multi-level comprehensive interventions are needed to develop effective programs. Health education specialists need to consider many levels of influence including behavioral, organizational, cultural, community, policy, and environmental. Theories and models can provide a framework for the needs assessment. Refer to Sub-competency 1.1.4 and 2.3.1 for more information on assessment and planning models.

Intervention Mapping. Bartholomew and colleagues (2016) first introduced intervention mapping with five steps: program objectives, theory-based intervention methods and practical strategies, designing and organizing a program, adoption and implementation plans, and program evaluation plans. Later, Bartholomew et al. (2016) made changes, such as adding a sixth step (needs assessment) and adding sustainability to program adoption and implementation. This framework can be used to help health education specialists plan and develop interventions (e.g.., the lifecycle from problem to solution).

Mobilizing for Action through Planning and Partnerships (**MAPP**) is a community-wide strategic planning framework for improving public health. MAPP has 6 phases for community data collection. These phases are as follows:

1. **Phase One:** Organizing for Success and Partnership Development
2. **Phase Two:** Visioning: Gathering collective vision of what the community should be
3. **Phase Three:** Conduct of the 4 Assessments:
   - **Community Themes and Strengths Assessment:** Assessment of qualitative data on how communities perceive their health and quality of life
   - **Local Public Health System Assessment:** Measurement of how well the public health system partners collectively offer health services through the analysis of national public health performance standards
   - **Community Health Status Assessment:** Analyses of the health indicators about the population
   - **Forces of change:** Assessment of positive and negative external forces that impact health promotion
4. **Phase Four:** Identifying Strategic Issues: Using gathered information from the 4 assessments to discern the strategic health and other issues that the community must address
5. **Phase Five:** Formulation of Goals and Strategies: Specifying goals and activities in a community health improvement plan
6. **Phase Six:** Action Cycle: Continuing with planning, implementation, and evaluation of the community plan (National Association of County and City Health Officials [NACCHO], 2019).

In addition to knowing community assessment models, it is necessary to review behavior change models to understand the diverse influences on health and behaviors. Refer to Sub-competency 2.4.3 for more information about factors that foster or hinder implementation.

Because health and health behaviors are influenced by many factors, it is important to collect data not only on what is happening but also why it is happening. Health education specialists should identify both a planning model and an implementation model in this stage to help identify the types of data that need to be collected to fully understand the complex influences on health (Doyle et al., 2019).

Applying theories and/or models in Implementation

Health education specialists are responsible for selecting a theory or model that will be used to inform program planning and implementation based on the concepts and constructs of a theory and the program goals and objectives. The following are a few current, popular textbooks that contain the most commonly used theories of health behavior and health promotion.

- *Health Behavior and Health Education: Theory, Research, and Practice,* 5th edition (Glanz et., 2015)
- *Emerging Theories in Health Promotion Practice and Research: Strategies for Improving Public Health* (DiClemente et al., 2009)
- *Theoretical Foundations of Health Education and Health Promotion* (Sharma, 2017)
- *Theory at a Glance* (NCI, 2005)

The following are some common theories and models used in health education and promotion. They are placed into individual, interpersonal, and community levels.

Individual Level

Transtheoretical Model. In the Transtheoretical Model, often called the Stages of Change Model, many theories are incorporated, thus the term "transtheoretical" (Prochaska et al., 2015). This theory is particularly useful in that its planned interventions can be used to reach people where they are in their motivation for changing a particular behavior. This model has several major constructs: stages of change, processes of change, decisional balance, and self-efficacy. The Stages of Change construct receives considerable attention due to its use in determining readiness to change.

Prochaska and colleagues (2015) proposed that change is a process, not an event, and that change occurs as people move through a series of stages to adopt a new behavior. The stages are:

- **Precontemplation:** person is not interested in addressing the problem; some people may be unaware of, or in denial about, the problem
- **Contemplation:** person is aware there is a problem and intends to do something in the next six months
- **Preparation:** person has taken steps and plans to address the problem in the next month
- **Action:** person has taken action (changed behavior) within the past six months
- **Maintenance:** person has maintained the behavior change for more than six months
- **Termination:** person has no temptation to return to the old behavior

(Prochaska et al., 2015)

A person can be in any stage with any behavior and move back and forth through the stages, depending on external factors affecting the individual. When using this model, health education specialists can develop materials and interventions for each stage to match individual needs for behavior change.

Health Belief Model. The Health Belief Model (HBM) is a popular behavior change model that has been extensively used and researched over the years (Rosenstock et al., 1988). HBM is an individual-level model first developed by social psychologists in the United States Public Health Service to provide an understanding about why individuals did not act on information specific to prevention or disease detection. In this model, there are six major constructs thought to affect behavior change:

- **Perceived susceptibility:** there is risk for the disease.
- **Perceived severity:** there are serious consequences to contracting/developing the disease.
- **Perceived benefits:** there are benefits to taking action to prevent or control the disease.
- **Perceived barriers:** there are consequences to taking action against the disease.
- **Cues to action:** cues or triggers that encourage a person to take action.
- **Self-efficacy:** there is confidence in taking action against the disease.

Theory of Reasoned Action and Theory of Planned Behavior. The Theory of Reasoned Action (TRA) was developed by Icek Ajzen first to focus on relationships among attitudes, behaviors, and intentions. The Theory of Planned Behavior (TPB) was built on the Theory of Reasoned Action with the behavioral control construct added. Both authors of the theories recognize behavioral intention as key in determining behavior and assume that behavior change is influenced by a person's attitude toward the outcome and the social or subjective norms of people important in the person's life (Montaño & Kasprzyk, 2015). In the TPB, the construct of perceived behavioral control was added. When using these theories, health education specialists should examine the individual's motivation to perform the behavior, determine what the individual's peers think of the behavior, and assess the difficulty the individual will have in performing the behavior.

Interpersonal Level

Social Cognitive Theory. Stated in the Social Cognitive Theory (SCT) by Albert Bandura is that learning is an interaction between a person and his or her environment, cognitive processes, and behavior (Heaney & Viswanath, 2015). In this theory, this interaction is referred to as reciprocal determinism. The several major constructs associated with this theory are: behavioral capability (knowledge and skills), outcomes expectations, expectancies, reciprocal determinism, and self-efficacy. Authors of other models have adopted Social Cognitive Theory constructs to serve as an underpinning for behavior change. More specifically, self-efficacy, a person's confidence in performing a behavior and overcoming possible barriers to that behavior, has been adopted by several other models. Major constructs in the SCT are displayed in Figure 8.1 and described in Table 8.4

Figure 8.1 *Social Cognitive Theory*

 Environment, Social support, Normative beliefs

 Behavior, Self-efficacy, Skills

Personal Knowledge, Expectations

Table 8.4
Social Cognitive Theory

Construct	Definition
Self-efficacy	Person's confidence in his ability to do a behavior
Knowledge	Person's understanding of the information on health topic or behavior, and risks and benefits of performing a behavior
Skills	Person's abilities to do a behavior
Outcome expectations	Person's judgement on the results of behavioral action
Observational learning	Learning new information and behaviors by watching others do a behavior
Normative beliefs	Norms and beliefs about the behavior (acceptability and prevalence) from those around the person
Social support or reinforcement	Encouragement and reinforcement a person gets from his or her networks of friends and relatives

Heaney & Viswanath, 2015

Social support. In changing behaviors or environmental conditions, social support has been studied and defined. Social supports the actual offering of support by other individuals in a person's life. The notion is that social support can help change behaviors such as smoking cessation and physical activity and can also has been linked to buffering stress and protective effect on mortality. Social support can take different forms, including tangible, informational, emotional, and appraisal (Holt-Lunstad & Uchino, 2015). In Table 8.5, these constructs are defined.

Table 8.5
Social Support Constructs

Construct	Definition
Tangible	Offering material assistance (e.g., money, food)
Emotional	Provision of caring or comfort
Informational	Offering advice or information
Appraisal	Support for self-evaluation or assessment

Holt-Lunstad & Uchino, 2015

Community Level

Diffusion of Innovations Theory. The Diffusion of Innovations Theory by Rogers (2003) is a community-level theory that is used to describe the rate at which a new program or activity will spread throughout a group of people. According to this theory, the characteristics of those accepting the new program helps to explain community readiness to change. People can fall into different categories of adopting change:

- *Innovators* are the first to adopt the new idea or program.
- *Early Adopters* wait until after the Innovators adopt.
- *Early Majority* adopt once the opinion leaders have done so.
- *Late Majority* adopt once the new idea or program becomes the norm.
- *Laggards* are the last to adopt or they may never adopt.

Health education specialists motivate groups of people to adopt a new idea or program by demonstrating how much better it is than the status quo. In the theory, constructs related to the innovation are incorporated; they include relative advantage, compatibility, complexity, observability, and trialability. Using the Diffusion of Innovations Theory, health education specialists integrate the idea into something already accepted in the community through communication channels.

Community Organizing/Mobilization. Community organizing is a process in which community groups identify problems or goals for change, mobilize internal and external resources, and deliver strategies to reach goals (Wallerstein et al., 2015). These activities can form the basis of policy and organizational change in communities. Strategies can include organizing coalitions, grassroots organizing, leadership development, building community identity, and legislative actions (Wallerstein et al., 2015).

Ecological Models. Ecological models are focused on the interaction of the individual and environment (Sallis & Owens, 2015). Applying ecological models requires that health education specialists be familiar with individual behavior change strategies as well as strategies to change the environment or physical surroundings. In health promotion, health education specialists need to have an understanding about behaviors having multiple levels of influence and perhaps intervene at multiple levels. Several ecological models have been proposed, each with a unique way to frame this interaction. Sallis and Owen (2015) proposed health behavior can be affected at five levels: individual or intrapersonal, interpersonal, organizational, community, and public policy.

Evidence-based Strategies

Evidence-based public health refers to the application of observation-, theory-, and science-based experiments (evidence) to improve the health of populations (Brownson et al., 2017). Examples of evidence-based interventions that have been proven to work can be found at several websites. These websites provide information about evidence-based strategies (e.g., one-on-one education for cancer screening), programs, or policies and may have the packaged materials available or a link to the program developers' site. Some of these websites include the following:

- The Guide to Community Preventive Services (http://thecommunityguide.org)
- Cochrane Reviews | The Cochrane Collaboration (http://www.cochrane.org)
- AHRQ Innovations Exchange (https://innovations.ahrq.gov/)
- National Cancer Institute's (NCI) Research-tested Intervention Programs (RTIPs) (http://rtips.cancer.gov/rtips)
- Diffusion of Effective Behavioral Interventions (DEBIs) for HIV programs (http://www.effectiveinterventions.org/)
- SAMSHAs Guide to Evidence-based Practices (EBP) (http://www.samhsa.gov/ebpwebguide)

- Partnership for Prevention (http://www.prevent.org/)
- Center for Training and Research Translation (http://centertrt.org/)

The Guide to Community Preventive Services is a free resource to help practitioners choose programs and policies to improve health and prevent disease at the community level. These programs or polices are grounded in evidence that work from systematic reviews of articles on that intervention and their findings. Programs, policies, or interventions that have sufficient evidence are recommended for the field of public health practice. Systematic reviews are used to answer these questions:

- Which program and policy interventions have been proven effective?
- Are there effective interventions that are right for my community?
- What might effective interventions cost?
- What is the likely return on investment? (The Community Guide for Preventive Services, 2019)

To impact health, health education specialists can implement policy, systems, or environmental (PSE) changes based on evidence. These change efforts often are more long-term, exist at the population vs. the individual level and can produce more sustained behavior change. Policies are usually written regulations at a wider community (e.g., federal or state law, local ordinances) or organizational level, while systems changes are rules within an organization. Environmental changes are alterations to physical structures (American Cancer Society (ACS), 2019). Examples of PSE changes follow in Table 8.6:

Table 8.6
Social Support Constructs

Setting	Policy	Systems Change	Environmental Change
General examples	Provision of public land for green spaces	Farm to school programs	Signage for bicycles and scooters Creation of walking or bike paths
Worksite	Healthy and lower calorie options are placed in all vending machines.	Employees receive reimbursement for healthy activities (e.g., screening tests).	Gym is provided onsite to increase availability of physical activity.
School	Schools prohibit the sales of sodas in vending machines and cafeterias.	Local procurement rule for schools to buy locally grown fruits and vegetables for meals	Fruits are available in the main cafeteria; some schools have gardens for growing vegetables.

Food Trust (2012)

Some examples of evidence-based strategies from the Guide for different health topics that are presented in Figure 8.2 (Community Guide Preventive Services, 2019).

Figure 8.2

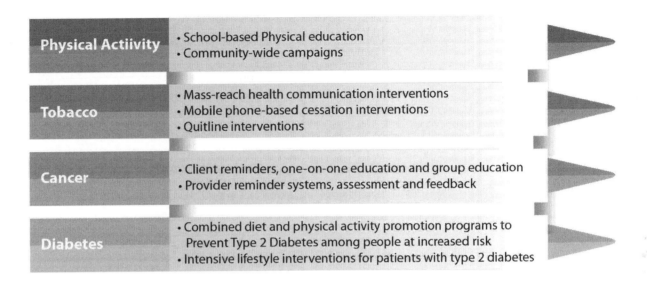

Physical Actiivity	• School-based Physical education • Community-wide campaigns
Tobacco	• Mass-reach health communication interventions • Mobile phone-based cessation interventions • Quitline interventions
Cancer	• Client reminders, one-on-one education and group education • Provider reminder systems, assessment and feedback
Diabetes	• Combined diet and physical activity promotion programs to Prevent Type 2 Diabetes among people at increased risk • Intensive lifestyle interventions for patients with type 2 diabetes

Evidence-based Policies

Hartsfield, Moulton, and McKie (2007) reviewed public health laws, identifying over 100 of them covering a variety of topics, most commonly tobacco control, injury prevention, and school health (Brownson et al., 2009). Only 6.5% of the reviewed laws, however, provided research evidence supporting such legislation (Brownson et. al, 2017).

Policy change to impact health status should include evidence that can be in two forms: quantitative (e.g., epidemiological or economic data, evaluation findings) or qualitative (e.g., health expert testimonies, expert opinions, narrative accounts). Results from studies have shown that the combination of both of these types of evidence has a stronger persuasive impact than one alone. Quantitative evidence may be derived from peer-reviewed journal articles, data from surveillance systems, and evaluation of programs or policies. Evidence-based resources have often been used as evidence for policymaking such as the Guide to Community Preventive Services or Cochrane Reviews (Brownson et al., 2017).

Laws and policies can affect population health and reduce long-term medical and other costs. Examples include:
- broad-based policies, such as smoking bans and laws.
- targeted laws, such as child safety seat laws.
- educational requirements, such as vaccinations for child care and school attendance.
- community-wide interventions, such as water fluoridation.

(The Guide to Community Preventive Services, 2019)

The Community Guide to Preventive Services (2019) (http://www.thecommunityguide.org/about/policy-development) provides information on public health interventions and policies that have been shown to be effective. Some examples of evidence-based strategies are listed in Table 8.7.

Table 8.7
Examples of Evidence-based Policies from The Community Guide

Physical Activity
• Creating or improving places for physical activity • Built environment approaches combining transportation system interventions with land use and environmental design • Interventions to increase active travel to school • Point-of-decision prompts to encourage use of stairs
Tobacco
• Smoke-free policies • Comprehensive Tobacco Control Programs • Interventions to increase the unit price for tobacco products
Motor Vehicle Injuries
• Laws mandating seat belt use • Universal helmet laws • Child safety seat laws

(The Guide to Community Preventive Services, 2019)

Legislators, policy makers, community leaders, and community members interested in specific issues can use these evidence-based policy recommendations to:

- identify what laws and policies promote public health and at what cost.
- draft evidence-based policies and legislation.
- justify funding decisions and proposals.
- support policies and legislation that promote the health of their communities and change policies and legislation that do not.

Authors who conduct Cochrane reviews provide systematic reviews of health care interventions and policy. Each review begins with a research question and interventions, and matching search criteria are found. The authors of the reviews aim to determine if there is or is not conclusive evidence for a recommended policy or intervention. The library is found at http://www.cochrane.org/.

8.1.6 Apply principles of cultural humility, inclusion, and diversity in all aspects of practice (e.g., Culturally and Linguistically Appropriate Services (CLAS) standards and culturally responsive pedagogy).

Regardless of the type of program strategy used, the method for behavior change must fit or meet the needs of the priority population for a program to be effective. The characteristics of the priority population will dictate how the intervention is received. Cultural competence is the ability of a person to understand and respect cultural values, attitudes, and beliefs of various people (Brown et al., 2012). Health education specialists should identify how the characteristics of a chosen strategy fit the population's culture and are relevant to the priority population (McKenzie et al., 2017). Cultural humility is an ongoing process of self-exploration for health education specialists in which they honor the beliefs, customs, culture, and values of the people with whom they work in communities (National Council on Aging, 2019). In health promotion, there needs to be recognition of the balance differences between specialists and the community they serve, importance of partnership and engagement of the community, and the need for holding health agencies accountable for provision of cultural competence practices (Tervalon & Murray-Garcia 1998).

Education and training on cultural competency may be obtained through federal agencies (e.g., Office of Minority Health, Health Resources and Services Administration), academic institutions (e.g., Georgetown University's National Center for Cultural Competence), articles published in peer-reviewed journals (e.g., European Journal of Cross-Cultural Competence and Management), and at conferences (e.g., Society for Public Health Education), among other sources. Other strategies to enhance organizations' cultural competency include identifying cultural factors that contribute to overall health, communicating in a culturally competent manner with patients and communities, and be willing to collaborate to overcome linguistic and literacy challenges in the clinical and community encounters (Expert Panel on Cultural Competence Education for Students in Medicine and Public Health, 2012).

Health education specialists work in various types of organizations. Culturally and linguistically appropriate services (CLAS) are methods to improve the quality of services provided to all individuals and can be applied to these settings. There are 15 CLAS standards that cover the topics of principle standard; governance and leadership; communication and language assistance; and engagement, continuous improvement, and accountability. These standards are located at https://thinkculturalhealth.hhs.gov/clas/standards. Examples of the standards and their practices that could increase culturally appropriate services are offered in Table 8.8.

Table 8.8
Culturally and Linguistically Appropriate Services Standards

Topic	Example of standard
Principal Standard	Offer effective, equitable, and respectful quality services and care that are responsive to diverse cultural beliefs and practices, preferred languages, and health literacy.
Governance, Leadership, and Workforce	Recruit, promote, and support a workforce that is culturally or linguistically diverse and addresses the needs of the population of interest.
Communication and Language Assistance	Offer easy-to-understand print and multimedia materials for the population one serves.
Engagement, Continuous Improvement, and Accountability	Conduct routine community analyses and develop programs or strategies that address diverse culture and language needs of the population. Partner with community to develop culturally relevant programs or policies.

The ability to match a particular program to the needs of the priority population is an essential skill for health education specialists. Disparities or inequities may be identified by gender, income, education, disability, geographic location, sexual orientation, and race/ethnicity (Mas et al., 2010).

According to the Prevention Institute (2014), the root causes of racial and ethnic disparities or inequities fall into four discrete yet often overlapping categories: 1) individual and behavioral, 2) societal, 3) environmental, and 4) medical care factors. See Table 8.9.

Table 8.9
Culturally and Linguistically Appropriate Services Standards

Category	Factor
Individual and behavioral factors	• Sedentary lifestyles • Poor eating habits • Lack of seat belt use • Smoking • Other high-risk behaviors
Societal	• Racism • Economics • Health illiteracy • Limited education • Educational inequality
Environmental	• Poor and unsafe physical and social environments • Viral and microbial agents • Exposure to toxins • Inadequate access to nutritious food • Limited options for exercise • Community norms that do not support prevention
Medical care	• Limited access to health care • Lack of quality health care • Gaps in cultural competence among providers

Adapted from Mas et al., 2010

Health education specialists need to involve the priority population in all aspects of program planning and delivery to ensure that the program addresses their identified health care needs, cultural preferences, and best modes of implementation. Health education specialists also should recruit and mentor diverse program staff to enhance the likelihood of success in reducing morbidity and mortality in any given community.

Culturally Responsive Pedagogy

Culturally and linguistically competent health education specialists value diversity, develop the capacity for self-assessment, raise awareness of dynamics inherent when cultures interact, use organizational processes to institutionalize cultural knowledge, and strive to develop individual and organizational adaptations to diversity (Institute of Medicine, 2002). In the design of health education materials, health education specialists should consider cultural attitudes, practices, and experiences. Delivering programs in a culturally sensitive manner requires conscientious attention by program planners. Health education specialists should provide an environment in which people from diverse backgrounds feel comfortable discussing culturally derived health beliefs and sharing cultural practices. Gonzalez Castro et al. (2010)

described health education as most relevant when relevance, comprehension, and motivation of the community of interest are considered. Health education materials should go beyond development of surface structure (pictures of foods and people, colors representing a culture); they should reflect deeper structures of factors (e.g., history, appropriate theoretical constructs) that influence health. Bernal and Rodríguez (2012) designed a framework of eight overlapping dimensions for understanding and adapting planning for a new culture: language, persons, metaphors, content, concepts, goals, methods, and context. Efforts should be made to understand all of these dimensions in planning educational events or instruction.

When crafting health information, health education specialists should use words and examples in the audience's primary language to ensure information is understandable (USDHHS, 2009). Literacy level, preferred language, and preferred media sources should be considered when delivering interventions. Health education specialist should use design techniques for low-literacy audiences to improve reception of the instruction, including oral delivery (Doak et al., 2002; Parvanta & Bass, 2020; Plain Language Action and Information Network, 2014). When an audience is culturally diverse, matching the source as closely to the audience in key demographics is important to message credibility. Where languages other than English are spoken, health education specialists must take care to ensure accurate translations or develop interventions with that culture in mind to put the behavior into the proper cultural context. Other strategies to enhance cultural competency in pedagogy include assessing needs for bilingual staff, adopting/adapting/creating materials for specific populations, considering the priority populations' learning and programmatic preferences, providing translators, if necessary, through use of in-person resources or language lines, and evaluating the use of health workers and advisors from the communities served.

Competency 8.2 Serve as an authoritative resource on health education and promotion.

Health education specialists are sometimes asked by individuals and partner organizations to serve as an authoritative resource on a particular public health or health education issue as subject matter experts, technical assistance providers, consultants, or in informal resource roles. Health education specialists also may serve on the leadership teams of collaboratives, coalitions, or in consultation roles. Consultants might be asked to facilitate organizations in planning, implementing, or evaluating programs. Consultants can provide services such as delivering educational seminars and skills-based trainings on a health topic or to deliver a program, such as a smoking cessation program, to employees of a company in which a health education specialist is not on staff. Health education specialists also may be sought as a resource for preparing health policy briefs for decision makers, developing talking points for administrative leaders and public information officers, or serving on continuing education committees for conferences and training events.

8.2.1 ▲ Evaluate personnel and organizational capacity to provide consultation.

An effective consultative relationship requires that the health education specialist has knowledge about the health issue/problem, as well as resources, a service-oriented attitude, and skills to provide advice and direction to meet the programmatic goals and objectives of an organization. Consultation or advice needs are similar to training needs. Refer to Competency 1.1 for more information about how to assess needs. The need for consultation should be established by meeting with key stakeholders of the organization, discussing of the reasons for consultation, and reviewing organizational documents supporting the need. Once this information is gathered, health education specialists can assess better the need for assistance and begin the consultative relationship.

8.2.2 ▲ Provide expert consultation, assistance, and guidance to individuals, groups, and organizations.

After the consultative or partnership relationships have been established, health education specialists will provide the assistance needed and outlined in the consultation agreement. Often, the tasks will involve the common skills of health education specialists, including assessing individual and community needs; planning, implementing, and evaluating effective health education programs; coordinating the provision of health education services; acting as a resource person; or communicating health and health education needs and resources. Health education specialists should keep in communication with the client or organization frequently as defined in the consultation agreement. Monitoring progress and keeping open communications with the client will make the relationship more effective.

Technical assistance (TA) is the provision of direct, hands-on aid that builds capacity to complete with quality and prevention tasks (Chinman et al., 2005). The focus of TA is to: (a) develop individual skills and the conditions to use the skills effectively, (b) build effective organizations, (c) strengthen interrelationships between organizations, and (d) create enabling environments for addressing health issues across social sectors. The provision of basic TA is to provide information and support (e.g., materials, overview workshops, tools) in an episodic or short-term timeframe. Intensive TA is required when new knowledge, skills, and abilities are called for and changes will need to occur at multiple levels to support and sustain the change (e.g., organization change, policy change) (Blasé, 2009).

TA methods can vary based on relationship and needs. Some formats of TA include the following:
- One-on-one consultation(s) (e.g., in person, telephone, e-mail, chat)
- Coaching (e.g., observation, feedback, data reviews)
- Group-based capacity building (e.g., group intensives, service learning)
- Informal (e.g., unplanned conversations at conferences) and formal networking among colleagues of similar interest (e.g., communities of practices)

Facilitate collaborative efforts to achieve program goals. Often, health education specialists may be asked to serve as partners, individuals, or groups who work with or convene other organizations to accomplish a shared goal to promote the health of the community. These collective efforts may be called partnerships, collaboratives, or coalitions. Some benefits of partnering are as follows:
- Increasing credibility beyond individual organizations
- Leveraging or maximizing resources
- Improving the reach to the community
- Encouraging organizations to work together that have not done so before
- Creating new ways to bring together novel talents and approaches
- Minimizing the duplication of efforts

(Cole & Sleet, 2016)

Skillful networking can provide health education specialists with an extensive contact list of other professionals working in a variety of settings who can be called upon for guidance, such as opinions, answers, and referrals, when appropriate. Many agencies, organizations, hospitals, and businesses (especially those in which full-time, in-house technical experts are not possible because of low finances) hire consultants to create interventions, conduct evaluations, or make program recommendations. Health education specialists often use the expertise of consultants when planning or modifying their programs.

8.2.3 ■ Conduct peer reviews (e.g., manuscripts, abstracts, proposals, and tenure folios).

Service to the profession is an important part of professionalism for health education specialists. An important service to the profession is to be a peer reviewer for scientific manuscripts and abstracts, grant proposals, and university tenure portfolios. These services are important to ensure that quality research and practice are being published, disseminated, or funded for health promotion.

Peer review of journal manuscripts and conference abstracts. Peer review is a process to ensure the quality of scientific or professional manuscripts and abstracts before articles are published or abstracts are selected. Peer review means that these documents are reviewed by qualified colleagues. In the peer review process, health education specialists will receive instructions on how to review manuscripts or abstracts based on quality or rating criteria. For a manuscript, the journal editors write a summary in which merits, key strengths and weaknesses, and a summative rating to accept, accept with revisions, or reject are identified. International groups have developed guidelines for reporting different types of research or practices and these are housed in the EQUATOR Network. EQUATOR stands for Enhancing the QUAlity and Transparency Of health Research and is found at http://www.equator-network.org/ (Equator Network, 2019). For example, EQUATOR has guidance for reporting different types of trials and studies (randomized, systematic review, qualitative research). For conference abstracts, health education specialists can review them based on established criteria for rating for annual meetings for their professional association or particular sections (e.g., SOPHE, ACHA, ASHA). For examples, ratings may include alignment with the conference themes, importance for the field, and coverage of abstract elements.

Peer review of proposals. Reviewing grant proposals helps innovative and necessary health promotion activities and research be awarded and executed. Health education specialists can review grant applications within their own agencies and for federal/state/local public health agencies and foundations. They can participate in a structured review process that could include written assessment of applications and/or an oral presentation of application assessments. The most important guidance for proposal reviews is to study the application request for application/proposal (RFA) instructions and apply evaluation criteria listed in the RFA and/or those given to the review panel. Refer to Sub-competency 7.4.6 for more information about considerations in reviewing grants.

Portfolio reviews. A tenure portfolio is the package that junior, and sometimes other faculty, in colleges and universities are required to compile and synthesize their research, teaching, and service contributions. Tenure is often an indefinite appointment at a university or organization. The tenure process includes formative and summative evaluations. Formative steps include guidance and reviews periodically with department chairs and/or mentors, while summative reviews happened when the professor submits materials for tenure review. (i.e., going from Assistant Professor to Associate). University department chairs or administrators will request senior researchers or professors in the field (typically 5-10 based on rank) to write letters in support of promotion to evaluate the faculty member. This service allows health education specialists to support the promotion, or tenure, of the faculty and/or researchers in a health promotion department within a university. When accepting a tenure or promotion folio review, a health education specialist will evaluate a particular candidate for attainment based on established criteria set by the professor's department and/

or university. The tenure packet often will include these sections: 1) research/scholarship statement; 2) peer-reviewed publications (if applicable); 2) teaching and mentoring statement; 3) letters from mentees and/or teaching evaluations (if applicable); and 4) service statement (Ortiz et al., 2017). Then, a full professor or veteran person in the field will write a letter in which the candidate's research, service, teaching, and mentoring are summarized. The letter is part of the tenure review packet that a university tenure committee(s) will use in the evaluation of a faculty for promotion.

Competency 8.3 Engage in professional development to maintain and/or enhance proficiency.

Health education specialists commit to a professional career of lifelong learning to stay updated in the field and improve their skills to better serve priority populations. Ongoing professional development not only benefits the individual professional, but also their colleagues, partners, and communities. Professionals can further develop their proficiency in health promotion skills through multi-faceted approaches such as engaging in associations and networks, seeking continuing education, creating a career plan, building relationships, and mentoring others.

8.3.1 Participate in professional associations, coalitions, and networks (e.g., serving on committees, attending conferences, and providing leadership).

Many professional development opportunities may arise for health education specialists from engaging in group settings such as professional organizations, coalitions, and networks. All of these situations offer prospects to grow in communication, networking, and relational skills through interaction with professionals who can share varied experiences and perspectives. Professional associations may offer opportunities to exercise leadership skills by serving on, or leading, committees and work groups.

Participating in local, state, and national professional associations promotes advancement of public health practice and science by helping practitioners stay current on the evidence and state of specific fields of expertise. Professional associations that may be of particular interest to health education specialists are the Society for Public Health Education (SOPHE), American Evaluation Association (AEA), and the American Public Health Association (APHA), which are national organizations with local affiliate chapters. Refer to the National Coalition of Health Education to see a list of health promotion-related professional associations: http://www.cnheo.org/. These associations among others provide growth opportunities through the following participation avenues:

- Attending and planning professional meetings
- Presenting at professional meetings
- Taking courses or skills-based workshops (in-person or distance-based)
- Reading and/or reviewing peer-reviewed professional journals
- Authoring journal articles, chapters, or books
- Providing resources, networking, job announcements, award recognition, and engagement in policy and advocacy
- Connecting people through service learning activities such as volunteering, mentoring, and serving as elected officers

(AEA, 2019; APHA, 2019; SOPHE, 2019c)

Involvement with coalitions, collaborative partnerships, communities of practice, and other networks also can be beneficial for professional growth. These groups may span across communities, professional networks, and multiple sectors in addition to public health and healthcare. Participation can create linkages and benefits such as:

- creating common ground and identity among interdisciplinary and/or multi-sector partners.
- facilitating ownership and trust among collaborators and organizations.
- enhancing learning by bringing together stakeholders with varied experiences.
- building capacity and competence among members and organizations to address community issues.
- advancing public health practice initiatives through tangible partnerships with shared knowledge/experience.

(Butterfoss & Kegler, 2012; Wenger et al, 2002)

8.3.2 Participate in continuing education opportunities to maintain or enhance continuing competence.

Sources of ongoing professional growth for health education specialists can come through job experience, professional training, and education, and obtaining individual certification. Below are just a few national resources for professional development and training to pursue continuing education and pursue increasing competence in specific skills. These training resources in Table 8.10 have searchable databases for the health education specialist to find specific topics and skills based on user needs.

Table 8.10
Sources of Continuing Education Training

Training Source	Description
TRAIN (Training Finder Real-time Affiliate Integrated Network) www.train.org	TRAIN is a nationwide database for on-site or distance learning courses. Some courses are available for free or low cost and offer continuing education credits. A user can store a personal training plan and learning record of competency-based training.
CDC Learning Connection www.cdc.gov/learning/index.html	In this resource, trainings and resources from the Centers for Disease Control and Prevention, other federal agencies, and federally funded partners are featured.
Public Health Learning Network (PHLN) https://nnphi.org/phtcs/	The PHLN is composed of the 10 Regional Public Health Training Centers funded by the Health Resources and Services Administration (HRSA) to train the public health workforce. The 10 centers each have local and national training resources and events including distance-based and in-person competency-based trainings.
Public Health Learning Navigator https://www.phlearningnavigator.org/	The PHLN supports the Learning Navigator, a streamlined, curated searchable database of self-paced online training modules, which are peer-reviewed using distance-based quality learning standards.
Center for Online Resources & Education (CORE) https://www.sophe.org/professional-development/core-elearning/	CORE is an online resource of SOPHE for continuing education and skills related to public health education and promotion. CORE provides CHES®/MCHES® credits to members and non-members. SOPHE and local affiliate chapters also offer additional training and education resources.

Other public health continuing education and training resources can be found through employers, universities, online training sources, and local public health agencies and organizations.

Health education specialists may want to pursue formal academic preparation through an advanced master or doctoral degree. Typical graduate degrees related to health education include the following:

- Master of Education (MEd)
- Master of Science (MS)
- Master of Arts (MA)
- Master of Public Health (MPH)
- Master of Science in Public Health (MSPH)
- Doctor of Public Health (DrPH)
- Doctorate in Education (EdD)
- Doctorate in Health Science (DHSC)
- Doctor of Philosophy (PhD)

The individual's personal plan for growth should help in choosing a degree, as well as college or university. In pursuing continuing education opportunities, health education specialists should be cognizant of how the activities may further develop their knowledge and skills in the Eight Areas of Responsibility. Many health education specialists choose to gain the nationally recognized CHES© and/or MCHES© certification to promote, demonstrate, and continue their professional development. Refer to Sub-competency 8.4.5 for more information on credentialing. Once employed, health education specialists can revisit a professional development plan annually with their supervisor and mentors to continually support their career goals.

8.3.3 Develop a career advancement plan.

Individual professional career plans

A career advancement plan is helpful to set specific short-term, mid-term, and long-term goals not only for a job position, but for an individual's career trajectory over time. As a health education specialist engages in ongoing professional development, different career path options may become more evident and evolve over time. Career decisions can be influenced by a variety of factors including personal passions and interests, talent in certain skills, guidance of mentors, and emerging priorities in communities. External economic, social, and political influences also may play a part in professional maturation.

Professionals should seek ongoing opportunities to grow in both technical and adaptive leadership skills. While technical leadership is focused on known problems with known solutions (e.g., implementing evidence-based programs to improve health outcomes), adaptive leadership is used to addresses complex challenges with no known or "right'" solution (e.g., addressing values and beliefs to shift organizational paradigms about institutional racism) (Heifetz et al., 2009). For example, one might need additional training in rigorous evaluation methodology to measure success of an intervention (a technical challenge). That same person, however, also may simultaneously need training in cultural humility (an adaptive challenge) to interact with a community with deeper empathy and understanding that transcends measurement of the intervention.

Development of competency-based professional development plans (PDPs)

To address multiple dimensions of learning, career plans should be structured using competencies and strategic skills. A health education specialist may start by referring to the *NCHEC Areas of Responsibilities for Health Education Specialists* (NCHEC, 2020) to determine what areas need development and are also most relevant to their interests, current job, and future career needs. The health education specialist also may refer to other competency sets, such as the Council on Linkages Ignite: *Getting your coalition fired up for change Core Competencies for Public Health Professionals* (Council on Linkages, 2014) and the eight strategic skills in the *Building Skills for a More Strategic Health Workforce: A Call to Action* (De Beaumont Foundation, 2017; McKeever et al., 2019). These competency lists can help professionals decide where their individual gaps and needs are to prioritize in which areas they need more training.

Career plans also may be called professional development plans (PDPs), which can be developed for short-term, mid-term, and long-term goals and objectives. These plans are used to document a health educators' goals, required knowledge and skills, and objectives which individuals will need to attain to support their career development. Table 8.11 provides an example of a competency-based PDP addressing an individual's priority training needs and has specific competencies or strategic skills and their sources. In the PDP, the health education specialist delineates the justification why training is needed, steps to take, possible training resources, support needed, and target date for each training priority. The structure of the plan can be tailored to a professional's needs.

While selecting potential training resources for the PDP, the learner should consider the learning needs to match them to the modalities, delivery methods, and complexity of training needed. They may refer to Bloom's taxonomy to determine the spectrum of training needed (e.g., introductory knowledge and awareness, ability to synthesize and evaluate) (Krathwohl, 2002). The learner also should consider whether the training need requires simple, complicated, or complex learning. For example, a webinar may be sufficient to obtain simple background knowledge, but in more complicated tasks that require application, the learner may need longer skills-based interactive trainings. Complex challenges may require ongoing coaching and more frequent or intensive training over time (Snyder 2013; Welter et al., 2018).

Table 8.11
Competency-based Professional Development Plan

Top 3 Priority Training Needs (competency or strategic skill)	Justification (e.g., help with job performance, support agency strategic priorities)	What do I need to do to learn this knowledge or skill? (e.g., take a training, talk to my supervisor, shadow another employee)	Possible training resources (e.g., r4phtc.org, in-house trainings, TRAIN) Note: Consider if need to address simple, complicated, or complex challenges when selecting training opportunities.	What support and resources will I need? (e.g., supervisor's approval, time off, registration fee, request to travel)	Target Date?
Examples: Facilitate the development of strategic and/or improvement plans using systems thinking to promote the mission, vision, and goal statements for health education and promotion (NCHEC Leadership & Management – Sub-competency 7.5.1)	Assist the local health department accreditation team to use systems thinking to update the strategic plan	Take a training course; discuss with accreditation team and administrators	Self-paced module: Introduction to Systems Thinking. New England Public Health Training Center https://www.nephtc.org/enrol/index.php?id=82 Search for local leadership institute or management training cohort for longer term training	Time to participate in module and debrief with team May need to apply to a leadership or certificate program	01/10/2024
Recommends policies, programs, and services for implementation (COL Policy Development/Program Planning Competency 2B8)	Prioritize policy and advocacy priorities for SOPHE Chapter implementation	Participate in module and discuss priority plan with advocacy committee	Self-paced module: Advocacy in Action. SOPHE & University of Maryland https://www.sophe.org/professional-development/advocacy-course/	Request financial support for registration fee from chapter board	04/30/202
Acquisition, retention, and management of people and fiscal resources (de Beaumont Strategic Skill – Resource Management)	Provide feedback to direct report employees before, during, and after performance reviews	Take a training, discuss with supervisors/mentors	*On-demand Webinar: Giving and Receiving Feedback For Personal and Professional Growth.* Region-IV Public Health Training Center. http://bit.ly/2xK4hRi	Supervisor's approval, time to watch webinar, meetings with supervisors/mentors	09/16/2024

Adapted from Creating a Personal Professional Development Plan, Region IV Public Health Training Center (2018) https://www.r4phtc.org/creating-a-personal-professional-development-plan/

Organizational level workforce development plans (WDPs)

At an organizational level, health education specialists may work with their agencies or systems to create workforce development plans (WDPs) for teams or organizations. Accreditation and strategic planning priorities are driving more agencies to create workforce development plans to improve quality in professional development. Competencies and strategic skills also can be used to create these WDPs which in turn may guide individual PDPs. For more information on Competency-Based Workforce Development Plans, visit websites for the Public Health Foundation (PHF), Public Health Accreditation Board (PHAB), National Association of County and City Health Officials (NACCHO) and Association of State and Territorial Health Officials (ASTHO).

8.3.4 Build relationships with other professionals within and outside the profession.

Health education specialists act as liaisons who build relationships and bridge silos between individuals, groups, and organizations within and outside of public health. Often, when health education specialists serve as liaisons and as part of coalitions, they can use their training, skillsets, and experience to assess needs. They also can address group fears and experiences regarding a health issue. Health education specialists may consider how the involved parties listen, reflect, and summarize ideas and questions.

Health education specialists and consultants who serve as liaisons between groups may need the following skills: facilitation, presentation, data collection, meeting management, resource material evaluation, networking, and report writing. They may be asked to facilitate relationships across different groups, coordinate communication, and enhance linkages with other agencies. They analyze and synthesize information about the problem or concern and interpret it for stakeholders. Health education specialists meet with stakeholders, assess the quality and appropriateness of materials, and develop data-driven reports that provide recommendations. They can take action on these steps while keeping in mind barriers and the political climate.

Relationships develop in multiple dimensions within health education, broader public health, healthcare, and other professions and sectors. Bridging gaps by nurturing and maintaining relationships can have an important role in finding and sustaining solutions to advance common public health goals.

Relationships within health education and health promotion

Even within health education, health promotion, and behavioral sciences there are many nuanced groups. Health education may encompass similar skill sets such as assessment, evaluation, and program planning (and other NCHEC Areas of Responsibility), yet there is wide diversity in expertise to share within the field of health education. There are generalists who have a broad sweeping knowledge of the health education field. There are topic-specific specialists in a health issue (e.g., chronic disease, infectious disease, emergency preparedness). Then, there are subject matter experts in specific skill sets of public health education (health equity, social determinants of health, systems thinking, advocacy, etc.). Health education specialists should stay connected to those across the field of health education to learn from one another and bridge siloed thinking. For example, those studying implementation science to disseminate evidence-based practice for cancer prevention can learn from those in HIV/AIDS and injury prevention who are developing similar cross-cutting frameworks, theories, and approaches. Those health education specialists in agencies, departments, and geographic areas who may be struggling may be able to learn from other agencies experiencing success, including positive deviants (the few who find unique and successful solutions) (Pascale et al., 2010).

Interactive relationships with other public health professions

Public health is an extremely diverse field consisting of epidemiology, biostatics, informatics, health policy, management, environmental health, and global health among other specialties. The people in the field of health education must work closely with people in other fields to more effectively improve health outcomes and share resources. Subject matter experts in different fields of public health work together to improve a population's health outcomes. A movement exists to unify diverse public health entities and multi-sector initiatives through braided and blended funding which brings public health, healthcare, and other professions to work together as well. Braided funding reflects combining funding from multiple sources to support one initiative (yet maintains distinguishable strands so each funder can track resources). Blended funding is used to pool funds to collectively meet needs in a way that is not easy to distinguish which funding streams support specific components. This blended model for funding public health not only brings together different public health disciplines, but also multiple professions and sectors to work in concert on community health issues (Clary & Riley, 2019; Urban Institute, 2018).

Interprofessional practice (IPP) relationships with healthcare and clinical professions

Professions in public health is increasingly working with clinical practice, including primary care clinics and healthcare systems. Through interprofessional practice (IPP), teams from different disciplines work together on health promotion, population health, and quality improvement efforts to provide the highest quality of care and preventive services. These may include teams and networks of public health professionals, health education specialists, nurses, physicians, physical therapists, physician assistants, oral health professionals, and behavioral health specialists among others (Reeves et al., 2018). The Practical Playbook: Public Health and Primary Care Together is a book that provides tools, case examples, and resources for primary care and public health to better collaborate to advance population health (Michener et al., 2015).

Multi-sector relationships across professions

Multi-sector collaboration is critical to promote thriving communities and address social determinants of health. Health education specialists and public health professionals need to work in synchronicity with other professionals in professions and sectors such as education, transportation, housing, agriculture, and varied business and industry partners to serve communities more comprehensively. This partnership may occur in informal relationships or more formal networks, collaborations, and coalitions. Public Health 3.0 (PH 3.0) is a model to advance the field and strengthen public health infrastructure through Community Health Strategists that are focused on cross-sector collaboration to leverage data and resources to address social, environmental, and economic conditions that impact health and health equity" (DeSalvo et al., 2017: NACCHO, 2019). PH 3.0 also is used to support recommendations for accreditation, quality improvement, documentation of success with data and metrics, and enhanced sustainable funding models. Multiple tools and initiatives can be used to help advance Public Health 3.0.

Health education specialists can increasingly develop skills to frame public health messages in ways that resonate with other sectors such as businesses or schools, using messages and metaphors consistent with the values and mission of partners. PHRASES (Public Health Reaching Across Sectors) is a workforce development initiative to help public health leaders communicate the value of public health to partners and decision makers in other sectors. Effective partnerships begin with asking partners what they need rather than starting the conversation with what public health needs. To connect meaningfully, health education has a role in helping public health map the gaps in communication, jargon, values, and understanding between sectors (L'Hôte et al., 2019). The PHRASES toolkit, a collaboration of the deBeaumont Foundation, Aspen Institute, and FrameWorks Institute, was developed as a result of framing research. In this toolkit, public health evidence is tied together with communication framing research and testing to help more effectively communicate the value of public health to other sectors. The toolkit includes stories from the field, a resource library about the art and science of framing, the evidence behind cross-sector collaboration, and samples of memoranda of understanding and governance structures for shared decision making (PHRASES, 2020). *The Practical Playbook II: Building Multisector Partnerships That Work* is built upon the prior work of The Practical Playbook (which is focused on public health/primary care partners) to offer practical tools, methods, and case examples about how to leverage resources through multisector partnerships that work to improve population health (Michener et al., 2019).

8.3.5 ■ Serve as a mentor.

Mentoring can take many forms informally and formally. To become an effective mentor, a professional must first be a humble mentee to learn as much as possible from many others continually throughout a lifetime (Youthbuild National Mentoring Alliance, 2020). A person can find multiple mentors for different specific areas of life and professionalism. For example, one might find a mentor for research and another for practice-based leadership. While there is the traditional idea of mentoring the less experienced practitioner, there is also mentorship laterally among peer colleagues, mentoring up, and coaching. Mentoring is assisting another person either with short-term or long-term development through a learning relationship. The mentor is a trusted, faithful guide to the mentee for personal, professional, or career development. The mentee or protégé learns by gaining new awareness, knowledge, ideas, and skills (Connor & Pokora, 2012). A mentor may be someone who teaches or gives help and advice to a less experienced (in general or in a specific area of expertise) and/or younger person (Merriam-Webster, 2014). To grow the profession and elevate its importance in society, it is important for health education specialists to reach out to new and emerging health education specialists to help them develop and build their professional growth.

In addition to informal mentorship, a health education specialist is encouraged to become an official mentor or coach to persons in the profession and help them succeed by finding ways to use their strengths while developing new skills and knowledge. Both parties can benefit from mentoring; it offers the opportunity to exchange skills. For example, seasoned health education specialists can enhance their technology and social media skills, generational perspectives, and cultural humility by working with and learning from younger colleagues. Results from previous research has shown that robust mentorship helps people with their career development and career satisfaction, supports faculty retention, and contributes to academic productivity (Straus et al., 2013). The National Mentoring Resource Center offers tools and guides on mentoring.

Mentors deliberately identify their protégés' talents and strengths. They communicate insights to them and affirm how they can enhance and utilize those strengths. They also help protégés acknowledge fears and areas of improvement in a way that is feasible to tackle and not overwhelming. Frequency and quality of face-to-face interaction enrich mentorship success, so mentors should be accessible and available (Johnson & Ridley, 2008). Mentors also can act as supporting peer partners and learning catalysts for mentees and among co-workers of similar experience and roles. This approach is focused more on the relationships than the hierarchy (Bell, 2013).

Mentoring up refers to a mentee's proactive engagement in the relationship in which the mentee takes on more responsibility for their own learning in a way that both parties mutually benefit from the relationship (Lee et al., 2015). The mentee also can guide and facilitate the mentor's efforts to develop a productive relationship (Youthbuild National Mentoring Alliance, 2020). Moreover, there is increased emphasis on mentors taking a **coaching** approach in leadership. Coaches use insightful questions to stimulate people to expand self-awareness, view the world with different perspectives, and solve challenges. Coaching incorporates more asking and listening rather than "teaching" to help the other person build their own capacity and self-efficacy. A coach supports, challenges, and encourages rather than offering direction (Cotrell & Layton, 2002; Creswell, 2008; Jones, 2019).

Competency 8.4 Promote the health education profession to stakeholders, the public, and others.

One responsibility of health education specialists is to promote the health education profession to stakeholders, the public, and others. This process includes explaining the responsibilities of health education specialists, the history of the profession, and the role of professional organizations and credentialing in advancing professional practice. Health education specialists also may engage in service to advance the health education profession such as serving as a mentor or contributing to professional literature.

8.4.1 Explain the major responsibilities, contributions, and value of the health education specialist.

The Eight Areas of Responsibility of health education specialists include:
  I.   Assessment of Needs and Capacity
  II.   Planning
  III. Implementation
  IV.   Evaluation and Research
  V.   Advocacy
  VI.   Communication
  VII. Leadership and Management
  VIII. Ethics and Professionalism
  (NCHEC, 2019)

The definition of health educators in the United States Department of Labor Bureau of Labor Statistics (USBLS) (2018) reveals that health educators (SOC 21-1091.00) are professionals who "provide and manage health education programs that help individuals, families, and communities maximize and maintain healthy lifestyles. [They] collect and analyze data to identify community needs prior to planning, implementing, monitoring, and evaluating programs designed to encourage healthy lifestyles, policies, and environments. [They] may serve as a resource to assist individuals, other professionals, or the community and may administer fiscal resources for health education programs." (USBLS, 2018, paragraph 1).

8.4.2 Explain the role of professional organizations and the benefits of participating in them.

In professional associations in health education, many of the functions necessary for continuing education in the profession are carried out. The purposes of professional associations include, but are not limited to, conducting continuing education programs, disseminating research findings, legislative advocacy, and establishing ethics and standards for the profession (Cottrell et al., 2009). Refer to Sub-competencies 8.3.1-8.3.5 for details about the benefits of engaging in professional organizations for development, career advancement, continuing education, relationships, and mentorship. The health education specialist should understand the personal benefits and have the ability to convey that benefit to other colleagues, including mentors, mentees, and leaders in the workplace.

The Coalition of National Health Education Organizations (CNHEO) is a collaboration of membership organizations. Members of the CNHEO are listed in Table 8.12. The primary mission of the CNHEO is the "mobilization of the resources of the Health Education Profession in order to expand and improve health education, regardless of setting"(CNHEO, 2020, par 1). CNHEO:
- facilitates national-level communication, collaboration, and coordination among the member organizations.
- provides a forum for the identification and discussion of health education issues.
- formulates recommendations and takes appropriate action on issues affecting member interests.
- serves as a communication and advisory resource for agencies, organizations, and persons in the public and private sectors on health education issues.
- serves as a focus for the exploration and resolution of issues pertinent to professional health education specialists.

(CNHEO, 2019)

Table 8.12
Members of the Coalition of National Health Education Organizations

Member	Mission	Publication
American College Health Association (ACHA)	To advocate and offer leadership organization for college and university health. http://www.acha.org	*Journal of American College Health*
American Public Health Association (APHA)	To be a strong advocate for health education, disease prevention and health promotion directed to individuals, groups, and communities in all activities of the association. To set, maintain and exemplify the highest ethical principles and standards of practice on the part of all professionals whose primary purpose is health education and disease prevention. http://www.acha.org	*American Journal of Public Health* *The Nation's Health*

Member	Mission	Publication
Public Health Education and Health Promotion (PHEHP) • Section of APHA	To be a strong advocate for health education and health promotion for individuals, groups, and communities, and systems and support efforts to achieve health equity in all activities of the Association. To set, maintain, and exemplify the highest ethical principles and standards of practice on the part of all professionals and disciplines whose primary purpose is health education, disease prevention, and/or health promotion. https://www.apha.org/apha-communities/member-sections/public-health-education-and-health-promotion	*American Journal of Public Health* *The Nation's Health*
American School Health Association (ASHA)	To protect and promote the health of children and youth by supporting coordinated school health programs as a foundation for school success. http://www.ashaweb.org	*Journal of School Health* *Health in Action*
Eta Sigma Gamma (ESG)	To foster professional competence and dedication of members in the health education profession. http://www.etasigmagamma.org	*The Health Educator* *Eta Sigma Gamma Student Monograph*
International Union for Health Promotion and Education (IUHPE)	To promote global health and wellbeing and to contribute to the achievement of equity in health between and within countries of the world. https://www.iuhpe.org/index.php/en/	*Global Health Promotion*
National Commission for Health Education Credentialing (NCHEC)	To enhance the professional practice of Health Education by promoting and sustaining a credentialed body of health education specialists. https://www.nchec.org/	*The Health Education Specialist: A Companion Guide for Professional Excellence, Eighth Edition* *A Competency Based Framework for Health Education Specialists 2020* *NCHEC News*
Society for Public Health Education (SOPHE)	To provide leadership in facilitating and promoting initiatives to achieve national health and education goals and objectives. The society promotes effective school programs and practices that involve collaboration with parents and community groups to positively impact healthy and active lifestyles. http://www.sophe.org	*Health Promotion Practice* *Health Education and Behavior Pedagogy in Health Promotion*
Society of State Leaders of Health and Physical Education (SSLHPE)	To utilize advocacy, partnerships, professional development, and resources to build the capacity of school health leaders to implement effective health education and physical education policies and practices that support success in school, work, and life. https://thesociety.org	

8.4.3 Advocate for professional development for health education specialists.

Once health education specialists understand the personal benefits of professional development and can convey that benefit to others, they also may need to serve as an advocate for themselves and other colleagues in the workplace. The health education specialist should be able to justify the investment of time, personnel, and financial resources to participate in professional development such as participating in organizations, conferences, and trainings, and clearly connect the personal benefits to how those benefits directly advance the team or organization's mission (e.g., dissemination of findings, marketing/branding, reaching partners). Refer to Sub-competencies 8.3.1-8.3.5 for details about the benefits of engaging in professional organizations for development, career advancement, continuing education, relationships, and mentorship. The following ideas are different ways to advocate for professional development at individual and organizational levels:

- Demonstrate personal participation in activities and organizations to model the importance of professional development.
- Initiate informal conversations with colleagues and leaders expressing the personal value, priority benefits, and tangible skills gained.
- Gauge readiness and interest of others to engage in local, regional, or national opportunities.
- Share information about available training and professional development opportunities.
- Support mentees and colleagues through sponsorships, award nominations, and encouragement to get involved.
- Suggest teams submit abstracts for presentations at specific conferences that fit the mission of the work place.
- Request financial support to attend conferences, especially if abstracts are accepted to disseminate relevant work.
- Plan in advance to promote attendance (of self and others) based on schedules of conference abstract submissions and registrations.

8.4.4 Educate others about the history of the profession, its current status, and its implications for professional practice.

Advocate for the health education profession

Advocacy for the profession can take on many forms. Attending conferences, educating others about the profession, mentoring young professionals, and advocating for policies to advance the profession are all examples. Many people may not understand the professional role and responsibilities the health education profession requires. By advocating for the profession, health education specialists help to distinguish the profession from others, secure potential jobs, and help improve collaboration between health education specialists and other allied and public health professionals.

Explain the history of the profession and its current and future implications for professional practice

The history of health education in the United States dates back to the late 19th century with the establishment of the first academic programs preparing school health educators (Allegrante et al., 2004) and public health educators (IOM, 2002). Interest in quality assurance and the development of standards for professional preparation of health educators emerged in the 1940s. Over the next several decades, professional associations produced guidelines for preparing health educators, and accreditation efforts were introduced (SOPHE, 1977). Yet, it was not until the 1970s that health education began evolving as a true profession in terms of a sociological perspective (Livingood & Auld, 2001). In addition to defining a body of research, SOPHE and other health education professional organizations began to promulgate a Health Education Code of Ethics, as well as agree upon the use of terminology, a skill-based set of competencies, rigorous systems for quality assurance, and a health education credentialing system (NCHEC & SOPHE 2020).

Beginning in the mid-1970s, the health education profession began the process of developing the steps necessary to establish the credentialing of health educators. This process is outlined in more detail in the publication, *A Competency-Based Framework for Health Education Specialists – 2020* (NCHEC & SOPHE 2020). The landmark Role Delineation Project was officially funded in 1978 (United States Department of Health, Education and Welfare, 1978). Through a series of conferences, workshops, and a national survey of health educators, the responsibilities, functions, skills, and knowledge expected of entry-level health educators were delineated. In the 1985 document, A Framework for the Development of Competency-Based Curricula for Entry-level Health Educators, the Areas of Responsibility, Competencies, and Sub-Competencies were delineated for the preparation and practice of health educators (National Task Force on the Preparation and Practice of Health Educators, 1985). The concept of a "generic role" common to all health educators, regardless of work setting, emerged and formed the basis for the credentialing process for health education specialists (NCHEC and SOPHE 2020)

The planning committee for the First Bethesda Conference in 1978 became the National Task Force on the Preparation and Practice of Health Educators (NTFPPHE). NTFPPHE formally became incorporated as the National Commission for Health Education Credentialing, Inc. (NCHEC) in 1988. In 1989, experienced health education professionals had the opportunity to become Certified Health Education Specialists via a charter certification phase that included meeting eligibility requirements, submitting an application, and a review of documented education and experience. The first CHES® exam was administered in 1990 and is now offered via Computer Based Testing twice a year at more than 400 Prometric Testing centers both nationally and internationally.

The role of the health educator was further defined in a six-year (1998-2004) study known as the National Health Educator Competencies Update Project (CUP), in which the roles of entry- and advanced-level health educators were defined (Gilmore et al., 2005). Results from the CUP study led to the release of a new Framework (NCHEC, SOPHE, & AAHE, 2006), a new study guide (NCHEC, 2007), and revisions to the CHES® examination in October 2007 to reflect the updated Responsibilities, Competencies, and Sub-competencies of the entry-level health educator. Very significantly, the CUP model introduced a hierarchical model in which advanced-levels were built on the entry-levels (Gilmore et al., 2005).

In June of 2008, the CHES® certification program was granted accreditation by the National Commission for Certifying Agencies (NCCA), a government-recognized accrediting body for professional certification organizations. This accreditation signifies that the CHES® exam complies with stringent testing and measurement standards among certification organizations. The NCCA standards require that a certification program conduct a periodic job analysis to verify the Competencies that are the basis of an exam.

The subsequent job analysis was held in 2008-2009 to again validate the contemporary practice of entry- and advanced-level health educators. This 18-month research project, known as the Health Educator Job Analysis-2010 (HEJA

2010) (Doyle et al., 2012) and confirmed a hierarchical model of entry- and advanced-level Competencies. As with the previous study, the results were used to update the framework publications, *A Competency-Based Framework for Health Education Specialists-2010*, and to revise the study material, *The Health Education Specialist: A Companion Guide for Professional Excellence, Sixth Edition* (NCHEC, 2010).

The presence of a hierarchical model of the advanced-level which builds upon the entry-level Competencies confirmed the concept first introduced in the CUP study and led to the creation of a second level of certification. The advanced-level Competencies were first used in the Experience Documentation Opportunity (2010-2011) of current CHES® to obtain the MCHES® first awarded in April 2011. The first MCHES® exam was released in October 2011. The next research study was held in 2013-2014 and known as the Health Education Specialist Practice Analysis I 2015 (HESPA I 2015). The name was changed to reflect the change in the recognized name from health educator to health education specialist. The purpose of this study was to validate the current practice of entry- and advanced-level health education specialists to determine any changes in health education practice since the last major job analysis study, HEJA 2010, and to inform certification, professional preparation, and continuing education initiatives. As with the previous studies, the results were used to update the framework publications, *A Competency-Based Framework for Health Education Specialists-2015*, and to revise the study material, *The Health Education Specialist: A Companion Guide for Professional Excellence, Seventh Edition* (NCHEC, 2015).

The most recent research study was held in 2017-2019 and known as the Health Education Specialist Practice Analysis II-2020 (HESPA 2020). In this study, differing from previous practice analysis, eight areas of responsibility were identified. Most significantly, Area VIII was identified as Ethics and Professionalism, creating one unified place for Competencies and Sub-competencies that were previously interspersed among other Areas of Responsibility.

The health education profession has a proud history of scientifically validating the Competencies that have become the basis of the professional credential(s), professional preparation, and professional development. The Responsibilities, Competencies and Sub-competencies are used to define the profession and distinguish individuals from those trained in other disciplines. See the Timeline for major achievements related to certification for the field of health education.

Health Education Certification History Timeline
- 1978 – National Task Force on the Preparation & Practice of Health Educators was established.
- 1978 – 1981 Role Delineation Project was conducted.
- 1985 – A Framework for the Development of Competency-Based Curricula for Entry-Level Health Educators published.
- 1988 – NCHEC was incorporated as a nonprofit organization.
- 1989 – Charter CHES® certification phase began.
- 1990 – First CHES® exam was given.
- 1997 – CHES® exam was offered twice a year.
- 2000 – Code of Ethics for Health Education Profession was adopted.
- 2005 – National Health Educator Competencies Update Project (CUP) results were released (1998 – 2004 study).
- 2006 – Revised framework, *A Competency- Based framework for Health Educators -2006* was published.

- 2007 – Revised study guide, *The Health Education Specialist: A Companion Guide for Professional Excellence, Sixth Edition*, was published.
- 2007 – CHES® exam was revised based on CUP results.
- 2008 – CHES® certification program was accredited by National Commission on Certifying Agencies (NCCA).
- 2010 – Health Educator Job Analysis (HEJA) results were released (2008-2009 study).
- 2010 – Revised framework, A Competency-Based Framework for Health Education Specialists-2010 was published.
- 2010 – Revised study material, *The Health Education Specialist: A Companion Guide for Professional Excellence, Sixth Edition* was published.
- 2011 – CHES® exam was revised based on HEJA results.
- 2011 – MCHES® certification was first conferred via Experience Documentation Opportunity (EDO) for existing CHES®.
- 2011 – MCHES® first examination was offered. EDO closed.
- 2013 – The CHES® certification program is re-accredited and the MCHES® certification program received accreditation by NCCA.
- 2015 - NCHEC is accredited by International Accreditation Service (IAS) NCHEC to ISO 17024 standard.
- 2015 - Health Education Practice Analysis I (HESPA I 2015) results were released (2013-2014 study).
- 2020 - Health Education Specialist Practice Analysis II (HESPA II 2020) results released (2017-2019 study) containing Eight Areas of Responsibility.
- 2020 – Revised Code of Ethics for the Health Education Profession was adopted.

8.4.5   Explain the role and benefits of credentialing (e.g., individual and program).

Credentialing is an umbrella term that refers to several processes put in place to ensure that persons who deliver a given service have obtained a minimum level of competency (skills, ability, and knowledge). These processes include the accreditation of institutions and licensure or certification/registration of individuals (Cottrell et al., 2012; National Task Force on the Preparation and Practice of Health Education Specialists, 1985; Taub et al., 2009); Certification is the method of individual credentialing for the profession.

The CHES® certification was developed by and for the health education profession to demonstrate the mastery of a set of fundamental skills across all practice settings. The CHES® credential has three components: academic preparation specifically in health education, successfully passing a written exam, and continued professional development (continuing education) of a minimum of 75 continuing education contact hours over a five-year period.

As a result of the CUP and the HEJA 2010 research findings, an advanced-level certification, MCHES®, was introduced in 2010. The MCHES® credential has four components: academic preparation in health education, experience in the field, successfully passing a written exam, and continued professional development (continuing education) of a minimum of 75 contact hours over a five year period, 30 of which must be at advanced-level. "CHES®" or "MCHES®" after a health education specialist's name is one indication of professional competence and a commitment to continued professional development.

NCHEC has committed to maintaining accreditation for the CHES® and MCHES® certification programs through NCCA and the NCHEC organization through the International Accreditation Service (IAS). Among the *NCCA Standards for the Accreditation of Certification Programs* and the ISO 17024 Standards Conformity assessment, there are general requirements for bodies operating certification of persons that a professional role delineation or job analysis be conducted and periodically validated. NCHEC, therefore, has committed to ongoing re-verification of the Responsibilities, Competencies, and Sub-competencies of health education specialists, which has implications beyond certification, including the areas of professional development and professional preparation in the field of health education. Thus, the accreditation standards for certifying agencies have had a critical impact on the progress of the health education profession.

In addition to individual certification, the health education profession has mechanisms for accreditation of institutions/programs preparing health education specialists. Efforts have been made to coordinate the system of quality assurance of health education programs under the guidance of three task forces starting with the National Task Force on Accreditation in Health Education (Allegrante et al., 2004; Taub et al., 2009). The Council on Education for Public Health (CEPH) accredits schools of public health, graduate programs in public/community health, and undergraduate programs affiliated with graduate program. The SOPHE/AAHE Baccalaureate Program Approval Committee (SABPAC), which previously approved undergraduate programs, ended in 2014 as CEPH began to also accredit standalone undergraduate programs in public health. The National Council for Accreditation of Teacher Education (NCATE) and Teacher Accreditation Council (TEAC) accredited teacher preparation programs consolidated as the Council for the Accreditation of Educator Preparation (CAEP) (TEAC, 2014; CAEP, 2015). Until June 2019, the Society of Health and Physical Educators (SHAPE) was recognized by CAEP as the Specialized Professional Association (SPA) in health education. In fall 2019, SOPHE was approved by CAEP to become the health education SPA based on the HESPA II 2020 results.

8.4.6 ▲ Develop presentations and publications that contribute to the profession

From any practice setting, health education specialists can participate in research/practice collaboration, including participating on writing teams for publication in peer-reviewed journals or electronic or print books, that are focused on their content or methodological expertise. Participation as a member of a cross disciplinary team in research or practice initiatives can enrich both health education literature and the other participating disciplines. Health education specialists can stay current with new health promotion concepts through reading one or more professional journals regularly and responding to articles in peer-reviewed journals or letters to the editor or commentaries.

Practitioners can publish lessons learned and evaluation findings in "notes for the field" opportunities in research journals or by contributing to more practice-oriented journals (such as *Health Promotion Practice*). Practitioners and researchers can serve on dissertation or master's thesis committees, co-author articles with masters or doctoral candidates, and mentor them to continue as contributors to the field. Research and practice collaborations also can lead to submission of theory driven practice tested model programs, policies, or practices to listings such as the Substance Abuse and Mental Health Services Administration's (SAMHSA) National Registry of Evidence-based Programs and Practices (NREPP) Evidence-based Practice Resource Center (SAMHSA, 2020). Developing white papers, guides, toolkits, fact sheets, infographics, and reports are additional ways to contribute to the knowledge base in the field.

All health education specialists can submit abstracts or presentations to local, state, and national meetings that can lead to being included as a part of meeting proceedings. Volunteering to be a reviewer for such abstracts or for health education, health communication, health promotion, or related journals not only contributes to the professional literature of the field but also can improve health education specialists' research and writing skills.

8.4.7 ▲ Engage in service to advance the profession.

Health education specialists can engage in service to directly advance the profession and serve in ways that represent the profession. Previous sections have referred to personal professional growth opportunities such as joining local, state, and national professional organizations, serving on committees or as an elected officer, and volunteering as a reviewer for conference abstracts or professional publications. Health education specialists can simultaneously provide service to the field of health education and serve other professionals in the field. Specifically, service to the field of health education may include:

- reviewing abstracts and volunteering for health education conferences.
- prioritizing involvement in health education committees and communities of practice.
- serving on continuing education review committees to approve CHES®/MCHES® trainings and events.
- advocating for credentialing and CHES®/MCHES® to employers.
- promoting CHES®/MCHES® to students, mentees, and colleagues.
- incorporating skills and certification for health education specialists in job postings and professional development plans.

Health education specialists also can represent the profession by serving on boards of local, state, or national health and human service nonprofit organizations or on community health coalitions. They can use their expertise in health assessment or planning to advance these efforts, encouraging others to tap into health education expertise in the future. In addition, they can serve on grant review panels for organizations using the health education perspectives and skills. Recruiting the best and brightest students and colleagues to the profession of health education, engaging them in professional organizations, and mentoring them in various roles and settings is a service that will continue to elevate all aspects of the profession.

Advocating for health education resources and making legislative visits to promote the inclusion of health education in state or federally funded health education, health communication, and health promotion activities are other ways to serve. Running for public office at the local, state, or federal level represents a long-term way to engage in service and promote health education, thus working to reach the "best in advocacy" (Galer-Unti et al., 2004). Health education specialists should seek positions of authority with responsibilities for making policy and apply many of the health education skills to improve organizational effectiveness.

Serving the profession of health education not only adds personal value to an individual's career, but it also inspires the continued engagement of future generations of leaders for successions planning and sustainability of the health education profession. The value of professional involvement and service is unquestionable. Health education specialists can derive the greatest satisfaction through service both to the field of health education and to communities. The struggles, accomplishments, and networking that emerge from working with peers who share a similar interest will help health education specialists develop an appreciation for how much can be accomplished by working collectively to achieve a common goal. More importantly than building one's own personal professional development, service helps health education specialists make connections, develop skills, and gain confidence in their abilities. All of these attributes yield rich rewards and an expansive network of inspired health education specialists that are better equipped and trained to serve communities and promote health equity.

Companion Guide References

Adams, S. A. (2012). Revisiting the online health information reliability debate in the wake of "web 2.0": An inter-disciplinary literature and website review. *International Journal of Medical Informatics, 79*(6), 391- 400.

Aday, L., & Cornelius, L. (2011). *Designing and conducting health surveys: A comprehensive guide.* (4th ed.). Jossey-Bass.

Adler, N., Glymour, M., & Fielding, J. (2016). Addressing social determinants of health and health inequalities. *Journal of the American Medical Association, 316*(16), 1641-1642.

Agency for Healthcare Research and Quality. (2014). *Care coordination measures atlas update.* https://www.ahrq.gov/ncepcr/care/coordination/atlas.html

Agency for Healthcare Research and Quality. (2019). *AHRQ health literacy universal precautions toolkit.* https://www.ahrq.gov/professionals/quality-patient-safety/quality-resources/tools/literacy-toolkit/index.html.

Allegrante, J. P., Airhihenbuwa, C. O., Auld, M. E., Birch, D. A., Roe, K. M., & Smith, B. J. (2004). Toward a unified system of accreditation for professional preparation in health education: Final report of the National Task Force on Accreditation in Health Education. *Journal of Health Education, 35*(6), 347-358.

Allegrante, J. P., Barry, M. M., Auld, M. E., Lamarre, M. C., & Taub, A. (2009). Toward international collaboration on credentialing in health promotion and health education: The Galway Consensus Conference. *Health Education & Behavior, 36*(3), 427-438.

American Cancer Society (ACS). (2019). Policy, systems and environmental change resource guide. https://smhs.gwu.edu/cancercontroltap/sites/cancercontroltap/files/PSE_Resource_Guide_FINAL_05.15.15.pdf

American Evaluation Association (AEA). (2019). https://www.eval.org/

American Psychological Association (APA). (2017). Ethical principles of psychologists and code of conduct. https://www.apa.org/ethics/code/ethics-code-2017.pdf

American Psychological Association (APA). (2019). *Publication manual of the American Psychological Association* (7th ed.). https://doi.org/10.1037/0000165-000

American Public Health Association (APHA). (2017). *The role of health education specialists in a post-health reform environment.* https://www.apha.org/policies-and-advocacy/public-health-policy-statements/policy-database/2016/01/27/13/58/role-of-health-education-specialists

American Public Health Association (APHA). (2019). *Advocacy for public health.* https://www.apha.org/policies-and-advocacy/advocacy-for-public-health

Anderson, M., Perrin, A., Jiang, J., & Kumar, M. (2019). 10% of Americans don't use the Internet. Who are they? https://www.pewresearch.org/fact-tank/2019/04/22/some-americans-dont-use-the-internet-who-are-they/

Anspaugh, D. J., Dignan, M. B., & Anspaugh, S. L. (2006). *Developing health promotion programs* (2nd ed.). Waveland Press.

Companion Guide References

Armstrong, S. (2010). *The essential performance review handbook.* Career Press.

Association for Talent Development (ASTD). (2019). *Five best practices of training and development professionals.* https://www.td.org/5-best-practices-of-training-and-development-professionals-offer

Babbie, E. R. (2016). *The practice of social science research* (14th ed.). Cengage Learning Solutions.

Baciu A., Negussie Y., Geller A., & Weinstein, J. N. (2017). *Communities in action: Pathways to health equity.* National Academies Press.

Baker, D. W., Wolf, M. S., Feinglass, J., & Thompson, J. A. (2008). Health literacy, cognitive abilities, and mortality among elderly persons. *Journal of General Internal Medicine, 23*(6), 723–726.

Ballotpedia. (n.d.). *Lifetime voting records of United States senators and representatives.* https://ballotpedia.org/Lifetime_voting_records_of_United_States_Senators_and_Representatives

Barnlund, D. (1970). *Foundations of communication theory. Communication: The context of change.* In Sereno K. K., & Mortensen (Eds), C. D. Harper & Row.

Bartholomew Eldredge, L. K., Markham, C. M., Ruiter, R. A. C., Fernandez, M. E., Kok, G., & Parcel, G. S. (2016). *Planning health promotion programs: An intervention mapping approach* (4th ed.). Jossey-Bass.

Baumgartner, F. R. (2016). *International encyclopedia of the social and behavioral sciences.* Elsevier.

Baumgartner, T. A., Hensley, L. D., Zhu, W., & Hodges Kulinna, P. (2021). *Conducting and reading research in kinesiology* (6th ed.). Jones and Bartlett.

Baur, C., & Prue, C. (2014). The CDC Clear Communication Index is a new evidence-based tool to prepare and review health information. *Health Promotion Practice, 15*(5), 629-637.

Beaulieu, L. J. (2002). *Mapping the assets of your community: A key component for building local capacity.* http://www.nebhands.nebraska.edu/files/227_asset_mapping.pdf

Bell, C. R. (2013). *Managers as mentors.* (3rd ed.). Berret-Koehlor Publishers, Inc.

Benedictine University. (2019). *Evaluating scores: The CRAAP test.* https://researchguides.ben.edu/source-evaluation

Bensley, R. J., Thackeray, R., & Stellefson, M. (2019). Using Social Media. In R. J. Bensley, R & J. Brookins-Fisher (Eds.), *Community and public health education methods: A practical guide* (4th ed. pp. 149-167). Jones & Barlett Learning.

Bernal, G. E., & Domenech Rodríguez, M. M. (2012). *Cultural adaptations: Tools for evidence-based practice with diverse populations.* American Psychological Association.

Bettman, J. R. (1979). *An information processing theory of consumer choice.* Addison-Wesley.

Bhattacharya, D. (2013). *The research policy brief: A primer.* In D. Bhattacharya (Ed.), *Public health policy: Issues, theory, and advocacy.* Jossey-Bass.

Bhattacherjee, A. (2012). Social science research: Principles, methods, and practices. http://scholarcommons.usf.edu/oa_textbooks/3/

Blase, K. (2009). *Technical assistance to promote service and system change. Roadmap to effective intervention practices #4*. University of South Florida, Technical Assistance Center on Social Emotional Intervention for Young Children.

Bolarinwa O. (2015). Principles and methods of validity and reliability testing of questionnaires used in social and health science researches. *Nigerian Postgraduate Medical Journal*, 22, 195-201.

Booth, V. L., Fierro, L. A., Laurent, A., & Shih, M. (2018). Sub-county life expectancy: A tool to improve community health and advance health equity. *Preventing Chronic Disease*, 15, E1-11. doi:10.5888/pcd15.170187

Borsari, B., & Carey, K. B. (2003). Descriptive and injunctive norms in college drinking: A meta-analytic integration. *Journal of Studies on Alcohol*, 64, 331-341.

Boyce, C. & Neale, P. (2006). Pathfinder international tool series: Monitoring and evaluation: Conducting in-depth interviews: A guide for designing and conducting in-depth interviews for evaluation input. http://www2.pathfinder.org/site/DocServer/m_e_tool_series_indepth_interviews.pdf

Braveman, P., Arkin, E., Orleans, T., Proctor, D., & Plough, A. (2017). *What is health equity? And what difference does a definition make?* Robert Wood Johnson Foundation.

Breny Bontempi, J. M., Fagen, M. C., & Roe, K. M. (2017). Implementation tools, program staff and budgets. In *Health Promotion Programs: From Theory to Practice* (pp.143-170. Jossey-Bass.

Brookhart, S. M., & Nitko, A. J. (2008). *Assessment and grading in classrooms*. Pearson.

Brown, K., Goekler, S., Torabi, M., Hormel, C., Anglin, T., & McKenzie, J. (2012). Report of the 2011 Joint Committee on Health Education and Promotion Terminology. *American Journal of Health Education*, 43, 1-19.

Brownson, R. C., Baker, E. A., Deshpande, A. D., & Gillespie, K. N. (2017). *Evidence-based public health* (3rd ed.). Oxford University Press.

Brownson, R. C., Chriqui, J. F., & Stamatakis, K. A. (2009). Understanding evidence-based public health policy. *American Journal of Public Health*, *99*(9), 1576-1583.

Brownson, R., & Eyler, A. (2016). *Future directions for improving public health through policy*. In Eyler, A., Chriqui, J., Moreland-Russell, S., & Brownson, R. *Prevention, policy, and public health*. Oxford University Press

Bryan, R. L., Kreuter, M. W., & Brownson, R. C. (2008). Integrating adult learning principles into training for public health practice. *Health Promotion Practice*, *10*(4), 557-563.

Buchar, J. (2011). *The barriers and enabling factors to public health advocacy skills in Kentucky local health departments*. Electronic Thesis and Dissertations, University of Louisville.

Bull, S. (2011). Technology-based health promotion. SAGE Publications, Inc., https://www.doi.org/10.4135/9781452230139

Bulmer, M., Gibbs, J., & Hyman, L. (2006, April). *The use of pre-existing survey questions: Implications for data quality*. In The Conference on Quality in Survey Statistics.

Butterfoss, F. D. (2007). *Coalitions and partnerships in community health*. Jossey-Bass.

Butterfoss, F. D. (2013). *Ignite: Getting your coalition fired up for change*. AuthorHouse.

Companion Guide References

Butterfoss, F. D. (2019). *Building and sustaining coalitions*. In R. J. Bensley, & J. Brookins-Fisher (Eds.), *Community and public health education methods: A practical guide*. (Chapter 11). Jones and Bartlett Learning.

Butterfoss, F. D., & Kegler, M. C. (2012). A coalition model for community action. *Community organizing and community building for health and welfare*, *3*, 309-336.

California Department of Public Health, California Tobacco Control Program. (2002). *STORE Campaign*. http://www.tcsstore.org/

California State University Chico. (n.d.). Evaluating information: Applying the CRAAP test. http://www.csuchico.edu/lins/handouts/eval_websites.pdf

Capwiz. (2019). *Elected officials*. https://capwiz.com/nra/dbq/officials/

Castro, F. G., Barrera, Jr, M., & Holleran Steiker, L. K. (2010). Issues and challenges in the design of culturally adapted evidence-based interventions. *Annual Review of Clinical Psychology*, 6, 213-239.

Centers for Disease Control and Prevention. (1999). Framework for program evaluation in public health. *Morbidity and Mortality Weekly Report*, *48*(RR-11), 1-40.

Centers for Disease Control and Prevention. (2007). CDCynergy social marketing edition (Version 2). http://www.orau.gov/cdcynergy/soc2web/

Centers for Disease Control and Prevention. (2010). *Health equity checklist: Considering health equity in the strategy development process*. U.S. Department of Health and Human Services. *https://www.cdc.gov/nchhstp/socialdeterminants/faq.html*

Centers for Disease Control and Prevention. (2011a). *Health marketing basics*. http://www.cdc.gov/healthcommunication/ToolsTemplates/Basics.html

Centers for Disease Control and Prevention. (2011b). *Introduction to program evaluation for public health programs: A self-study guide*. https://www.cdc.gov/eval/guide/cdcevalmanual.pdf

Centers for Disease Control and Prevention. (2013a). *Evaluation reporting: A guide to help ensure use of evaluation findings*. https://www.cdc.gov/dhdsp/docs/Evaluation_Reporting_Guide.pdf

Centers for Disease Control and Prevention. (2013b). *Program planning participant workbook*. https://www.cdc.gov/globalhealth/healthprotection/fetp/training_modules/17/Program-Planning_PW_Final_09252013.pdf

Centers for Disease Control and Prevention. (2014a). *Best practices for comprehensive tobacco control programs*—2014. U.S. Department of Health and Human Services, Centers for Disease Control and Prevention, National Center for Chronic Disease Prevention and Health Promotion, Office on Smoking and Health. https://www.cdc.gov/tobacco/stateandcommunity/best_practices/index.htm

Centers for Disease Control and Prevention. (2014b). *CDCynergy lite, social marketing made simple: A guide for creating effective social marketing plans*. www.cdc.gov/healthcommunication/pdf/cdcynergylite.pdf

Centers for Disease Control and Prevention. (2016a). *What is health literacy?* https://www.cdc.gov/healthcommunication/toolstemplates/Basics.html

Centers for Disease Control and Prevention. (2016b). *Understanding literacy and numeracy*. https://www.cdc.gov/healthliteracy/learn/UnderstandingLiteracy.html

Centers for Disease Control and Prevention. (2018a). *Social determinants of health: Know what affects health*. https://www.cdc.gov/socialdeterminants/index.htm

Centers for Disease Control and Prevention. (2018b). *Resources for writing briefs*. https://www.cdc.gov/policy/polaris/training/policy-resources-writing-briefs.html

Centers for Disease Control and Prevention. (2018c). *CDC Program Evaluation Framework: checklist for step 2, Describe the program*. https://www.cdc.gov/eval/steps/step2/Step-2-Checklist-Final.pdf

Centers for Disease Control and Prevention. (2019a). *Tips from former smokers campaign*. https://www.cdc.gov/tobacco/campaign/tips/index.html

Centers for Disease Control and Prevention. (2019b). *The CDC Clear Communication Index*. https://www.cdc.gov/ccindex/index.html

Centers for Disease Control and Prevention. (2019c). *Health communication basics*. https://www.cdc.gov/healthcommunication/healthbasics/index.html

Centers for Disease Control and Prevention. (2019d). *Understanding the training of trainers model*. https://www.cdc.gov/healthyschools/tths/train_trainers_model.htm

Centers for Disease Control and Prevention. (2020). *CERC templates and tools*. https://emergency.cdc.gov/cerc/resources/templates-tools.asp

Chen, W. W., Sheu, J. J., & Chen, H. S. (2016). Making decisions to create and support a program. In C. I. Fertman & D. D. Allensworth (Eds.), *Health promotion programs: From theory to practice* (pp.121-150). Jossey-Bass.

Chen, X., Hay, J. L., Waters, E. A., Kiviniemi, M. T., Biddle, C., Schofield, E., Li, Y., Kaphingst, K.,& Orom, H. (2018). Health literacy and use and trust in health information. *Journal of health communication*, *23*(8), 724-734.

Chenoweth, D. H. (2011). *Worksite health promotion* (3rd ed.). Human Kinetics.

Chinman, M., Hannah, G., Wandersman, A., Ebener, P., Hunter, S. B., Imm, P., & Sheldon, J. (2005). Developing a community science research agenda for building community capacity for effective preventive interventions. *American journal of community psychology*, *35*(3-4), 143-157.

Clary, A., & Riley, T. (2019). Braiding, blending, or block granting? How to sustainably fund public health and prevention in states (Chapter 36). *The practical playbook II: Building multisector partnerships that work*. https://www.practicalplaybook.org/page/ppb2-table-contents

Clinical and Translational Science Awards Consortium. (2011). *Principles of community engagement*. https://www.atsdr.cdc.gov/communityengagement/pdf/PCE_Report_508_FINAL.pdf

Coalition of National Health Education Organizations (CNHEO). (2019). *Coalition of National Health Education Organizations*. http://www.cnheo.org/

Coalition of National Health Education Organizations (CNHEO). (2020). *Code of ethics for the health education profession*. http://www.cnheo.org/code-of-ethics.html

Companion Guide References

Cole, S., & Sleet, D. (2016). Leadership for sustainability. In C. Fertman & D. Allensworth (Eds.) *Health promotion programs: From theory to practice* (2nd ed., pp. 295-321). Jossey-Bass.

Community Guide to Preventive Services. (2019). About the community guide. https://www.thecommunityguide.org/about/about-community-guide

Connelly, L. (2013). Limitation section. *MedSurg Nursing, 22*(5), 325.

Connor, M., & Pokora, J. (2012). *Coaching and mentoring at work: Developing effective practice.* McGraw-Hill.

Cottrell, D., & Layton, M. (2002). *The manager's coaching handbook: A practical guide to improving employee performance.* The WALK THE TALK Company.

Cottrell, R. R., Auld, M. E., Birch, D. A., Taub, A., King, L. R., & Allegrante, J. P. (2012). Progress and directions in professional credentialing for health education in the United States. *Health Education & Behavior, 39*(6), 681-694.

Cottrell, R. R., Girvan, J. T., McKenzie, J. F., & Seabert, D. (2018). *Principles and foundations of health promotion and education* (7th ed.). Pearson.

Cottrell, R. R., Lysoby, L., King, L. R., Airhihenbuwa, C. O., Roe, K. M., & Allegrante, J. P. (2009). Current developments in accreditation and certification for health promotion and health education: A perspective on systems of quality assurance in the United States. *Health Education & Behavior, 36*(3), 451–463.

Cottrell, D., & Layton, M. (2002). *The manager's coaching handbook: A practical guide to improving employee performance.* Dallas, TX: The WALK THE TALK Company.

Cottrell, R. R., & McKenzie, J. F. (2011). *Health promotion and education research methods: Using the five-chapter thesis/dissertation model* (2nd ed.). Jones & Bartlett.

Council for the Accreditation of Educator Preparation (CAEP). (2015). *History of CAEP.* http://caepnet.org/about/history/

Council on Linkages. (2012). *Improving and measuring the impact of trainings: Strategies & methods.* Council on Linkages.

Council on Linkages. (2014). *Core competencies for public health professionals.* http://www.phf.org/resourcestools/Pages/Core_Public_Health_Competencies.aspx

Couper, M. (2008). *Designing effective web surveys.* Cambridge University Press.

Creswell, J. (2008). *The complete idiot's guide to coaching for excellence.* Alpha Books.

Cunningham, C. J. L., Weathington, B. L., & Pittenger, D. J. (2013). *Understanding and conducting research in the health sciences.* Wiley Publishers.

Dake, J. A., & Jordan, T. R. (2016). Evaluating health promotion programs. In C. Fertman & D. Allensworth (Eds.). *Health promotion programs: From theory to practice* (2nd ed., pp. 245-274). Jossey-Bass.

Davidov, E., Schmidt, P., & Billiet, J. (2018). *Cross-cultural analysis : Methods and applications* (2nd ed.). Routledge.

De Beaumont Foundation. (2017). *Building skills for a more strategic health workforce: A call to action. National consortium for public health workforce development report.* https://www.debeaumont.org/consortiumreport/

DeCenzo, D. A., Robbins, S. P., & Verhulst, S. L. (2016). *Fundamentals of human resource management* (12th ed.). John Wiley & Sons.

DeSalvo, K. B., Wang Y. C., Harris, A., Auerbach, J., Koo, D., & O'Carroll, P. (2017). Public health 3.0: A call to action for public health to meet the challenges of the 21st century. *Preventing Chronic Disease*, 14, 170017.

Diaz-Cuellar, A. L., & Evans, S. F. (2013). Diversity and health education. In M. A Perez & R.R. Luquis (Eds.), Cultural competence in health education and health promotion (2nd ed., pp. 43-65). Jossey-Bass.

DiClemente, R. A., Crosby, R. J., & Kegler, M. C (Eds.) (2009). *Emerging theories in health promotion practice and research*. (2nd ed., pp. 237-276). Jossey-Bass.

DiClemente, R. J., Salazar, L. F., & Crosby, R. A. (2019). *Health behavior theory for public health*. Jones & Bartlett Learning.

DNL Media. (2019). *TakeAction! advocacy and peer-to-peer fundraising app*. https://www.dnlomnimedia.com/products/dnl#takeaction-app

Doak, C. C., Doak, L. G., Gordon, L., & Lorig, K. (2001). Selecting, preparing, and using materials. In K. Lorig (Ed.), *Patient education: A practical approach* (3rd ed., pp. 183-197). Sage Publications.

Doak, C. C., Doak, L .G., & Root, J. H. (Eds.). (2002). *Pfizer health literacy principles: A handbook for creating patient education materials that enhance understanding and promote health outcomes*. Pfizer.

Dorfman, L., & Bakal, M. (2019). Using media advocacy to influence policy. In R. J. Bensley, & J. Brookins-Fisher (Eds.). *Community and public health education methods: A practical guide* (pp. 333-360.). Jones and Bartlett Learning.

Dover, R. V. H., & Lambert, E. V. (2016). "Choice Set" for health behavior in choice-constrained settings to frame research and inform policy: Examples of food consumption, obesity, and food security. *International Journal of Equity in Health*, *15*(1), 48-56.

Doyle, E. I., Caro, C. M., Lysoby, L., Auld, M. E., Smith, B. J., & Muenzen, P. M. (2012). The national health educator job analysis 2010: Process and outcomes. *Health Education & Behavior*, *39*(6), 695-708.

Doyle, E., Ward, S., & Early, J. (2019a). *The process of community health education and promotion*. Waveland Press.

Doyle, E., Ward, S., & Early, J. (2019b). *Communicating health information. In the process of community health education and promotion* (3rd Ed.). Waveland Press.

Doyle, E., Ward, S., & Early, J. (2019c). *Advocating for community health needs. In the process of community health education and promotion* (3rd ed.). Waveland Press.

Dreier, M., Borutta, B., Seidel, G., Kreusel, I., Töppich, J., Bitzer, E.M., Dierks, M., & Walter, U. (2013). Development of a comprehensive list of criteria for evaluating consumer education materials on colorectal cancer screening. *BMC Public Health*, *13*(1), 1-12.

Edlund, E., & Nichols, A.L. (2019). *Advanced research methods for the social and behavioral sciences*. Cambridge University Press.

Egger, M., & Zellweger-Zahner, T. (1997). Language bias in randomised controlled trials published in English and German. *Lancet, 350*(9074), 326.

Emory University. (2018). *Creating a personal professional development plan. Professional development plans for tiers 1, 2, and 3 public health professionals.* Region IV Public Health Training Center (R-IV PHTC), Rollins School of Public Health, Emory University. https://www.r4phtc.org/creating-a-personal-professional-development-plan/

EQUATOR Network. (2019). *Enhancing the QUAlity and transparency of health research.* http://www.equator-network.org/

Escoffery, C., Lebow-Skelley, E., Udelson, H., A Böing, E.A., Wood, R., Fernandez, M.E., & Mullen, P. D. (2018). A scoping study of frameworks for adapting public health evidence-based interventions. *Translational Behavioral Medicine, 9*(1) 1–10.

Expert Panel on Cultural Competence Education for Students in Medicine and Public Health. (2012). *Cultural competence education for students in medicine and public health: Report of an expert panel.* Association of American Medical Colleges and Association of Schools of Public Health.

Eyler, A. & Brownson, R. (2016). *The power of policy to improve health.* In A. Eyler, J. Chriqui, S. Moreland-Russell, & R. Brownson (Eds.). *Prevention, policy, and public health.* (Chapter 1). Oxford University Press.

Eysenbach, G., Powell, J., Kuss, O., & Sa, E. (2002). Empirical studies assessing the quality of health information for consumers on the World Wide Web: A systematic review. *Journal of the American Medical Assocation, 287*(20), 2691-2700.

Fadlallah, R., El-Jardali, F., Nomier, M., Hemadi, N., Arif, K., Langlois, E. V., & Akl, E. A. (2019). Using narratives to impact health policy-making: A systematic review. *Health Research Policy and Systems,* 17. https://health-policy-systems.biomed central.com/articles/10.1186/s12961-019-0423-4

Fallon, L. F., & Zgodzinski, E. (2011). *Essentials of public health management.* Jones & Barlett Publishers.

Fertman C, & Allensworth, D. (2016). *Health promotion programs: From theory to practice.* (2nd ed.). Jossey-Bass.

Fertman, C., Karen A. Spiller, K., & Mickalide, A. (2019). Where money meets mission: Developing and increasing program funding. In C. Fertman & D. Allensworth (Eds.). *Health promotion programs: From theory to practice.* (Chapter 9). Jossey-Bass.

Fink, A. (2013). *Conducting research literature reviews: From the internet to paper* (4th ed.). Sage Publications, Inc.

Food Trust. (2012). *What is policy, systems and environmental (PSE) change?* https://www.communitycatalyst.org/doc-store/publications/Tips_Advocates_Decision-maker-advocacy.pdf

Forister, J. G. & Blessing, J.D. (2020). *An introduction to research and medical literature.* Jones and Bartlett.

Freitas, F. A., & Leonard, L. J. (2011). Maslow's hierarchy of needs and student academic success. *Teaching and Learning in Nursing, 6*(1), 9-13.

Fresina, L., & Pickles, D. (2013). *Power Prism. Tips for advocates: Decision-maker advocacy.* http://healthtrust.org/wp-content/uploads/2013/11/2012-12-28-Policy_Systems_and_Environmental_Change.pdf

Frieden, T. R. (2014). Six components for effective public health program implementation. *American Journal of Public Health, 104*(1), 17-22.

Friedman, R., & Schwartz, M. (2016). Advocacy and public health policy. In A. Eyler, J. Chriqui, S. Moreland-Russell & R. Brownson (Eds.). *Prevention, policy, and public health.* (Chapter 17). Oxford University Press.

Friere, P. (2000). *Pedagogy of the oppressed.* Continuum.

Friis, R. H., & Sellers, T. A. (2014). *Epidemiology for public health practice* (5th ed.). Jones and Bartlett.

Gagne, R. M., Wager, W. W., Golas, K,. & Keller, J. M. (2005). *Principles of instructional design* (5th ed). Cengage Learning.

Galer-Unti, R. A., Bishop Alley, K., & McCoy Pulliam, R. (2016). Advocacy 101. In C. Fertman, & D. Allensworth, D (Eds.). *Health promotion programs: From theory to practice.* (Chapter 7). Jossey-Bass.

Galer-Unti, R., Tappe, M., & Lachenmayr, S. (2004). Advocacy 101: Getting started in health education advocacy. *Health Promotion Practice*, 5, 280-288.

Georgia Health Policy Center. (2011). *Sustainability framework*. Georgia Health Policy Center. http://www.raconline.org/ sustainability/pdf/georgia-health-policy-center-sustainability-framework.pdf

Gilmore, G. D. (2012). *Needs and capacity assessment strategies for health education and health promotion* (4th ed). Jones and Bartlett.

Gilmore, G. D., Olsen, L. K., Taub, A., & Connell, D. (2005). Overview of the national health educator competencies update project, 1998-2004. *Journal of Health Education*, *36*(6), 363-372.

Glanz, K., Rimer, B. K., & Viswanath, K. (Eds.). (2015). *Health behavior and health education: Theory research and practice* (5th ed.). Jossey-Bass.

Gonzalez Castro, F., Barrera, M., & Holleran Steiker, L. K. (2010). Issues and challenges in the design of culturally adapted evidence-based interventions. *Annual Reviews, Clinical Psychology*, 6, 213-39.

Goodman, M. S., & Thompson, V. L. (2018). *Public health research methods for partnerships and practice*. Routledge.

Grabeel, K., Russomanno, J., Tester, E., & Heidel, R. (2018). Computerized versus hand-scored health literacy tools: A comparison of Simple measure of Gobbledygook (SMOG) and Flesch-Kincaid in printed patient education materials. *Journal of Medical Library Association*, *106*(1), 38-45.

Green, L. W., & Kreuter, M. W. (2005). Health program planning: *An educational and ecological approach* (4th ed.). McGraw-Hill.

Hall, N. & Ireland, P. (2016). In Stanford social innovation review: *Transforming activism – digital era advocacy organizations*. https://ssir.org/articles/entry/transforming_activism_digital_era_advocacy_organizations

Hampton, C., & Lachenmayr, S. (2019). Advocating for health policy. In R. J. Bensley.& J. Brookins-Fisher (Eds.). *Community and public health education methods: A practical guide.* (pp. 299-332). Jones and Bartlett Learning.

Harrington, N. G. (2016). *Persuasive health message design*. https://oxfordre.com/communication/view/10.1093/acrefore/9780190228613.001.0001/acrefore-9780190228613-e-7

Harris, M. (2016). *Evaluating public and community health programs* (2nd ed.). Jossey-Bass.

Hartsfield, D., Moulton, A. D., & McKie, K. L. (2007). A review of model public health laws. *American Journal of Public Health*, *97*(Supplement_1), S56-S61.

Hawkins, R. P., Kreuter, M., Resnicow, K., Fishbein, M., & Dijkstra, A. (2008). Understanding tailoring in communicating about health. *Health Education Research*, *23*(3), 454-466.

Health Communication Capacity Collaborative. (2014). *The extended parallel processing model.* https://www.healthcomm capacity.org/wp-content/uploads/2014/09/Extended-Parallel-Processing-Model.pdf

Health Communication Capacity Collaborative. (2020). *Identify a set of SMART communication objectives.* https://sbcc implementationkits.org/sbcc-in-emergencies/identify-a-set-of-smart-communication-objectives/

Health Resources & Services Administration. (2018). *Dictionary of grant terms.* https://www.hrsa.gov/grants/apply/grant-dictionary.html

Healey, B. J., & Lesneski, C. D. (2011). *Transforming public health practice: Leadership and management essentials.* John Wiley & Sons.

Healey, B. J., & Zimmerman, R. S. (2010). *The new world of health promotion: New program development, implementation, and evaluation.* Jones and Bartlett.

Heaney, C. A., & Viswanath, K. (2015). Introduction to models of interpersonal influences on health behavior. In K. Glanz, B. K. Rimer, K. Viswanath (Eds). *Health behavior and health education: theory, research, and practice,* 151-158.

Heifetz, R. A., Linsky, M., & Grashow, A. (2009). *The practice of adaptive leadership: Tools and tactics for changing your organization and the world.* Harvard Business Press.

Hellriegel, D., & Slocum, J. W. (2013). *Organizational behavior* (13th ed.). Cengage Learning.

Hernandez, S. R., & O'Connor, S. J. (2009). *Strategic management of human resources in health services organizations* (3rd ed.). Cengage Learning.

Hinyard, L. J., & Kreuter, M. W. (2007). Using narrative communication as a tool for health behavior change: A conceptual, theoretical and empirical overview. *Health Education and Behavior, 34*(5), 777-792.

Hodges, B., & Videto, D. M. (2011). *Assessment and planning in health programs.* Jones & Bartlett Learning.

Holmes, B., Finegood, D.T., Riley, B.L. & Best, A. (2012). *Systems thinking in dissemination and implementation research. Dissemination and implementation research in health: Translating science to practice.* Oxford Scholarship Online.

Holt-Lunstad, J., & Uchino, B. N. (2015). Social support and health. In K. Glanz, B. K. Rimer, & K. Viswanath (Eds.). *Health behavior: Theory, research and practice,* 183-204.

Indeed. (2020). How to write a professional development plan (with examples). https://www.indeed.com/career-advice/career-development/professional-development-plan

Institute of Medicine, Committee on Communication for Behavior Change in the 21st Century: Improving the Health of Diverse Populations. (2002). *Speaking of health: Assessing health communication strategies for diverse populations.* National Academies Press.

Internal Revenue Service. (2019). *Lobbying.* https://www.irs.gov/charities-non-profits/lobbying

International Centre for Policy Advocacy. (2014). *Choose the advocacy activities that fit the role, process, and objectives.* https://advocacyguide.icpolicyadvocacy.org/641-choose-the-advocacy-activities-that-fit-the-role-process-and-objectives

Issel, L. M., & Wells, R. (2018). *Health program planning and evaluation: A practical, systematic approach for community health.* Jones & Bartlett Learning.

Jack, L., Jr., Hayes, S., Scharalda, J. G., Stetson, B., Jones-Jack, N., Valliere, M., Kirchain, W.R., & LeBlanc, C. (2010). Appraising quantitative research in health education: Guidelines for public health educators. *Health Promotion Practice, 11*(2), 161-165.

Jacobsen, K. H. (2017). *Introduction to health research methods: A practical guide* (2nd ed.).Jones & Bartlett.

Jensen, J., & Krakow, M. (2014). Customization as tailoring 2.0. In T. L. Thompson (Ed.), *Encyclopedia of health communication.* SAGE Publications.

Johnson, D. W., & Johnson, F.P. (2012). *Joining together: Group theory and group skills* (11th ed.). Pearson.

Johnson, J., & Breckon, D. (2007). *Managing health education and promotion programs: Leadership skills for the 21st century.* Jones and Bartlett.

Johnson, W. B., & Ridley, C. R. (2008). *The elements of mentoring.* Palgrave Macmillan.

Jones, C. (2019, November 21). *Leading as a coach and mentor.* https://www.forbes.com/sites/forbescoachescouncil/2019/11/21/leading-as-a-coach-and-mentor/#5ad6affe3bfe

Kahneman, D., & Tversky, A. (1979). Prospect theory: An analysis of decision under risk. *Econometrica,* 47, 263-292.

Kaiser Family Foundation. (2018). *Disparities in health: Five key questions and answers.* https://www.kff.org/disparities-policy/issue-brief/disparities-in-health-and-health-care-five-key-questions-and-answers/

Kaplan, A. M., & Haenlein, M. (2010). Users of the world, unite! The challenges and opportunities of social media. *Business Horizons, 53*(1), 59-68.

Kaplan, R. M., Riley, W. T., & Mabry, P. L. (2014). News from the NIH: Leveraging big data in the behavioral sciences. *Translational Behavioral Medicine, 4*(3), 229-231.

Karlsson, J., & Beaufils, P. (2013). Legitimate division of large data sets, salami slicing and dual publication, where does a fraud begin? *Knee Surgery, Sports Traumatology, Arthroscopy,* 21, 751-752.

Kimberlin, C. L., & Winterstein, A. G. (2008). Validity and reliability of measurement instruments used in research. *American Journal of Health-Systems Pharmacy, 65*(23), 2276-2284.

Kirkpatrick J. D., & Kirkpatrick W. K. *Evaluation.* (2016). ATD Press.

Klasnja1, P., & Pratt, W. (2012). Healthcare in the pocket: Mapping the space of mobile-phone health interventions. *Journal of Biomedical Informatics, 45*(1), 184-198.

Knowles, M. S., Holten, E. F., & Swanson, R. A. (2015). *The adult learner: The definitive classic in adult education and human resource development* (8th ed.). Routledge.

Kolfschoten, G. L., Niederman, F., Briggs, R. O. & de Vreede, G. (2012). Facilitation roles and responsibilities for sustained collaboration support in organizations, *Journal of Management Information Systems, 28*(4), 129-162.

Korlaar, C. V. (2019). *Guide to creating mission & vision statements.* http://topnonprofits.com/vision-mission

Krathwohl, D. R. (2002). *A revision of Bloom's taxonomy: An overview. Theory into Practice. 41*(4), 212–218.

Kreps, G., Thackeray, R., & Barnes, M., (2019). Building a health communication framework. In R.J. Bensley & J. Brookins-Fisher (Eds.), *Community health education methods: A practical guide* (4th ed., pp. 69-92). Jones and Bartlett.

Companion Guide References

Kreslake, J. M., Elkins, A., Thomas, C. N., Gates, S., Lehman, T., (2019). Use of mass communication by public health programs in nonmetropolitan Regions. *Prev Chronic Dis.*

Kreuter, M. W., Farrell, D., Olevitch, L., & Brennan, L. (2000). *Tailoring health messages: Customizing communications with computer technology.* Lawrence Erlbaum and Associates.

Kreuter, M. W., Lezin, N. A., Kreuter, M. W., & Green, L. W. (2003). *Community health promotion ideas that work* (2nd ed.). Jones and Bartlett.

Kwon, H., & Nelson, D. (2016). Communicating research to influence policy and practice. In A. Eyler, J.Chriqui, S. Moreland-Russell & R. Brownson. *Prevention, policy, and public health.* (Chapter 16). Oxford University Press.

Lawson, K. (2008). *The trainer's handbook: Updated edition* (3rd ed.). San Francisco, CA: Pfieffer.

LeBlanc, C. (2010). Appraising quantitative research in health education: Guidelines for public health educators. *Health Promotion Practice, 11*(2), 161-165.

Lehmann, D., Li, Y., Saran R., & Li, Y. (2017). Strengthening instrumental variables through weighting. *Statistics in Biosciences, 9*(2), 320-338.

L'Hôte, E., Volmert, A., Davis, C., & Down, L. (2019). *Public health reaching across sectors mapping the gaps between how public health experts and leaders in other sectors view public health and cross-sector collaboration.* [Unpublished manuscript]. The Frameworks Institute.

Lee, N. R., & Kotler, P. (2016). *Social marketing: Changing behaviors for good.* SAGE Publications.

Lee, S. P., McGee, R., Pfund, C, & Branchaw J. (2015). *"Mentoring up:" Learning to manage your mentoring relationships.* (Chapter 7) The Mentoring Continuum. The Graduate School Press, Syracuse University.

Library of Congress. (n.d.). *Current legislative activities.* https://www.congress.gov/

Livet, M., Courser, M., & Wandersman, A. (2008). The prevention delivery system: Organizational context and use of comprehensive programming frameworks. *American Journal of Community Psychology, 41*(3-4), 361-378.

Livingood, W. C., & Auld, M. E. (2001). The credentialing of a population-based health profession: Lessons learned from health education certification. *Journal of Public Health Management and Practice, 7*(4), 38-45.

Livingstone, S. (2004). Media literacy and the challenge of new information and communication technologies. *The Communication Review, 7*(1), 3-14.

Lloyd, L. S., Loue, S., & O'Shea, D. J. (2002). *Evaluating the advocacy effort. Community health advocacy* (pp. 139-157). Springer.

Longest, B. B., Jr. (2011). *Managing health programs and projects.* Jossey-Bass.

Malterud, K. (2012). Systematic text condensation: A strategy for qualitative analysis. *Scandinavian Journal of Public Health, 40*(8), 795-805.

Mas, F. S., Allensworth, D. D., Jones, C. P., & Jacobson, H. E. (2010). Making decisions to create and support a program. In C. I. Fertman & D. D. Allensworth (Eds.), *Health promotion programs: From theory to practice* (Chapter 2). Jossey-Bass.

Mattson, M., & Lam, C. (2016). *Health advocacy: A communication approach.* Peter Lang Publishing.

McCrorie, A. D., Donnelly, C., & McGlade, K. J. (2016). Infographics: Healthcare communication for the digital age. *Ulster Medical Journal, 85*(2), 71-75.

McGuire, W. J. (1984). Public communication as a strategy for inducing health-promoting behavioral change. *Preventive Medicine, 13*(3), 299–313.

McKeever, J., Leider, J. P., Alford, A. A., & Evans, D. (2019). Regional training needs assessment: A first look at high-priority training needs across the United States by region. *Journal of Public Health Management and Practice, 25*(2), S166-S176.

McKenzie, J. F., & Neiger B. L., Thackeray R. (2017). *Planning, implementing & evaluating health promotion programs: A primer* (7th ed.). Pearson.

McRobert, C. J., Hill, J. C., Smale, T., Hay, E. M., & van der Windt, D. A. (2018). A multi-modal recruitment strategy using social media and internet-mediated methods to recruit a multidisciplinary, international sample of clinicians to an online research study. *PLOS ONE, 13*(7), e0200184.

Merriam, S. B., & Baumgartner, L.M. (2020). *Learning in adulthood: A comprehensive guide* (4th ed.). Wiley.

Merriam-Webster. (2014). *Social media.* http://www.merriam-webster.com/dictionary/socialmedia

Michener, J. L., Koo, D., Castrucci, B. C., & Sprague, J. B. (Eds.). (2015). *The practical playbook: Public health and primary care together.* Oxford University Press.

Michener, L., Castrucci, B. C., Bradley, D. W., Hunter, E. L., Thomas, C. W., Patterson, C. & Corcoran E. (Eds.). (2019). *Practical playbook II: Building multisector partnerships that work.* Oxford University Press. https://www.practicalplaybook.org/page/ppb2-table-contents

Miles, M. B., Huberman, A. M., & Saldana, J. (2019). *Qualitative data analysis.* Sage Publishing.

Minelli, M. J., & Breckon, D. J. (2009). *Community health education: Settings, roles, and skills for the 21st century* (5th ed.). Jones and Barlett.

Miner, J. T., & Ball, K. C. (2019). *Proposal planning & writing* (6th ed). ABC-CLIO.

Miner, J. T., & Miner, L. E. (2013). *Proposal planning & writing* (5th ed). ABC-CLIO.

Montano, D. E., & Kasprzyk, D. (2015). Theory of reasoned action, theory of planned behavior, and the integrated behavioral model. In K. Glanz, B. R. Rimer & K. Viswanath (Eds). *Health behavior: Theory, research and practice.* Jossey-Bass.

Moore, J. E., Bumbarger, B. K., & Cooper, B. R. (2013). Examining adaptations of evidence-based programs in natural contexts. *The Journal of Primary Prevention, 34*(3), 147-161.

Murphy, M., Staffileno, B., & Foreman, M. (2017). *Research for advanced practice nurses: From evidence to practice* (3rd ed.). Springer.

Nabi, R. L., & Green, M. C. (2015). The role of narrative's emotional flow in promoting persuasive outcomes. *Media Psychology, 18,* 137-162.

National Academies of Sciences, Engineering, and Medicine. (2017). *Communities in action: Pathways to health equity.* The National Academies Press.

National Association for County and City Health Officials (NACCHO). (2019). *Mobilizing for action through planning and partnerships (MAPP)*. https://www.naccho.org/programs/public-health-infrastructure/performance-improvement/community-health-assessment/mapp

National Association for County and City Health Officials (NACCHO). (2019). *Public health 3.0*. https://www.naccho.org/programs/public-health-infrastructure/public-health-3-0

National Cancer Institute (NCI). (2005). *Theory at a glance* (2nd ed.). NCI.

National Cancer Institute (NCI). (2008). *Making health communication programs work : A planner's guide. U.S. Dept. of Health and Human Services*, Public Health Service, National Institutes of Health, [Office of Cancer Communications, National Cancer Institute].

National Cancer Institute (NCI). (2014). *Evaluating online sources of health education*. http://www.cancer.gov/cancertopics/cancerlibrary/health-info-online

National Cancer Institute (NCI). (2015). *Using trusted resources*. http://www.cancer.gov/cancertopics/managing-care/using-trusted-resources

National Center on Quality Teaching and Learning. (2014). *Creating a learning environment for children*. http://eclkc.ohs.acf.hhs.gov/hslc/tta-system/teaching/eecd/learning%20environments/planning%20and%20arranging%20spaces/edudev_art_00400_060906.html

National Commission for the Protection of Human subjects of Biomedical and Behavioral Research. (1979). *Belmont report*. https://www.hhs.gov/ohrp/sites/default/files/the-belmont-report-508c_FINAL.pdf

National Commission for Health Education Credentialing. (2007). *The health education specialist: A companion guide for professional excellence* (5th ed). Author.

National Commission for Health Education Credentialing. (2010). *The health education specialist: A companion guide for professional excellence* (6th ed). Author.

National Commission for Health Education Credentialing. (2015). *The health education specialist: A companion guide for professional excellence* (7th ed). Author.

National Commission for Health Education Credentialing. (2019). *Responsibilities and competencies for health education specialists*. https://www.nchec.org/responsibilities-and-competencies

National Commission for Health Education Credentialing, Inc., & Society for Public Health Education. (2020). *A competency-based framework for health education specialists – 2020*. Author.

National Commission for Health Education Credentialing, Inc., Society for Public Health Education, & American Association for Health Education. (2006). *A competency-based framework for health educators – 2006*. Author.

National Commission for the Protection of Human Subjects of Biomedical and Behavioral Research, & U.S. Department of Health and Human Services. (1979). *Belmont report*. https://www.hhs.gov/ohrp/regulations-and-policy/belmont-report/index.html

National Conference of State Legislatures. (2019). *You have to know the rules*. http://www.ncsl.org/research/about-state-legislatures/glossary-of-legislative-terms.aspx

National Council. (2017). *A handbook for advocates.* https://www.thenationalcouncil.org/wp-content/uploads/2017/07/AdvocateHandbook-v9.pdf?daf=375ateTbd56

National Council on Aging. (2019). *Cultural humility.* https://www.ncoa.org/article/cultural-humility-webinar

National Council on Nonprofits. (2019). *Why diversity, equity, and inclusion matter for nonprofits.* https://www.councilofnonprofits.org/tools-resources/why-diversity-equity-and-inclusion-matter-nonprofits

National Implementation Research Network. (2014). *Implementation defined.* https://nirn.fpg.unc.edu/resources/practice-profile-planning-tool

National Institute on Aging. (2018). *Online health information: Is it reliable?* https://www.nia.nih.gov/health/online-health-information-it-reliable

National Institutes of Health. (2012). *NIH policies and procedures for promoting scientific integrity.* NIH Office of the Director.

National Library of Medicine. (2009). *Resources: A user's guide to finding and evaluating health information on the web.* http://www.mlanet.org/resources/userguide.html

National Prevention Information Network. (n.d.). *HIV/AIDS training.* https://npin.cdc.gov/training/hiv/hiv

National Task Force on the Preparation and Practice of Health Educators. (1985). *Framework for the development of competency-based curricula for entry-level health educators.* Author.

Neiger, B. L., Thackeray, R., Van Wagenen, S. A., Hanson, C. L., West, J. H., Barnes, M. D. & Fagen, M. C. (2012). Use of social media in health promotion: Purposes, key performance indicators, and evaluation metrics. *Health Promotion Practice, 13*(2), 159-164.

Neutens, J. J., & Rubinson, L. (2014). *Research techniques for health sciences* (5th ed.) Pearson.

Noar, S. M., Harrington, N. G., & Aldrich, R. S. (2009). The role of message tailoring in the development of persuasive health communication messages. In C. S. Beck (Ed.), *Communication yearbook.* Taylor & Francis Group.

Noar, S. M., & Van Stee, S. K. (2012). Designing messages for individuals in different stages of change. In H. Cho (Ed.), *Health communication message design: Theory and practice.* SAGE Publications, Inc.

Northwest Center for Public Health Practice. (2020). *Effective adult learning: A toolkit for teaching adults.* https://www.nwcphp.org/training/effective-adult-learning-a-toolkit-for-teaching-adults

Occupational Health and Safety Administration (OSHA). (n.d.). *Best practices for development, delivery, and evaluation of Susan Harwood training grants.* https://www.osha.gov/harwoodgrants/best-practices

Olson, S. J. (2010). Partnerships and collaboration, critical components to promoting health. In Healey and Zimmerman (Eds), *The New World of Health Promotion.* Jones and Bartlett.

Ortiz, A. M., Haviland, D, & Henriques, L. (2017). *The road to tenure: Understanding the process.* https://www.insidehighered.com/advice/2017/10/26/guidance-process-gaining-tenure-essay

Paige, S. R., Krieger, J. L., & Stellefson, M. (2017). The influence of eHealth literacy on perceived trust in online health communication channels and sources. *Journal of Health Communication, 22*(1), 53-65.

Companion Guide References

Paige, S. R., Stellefson, M., Krieger, J., Anderson-Lewis, C., Cheong, J., & Stopka, C. (2018). Proposing a transactional model of eHealth literacy: Concept analysis. *Journal of Medical Internet Research*, *20*(10), e10175.

Parvanta, C. (2011). Public health communication: a planning framework. In C. F. Parvanta, D. E. Nelson, S. A. Parvanta, & R. N. Harner (Eds.), *Essentials of public health communication* (pp. 19-38). Jones and Bartlett Learning.

Parvanta, C. F., & Bass, S. B. (2020). *Health communication: Strategies and skills for a new era.* Jones & Barlett.

Parvanta, C. F., Nelson, D. E., & Harner, R. N. (2018). *Public health communication: Critical tools and strategies.* Jones & Bartlett Learning.

Pascale, R. T., Sternin, J., & Sternin, M. (2010). *The power of positive deviance: How unlikely innovators solve the world's toughest problems.* Harvard Business Press.

Patton, M. Q. (2011). *Essentials of utilization-focused evaluation.* Sage.

Patton, M. Q. (2015). *Qualitative research and evaluation methods* (4th ed.). Sage.

Perkins, H. W., & Berkowitz, A. D. (1986). Perceiving the community norms of alcohol use among students: Some research implications for campus alcohol education programming. *International Journal of Addiction*, *21*, 961–976.

Perrin, A., & Andersen, M. (2019). Share of U.S. adults using social media, including Facebook, is mostly unchanged since 2018. https://www.pewresearch.org/fact-tank/2019/04/10/share-of-u-s-adults-using-social-media-including-facebook-is-mostly-unchanged-since-2018/

Peters, E., Hibbard, J., Slovic, P., & Dieckmann, N. (2007). Numeracy skill and the communication, comprehension, and use of risk-benefit information. *Health Affairs*, *26*(3), 741-748.

Petty, R. E., Barden, J., & Wheeler, S. C. (2009). The elaboration likelihood model persuasion: Developing health promotions for sustained behavioral change. In R. J. DiClemente, R. A. Crosby & M. C. Kegler (Eds.), *Emerging theories in health promotion practice and research* (2nd ed., pp. 185-214). Josey-Bass.

Pew-MacArthur Foundation. (2016). *Implementation oversight for evidence-based programs: A policymaker's guide to effective program delivery.* https://www.pewtrusts.org/-/media/assets/2016/05/rf_programimplementationbrief.pdf

Plain Language and Information Network. (2019). *Plain language.* https://www.plainlanguage.gov/

Plomer, K. D. & Bensley, R. J. (2009). Developing and selecting print materials. In R.J. Bensley & J. Brookins Fisher (Eds.), *Community health education methods: A practical guide* (3rd ed.) (pp. 209-236). Jones and Bartlett.

Ponto J. (2015). Understanding and evaluating survey research. *Journal of the Advanced Practitioner in Oncology*, *6*(2), 168-171.

Porta, M. (2014). *A dictionary of epidemiology.* (6th ed.). Oxford University Press.

Practice Development. (2008). SAM Suitability Assessment of Materials for evaluation of health-related information for adults. http://aspiruslibrary.org/literacy/sam.pdf

Prevention Institute. (2014). Developing effective coalitions: An eight-step guide. https://www.preventioninstitute.org/publications/developing-effective-coalitions-an-eight-step-guide

Prochaska, J. O., Redding, C. A., & Evers, K. E. (2015). The transtheoretical model and stages of change. *Health behavior: Theory, Research, and Practice*, 125-148.

Project Management Institute. (2019). *What is project management?* https://www.pmi.org/about/learn-about-pmi/what-is-project-management

Public Health Reaching Across Sectors (PHRASES). (2020). *An initiative and toolkit of the de Beaumont Foundation.* https://www.phrases.org/

R Core Team. (2017). *R: A language and environment for statistical computing. R Foundation for Statistical Computing* https://www.R-project.org/

Reeves, S, Xyrichis, A, & Zwarenstein, M. (2018). Teamwork, collaboration, coordination, and networking: Why we need to distinguish between different types of interprofessional practice. *Journal of Interprofessional Care*, 32, 1–3.

Region IV Public Health Training Center *(R-IV PHTC)*. (2018). *Creating a personal professional development plan* https://www.r4phtc.org/creating-a-personal-professional-development-plan/

Resnick, E., & Siegel, M. (2013). *Marketing public health: Strategies to promote social change.* Jones & Bartlett. (3rd ed.).

Riegelman, R., & Kirkwood, B. (2019). *Public health 101: Improving community health*, (3rd ed.).

Riley, K .E., Ulrich, M. R., Hamann, H. A., & Ostroff, J. (2017). Decreasing smoking but increasing stigma? Anti-tobacco campaigns, public health, and cancer care. *American Medical Association Journal of Ethics*, 19(5), 475-485.

Robert Wood Johnson Foundation. (2018). *Could where you live influence how long you live?* https://www.rwjf.org/en/library/interactives/whereyouliveaffectshowlongyoulive.html

Robbins, S. P., Judge, T. A., & Millett, B. (2015). *Organization behavior: The essentials.* Pearson Higher Education AU.

Rogers, E. M. (2003). *Diffusion of innovations* (3rd ed.). Free Press.

Rogers, R. W., & Prentice-Dunn, S. (1997). Protection motivation theory. In D. Gochman (Ed.), *Handbook of health behavior research: Vol. 1. personal and social determinants* (pp. 113-132). Plenum.

Rosenstock, I. M., Strecher, V. J., & Becker, M. H. (1988). Social learning theory and the health belief model. *Health education quarterly*, 15(2), 175-183.

Rowitz, L. (2013). *Public health leadership: Putting principles into practice* (3rd ed.). Jones & Bartlett.

Rudd, J., & Glanz, K. (1990). How individuals use information for health action and consumer information processing. In K. Glanz, F. Lewis & B. Rimer Eds.). *Health behavior and health education: Theory, research and practice.* Jossey-Bass.

Sage. (2018). *The SAGE handbook of qualitative data collection.* Author.

Saks, A. M., Haccoun, R. R., & Belcourt, M. (2010). *Managing performance through training and development.* Cengage Learning.

Salazar, L. F., Crosby, R. A., & DiClemente, R. J. (2015). *Research methods in health promotion* (2nd ed.). Jossey-Bass.

Sallis, J. F., & Owen, N. (2015). Ecological models of health behavior. In K. Glanz, B. K. Rimer, & K. V. Viswanath (Eds.), *Health behavior: Theory, research, and practice* (pp. 43-64). Jossey-Bass.

Sarris, W. E. (2014). *Design, evaluation, and analysis of questionnaires for survey research* (2nd ed.). Wiley.

Companion Guide References

Schiavo, R. (2013). *Health Communication: From theory to practice* (2nd ed.). Jossey Bass.

Seper, M., Patzer, R. E., Curtis, L. M., Smith, S. G., O'Conor, R., Baker, D. W., & Wolf, M. S. (2014). Health literacy, cognitive ability, and functional health status among older adults. *Health Services Research, 49*(4), 1249–1267.

Sharma, M. (2017). *Theoretical foundations of health education and health promotion.* Jones & Bartlett.

Sharma, M., & Petosa, R. L. (2014). *Measurement and evaluation for health educators.* Jones & Bartlett.

Shi, L., & Johnson, J. A. (2013). *Novick & Morrow's public health administration: Principles for population-based management.* Jones and Bartlett.

Simons-Morton, B. G., Greene, W. H., & Gottlieb, N. H. (1995). *Introduction to health education and health promotion* (2nd ed.). Waveland Press.

Simons-Morton, B., McLeroy, K. R., & Wendel, M. L. (2012). *Behavior theory in health promotion practice and research.* Jones and Bartlett Learning.

Sleezer, C. M., Russ-Eft, D. F., Gupta, K. (2014). *A practical guide to needs assessment* (3rd ed). Wiley.

Snyder, S. (2013). *The Simple, the complicated, and the complex: Educational reform through the lens of complexity theory.* OECD Education Working Papers, No. 96, OECD Publishing. http://dx.doi.org/10.1787/5k3txnpt1lnr-en

Society for Public Health Education. Ad Hoc Task Force on Professional Preparation and Practice of Health Education. (1977). Guidelines for the preparation and practice of professional health educators. *Health Education Monographs, 5*(1), 75-89.

Society for Public Health Education. (2019a). *Advocacy summit.* https://www.sophe.org/advocacy/advocacy-summit/

Society for Public Health Education. (2019b). *Take action!* https://www.sophe.org/advocacy/take-action/#/

Society for Public Health Education (SOPHE). (2019c). *Membership and membership benefits.* https://www.sophe.org/membership/

Society for Public Health Education (SOPHE). (2020). *Resolution for addressing the health impact on climate change.* https://www.sophe.org/wp-content/uploads/2020/05/Final-SOPHE-Climate-Change-Resolution-5.4.20-2.pdf

Souza, A., Alexandre, N., & Guirardello, E. (2017). Psychometric properties in instruments evaluation of reliability and validity. *Epidemiologia e serviços de saúde, 26*(3), 649-659.

Stamatakis, K. A., McBride, T. D., & Brownson, R. C. (2010). Communicating prevention messages to policy makers: The role of stories in promoting physical activity. *Journal of Physical Activity and Health, 7*(Suppl 1), S99-S107.

Sterne, J. (2010). *Social media metrics: How to measure and optimize your marketing investment.* John Wiley.

Straus, S. E., Johnson, M. O., Marquez, C., & Feldman, M. D. (2013). Characteristics of successful and failed mentoring relationships: a qualitative study across two academic health centers. *Academic Medicine, 88*(1), 82.

Strunke, W., & A-Morelli, R. D. (2018). *Elements of style.* Spectrum Inc.

Substance Abuse and Mental Health Services Administration (SAMHSA). (2012). *The non-researcher's guide to evidence-based program evaluation.* http://www.eblcprograms.org/docs/pdfs/NREPP_Non-researchers_guide_to_eval.pdf

Substance Abuse and Mental Health Services Administration (SAMHSA). (2020). Evidence-based practice resource center. https://www.samhsa.gov/ebp-resource-center

Tannenbaum, M. B., Hepler, J., Zimmerman, R. S., Saul, L., Jacobs, S., Wilson, K., & Albarracin, D. (2015). Appealing to fear: A meta-analysis of fear appeal effectiveness and theories. *Psychological Bulletin*, *141*(6), 1178-1204.

Taub, A., Birch, D. A., Auld, M. E., Lysoby, L., & Rasar King, L. (2009). Strengthening quality assurance in health education: Recent milestones and future directions. *Health Promotion Practice*, 10(2), 192-200.

Taub, A., Goekler, S., Auld, M. E., Birch, D. A., Muller, S., Wengert, D., & Allegrante, J. P. (2014). Accreditation of professional preparation programs for school health educators: The changing landscape. *Health Education & Behavior*, *41*(4), 349-358.

Teacher Education Accreditation Council (TEAC). (2014). https://www.chea.org/teacher-education-accreditation-council

Tervalon, M., & Murray-García, J., (1998). Cultural humility versus cultural competence: A critical distinction in defining physician training outcomes in multicultural education. *Journal of Health Care for the Poor and Underserved*, 2, 177-124.

The Guide to Community Preventive Services. (2019). *The community guide*. https://www.thecommunityguide.org/

Theodoulou, S. Z., & Cahn, M. A. (2013). *Public policy: The essential readings*. Pearson Education.

Tolley, E. E. (2016). *Qualitative methods in public health : A field guide for applied research* (2nd ed.). Jossey-Bass.

Trust for America's Health (TFAH). (2018, September). *Issue brief: Braiding and blending funds to support community health improvement: A compendium of resources and examples*. https://www.tfah.org/wp-content/uploads/2018/01/TFAH-Braiding-Blending-Compendium-FINAL.pdf

United Nations Development Programme. (2008). *Capacity assessment methodology user's guide. UNDP*. https://www.undp.org/content/dam/aplaws/publication/en/publications/capacity-development/undp-capacity-assessment-methodology/UNDP%20Capacity%20Assessment%20Users%20Guide.pdf

United States Bureau of Labor and Statistic (BLS). (2018). *Occupational employment and wages, May 2018 21-1091 Health Educators. Occupational employment statistics*. https://www.bls.gov/oes/current/oes211091.htm

United States Centers for Medicare and Medicaid Services. (n.d.). *Read the affordable care act*. https://www.healthcare.gov/where-can-i-read-the-affordable-care-act/

United States Department of Health, Education, and Welfare. (1978). *Preparation and practice of community, patient and school health educators: Proceedings of the workshop on commonalities and differences*. Author.

United States Department of Health and Human Services. (2020). *Healthy people 2030*. https://health.gov/healthypeople

United States Department of Health and Human Services, Health Resources and Services Administration [HRSA]. (2019). *Rural health information hub*. https://www.ruralhealthinfo.org/toolkits/health-promotion/2/strategies/health-communication

United States Department of Health and Human Services, Office of Disease Prevention and Health Promotion. (2009). *Quick guide to health literacy*. https://health.gov/healthliteracyonline/2010/Web_Guide_Health_Lit_Online.pdf

United States Department of Health and Human Services, Office of Disease Prevention and Health Promotion. (2010). *National action plan to improve health literacy*. Author.

Companion Guide References

United States Department of Health and Human Services, Office of Disease Prevention and Health Promotion. (2014). *Healthy people 2020: Health communication and health information technology*. https://www.healthypeople.gov/2020/topics-objectives/topic/health-communication-and-health-information-technology

United States Department of Health and Human Services. (2014). *Information collection/paperwork reduction act*. http://www.hhs.gov/ocio/policy/collection

United States Department of Justice. (2014). *A comprehensive tool for federal employees who work with comprehensive community initiatives*. https://www.hhs.gov/cto/initiatives/open-innovation/faqs/index.html#pra

United States Federal Election Commission. (2020). *Political action committees (PACs)*. https://www.fec.gov/press/resources-journalists/political-action-committees-pacs/

United States General Services Administration. (2018). *Section 508 laws*. http://www.section508.gov/section508-laws

United States Senate. (n.d.). *Glossary terms*. https://www.senate.gov/reference/glossary_term/act.htm

United States Department of Health and Human Services. (2011). *HHS action plan to reduce racial and ethnic health disparities*. Author. http://minorityhealth.hhs.gov/npa/files/plans/hhs/hhs_plan_complete.pdf

United States Department of Health and Human Services. (2019a). *Disparities*. https://www.healthypeople.gov/2020/about/foundation-health-measures/Disparities

United States Department of Health and Human Services. (2019b). *Social determinants of health*. https://www.healthypeople.gov/2020/topics-objectives/topic/social-determinants-of-health

United States Department of Health and Human Services. (2019c). *Web analytics basics*. https://www.usability.gov/what-and-why/web-analytics.html

University of Chicago Press. (2017). *Chicago manual of style* (17th ed.). Author.

University of Iowa Injury Prevention Research Center. (2017). *Writing and disseminating policy briefs: A communications guide for injury and violence researchers and practitioners* https://iprc.public-health.uiowa.edu/wp-content/uploads/2018/03/Writing-and-Disseminating-Policy-Briefs.pdf

University of Kansas, Center for Community Health and Development. (2018a). *Recognizing allies*. https://ctb.ku.edu/en/table-of-contents/advocacy/advocacy-principles/recognize-allies/main

University of Kansas, Center for Community Health and Development. (2018b). *Identifying opponents*. https://ctb.ku.edu/en/table-of-contents/advocacy/advocacy-principles/identify-opponents/main

University of Kansas, Center for Community Health and Development. (2018c). *Using principles of persuasion*. https://ctb.ku.edu/en/table-of-contents/participation/promoting-interest/principles-of-persuasion/main\

University of Kansas, Center for Community Health and Development. (2019a). *Conducting focus groups*. https://ctb.ku.edu/en/table-of-contents/assessment/assessing-community-needs-and-resources/conduct-focus-groups/main

University of Kansas, Center for Community Health and Development. (2019b). *Conducting interviews*. https://ctb.ku.edu/en/table-of-contents/assessment/assessing-community-needs-and-resources/conduct-interviews/main

University of Kansas center for Community Health and Development (2019c). *Qualitative methods to assess community issues.* https://ctb.ku.edu/en/table-of-contents/assessment/assessing-community-needs-and-resources/qualitative-methods/main

University of Kansas, Center for Community Health and Development. (2019d). Community tool box: Identify community assets. https://ctb.ku.edu/en/table-of-contents/assessment/assessing-community-needs-and-resources/identify-community-assets/main

University of Kansas, Center for Community Health and Development. (2019e). Section 23. Developing and using criteria and processes to set priorities. https://ctb.ku.edu/en/table-of-contents/assessment/assessing-community-needs-and-resources/criteria-and-processes-to-set-priorities/main

University of Kansas, Center for Community Health and Development. (2019f). Developing a plan for advocacy. https://ctb.ku.edu/en/table-of-contents/advocacy/advocacy-principles/advocacy-plan/main

University of Kansas, Center for Community Health and Development. (2019g). Section 1. Overview: getting an advocacy campaign off the ground. https://ctb.ku.edu/entable-of-contents/advocacy/advocacy-principles/overview/main

University of Kansas Center for Community Health and Development. (2019h). Community tool box: Participation. https://ctb.ku.edu/en/table-of-contents/participation/encouraging-involvement/identify-stakeholders/main

University of Kansas, Center for Community Health and Development. (2019i). Influencing policy development. https://ctb.ku.edu/en/influencing-policy-development

University of Kansas, Center for Community Health and Development. (2019j). Section 1. overview: getting an advocacy campaign off the ground. https://ctb.ku.edu/entable-of-contents/advocacy/advocacy-principles/overview/main

University of Kansas, Center for Community Health and Development. (2019k). Group facilitation and problem-solving. https://ctb.ku.edu/en/table-of-contents/leadership/group-facilitation

University of Kansas Center for Community Health and Development. (2019l). Conducting effective meetings. https://ctb.ku.edu/en/table-of-contents/leadership/group-facilitation/main

University of Kansas Center for Community Health and Development. (2019m). Selecting an appropriate design for the evaluation. https://ctb.ku.edu/en/table-of-contents/evaluate/evaluate-community-interventions/experimental-design/main

University of Kansas Center for Community Health and Development. (2019n). Identifying and analyzing stakeholders and their interests. https://ctb.ku.edu/en/table-of-contents/participation/encouraging-involvement/identify-stakeholders/main

University of Kansas, Center for Community Health and Development. (2019o). Community tool box: Creating and maintaining coalitions and partnerships. https://ctb.ku.edu/en/creating-and-maintaining-coalitions-and-partnerships

University of Kansas, Center for Community Health and Development. (2019p). Developing a training program for staff. https://ctb.ku.edu/en/table-of-contents/structure/hiring-and-training/training-programs/main

University of Kansas Center for Community Health and Development. (2019q). Community tool box: Cultural competence. https://ctb.ku.edu/en/table-of-contents/culture/cultural-competence/culturally-competent-organizations/main

Companion Guide References

University of Kansas, Center for Community Health and Development. (2019r). Community toolbox: Hiring and training. https://ctb.ku.edu/en/table-of-contents/structure/hiring-and-training/training-programs/main

University of Kansas, Center for Community Health and Development. (2019s). Managing finances. https://ctb.ku.edu/en/table-of-contents/finances/managing-finances/annual-budget/main

University of Kansas, Center for Community Health and Development. (2019t). *Developing a financial plan for sustainability.* https://ctb.ku.edu/en/table-of-contents/finances/grants-and-financial-resources/financial-sustainability/main

University of Kansas, Center for Community Health and Development. (2019u). *Planning and writing an annual budget.* https://ctb.ku.edu/en/table-of-contents/finances/managing-finances/annual-budget/main

University of Kansas, Center for Community Health and Development. (2019v). *Community tool box: Applying for grants.* https://ctb.ku.edu/en/applying-for-grants

United States Department of Health and Human Services. (2011). *HHS action plan to reduce racial and ethnic health disparities. Department of Health and Human Services.* https://www.hrsa.gov/sites/default/files/about/reduceracialdisparities.pdf

United States Department of Health and Human Services. (2019a). *Disparities.* https://www.healthypeople.gov/2020/about/foundation-health-measures/Disparities

United States Department of Health and Human Services. (2019b). *Social determinants of health.* https://www.healthypeople.gov/2020/topics-objectives/topic/social-determinants-of-health

United States Department of Health and Human Services. (2019c). Usability.gov *Web analytics basics.* https://www.usability.gov/what-and-why/web-analytics.html

Urban Institute. (2018). *Examples of braiding and blending to support community health: A compendium of resources.* https://pfs.urban.org/pay-success/pfs-perspectives/examples-braiding-and-blending-support-community-health-compendium

Virginia Polytechnic Institute and State University. (2015). *RE-AIM.org.* https://www.re-aim.org/about/what-is-re-aim/

W. K. Kellogg Foundation. (2017). The step-by-step guide to evaluation: How to become savvy evaluation consumers. *W.K. Kellogg Foundation Evaluation Handbook,* https://www.wkkf.org/resource-directory/resources/2017/11/the-step-by-step-guide-to-evaluation--how-to-become-savvy-evaluation-consumers

Wagenschutz, H. M., & Rivas, J. (2009). Developing effective presentations. In R. J. Bensley, & J. Brookins-Fisher (Eds.), *Community health education methods: A practical guide* (3rd ed.) (pp. 183-208). Jones and Barlett.

Wallerstein, N., Minkler, M., Carter-Edwards, L., Avila, M., & Sanchez, V. (2015). Improving health through community engagement, community organizing and community building. In K. Glanz, B. K .Rimer, & K. Viswanath, *Health behavior: Theory, research, and practice* (5th ed., pp. 287-312). Jossey-Bass.

Welter, C., Jarpe-Ratner, E., Najo, S. Scallan, E., Davis, S., Mousavi, C, Guthrie, M, & Miner, K. (2018). *A Typology of Learning: Approaches to addressing 21st century public health challenges.* Society for Public Health Education, 69th Annual Conference, Columbus, OH.

Wenger, E., McDermott, R., & Snyder, W. M. (2002). *Cultivating communities of practice: A guide to managing knowledge - Seven principles for cultivating communities of practice.* Harvard Business School Publishing.

West, G. R., Clapp, S. P., Averill, E. M. D., & Cates Jr, W. (2012). Defining and assessing evidence for the effectiveness of technical assistance in furthering global health. *Global public health*, *7*(9), 915-930.

White, S. (2010). Public speaking revisited: Delivery, structure, and style. *American Journal of Health System Pharmacy*, *67*(15), 1225-1227.

Wilensky, S. E., & Teitelbaum, J. B. (2020). *Essentials of health policy and law.* Jones & Bartlett Learning.

Witte, K., & Allen, M. (2000). A meta-analysis of fear appeals: Implications for effective public health campaigns. *Health Education and Behavior*, *27*(5), 591-615.

Windsor, R. (2015). *Evaluation of health promotion and disease prevention programs: Improving population health through evidence-based practice* (5th ed.). Oxford University Press.

World Health Organization. (2019a). *Health impact assessment: The determinants of health.* https://www.who.int/hia/evidence/doh/en/

World Health Organization. (2019b). *Social determinants of health.* https://www.who.int/social_determinants/en/

Wright, K. (2005). Researching internet-based populations: Advantages and disadvantages of online survey research, online questionnaire authoring software packages, and web survey services. *Journal of Computer-Mediated Communication*, *10*(3), 1034.

Wurzbach, M. E. (Ed.). (2004). Community health education and promotion: *A guide to program design and evaluation* (2nd ed.). Aspen Reference.

Youthbuild National Mentoring Alliance. (2020). *Mentee training toolkit: A guide for staff.* https://nationalmentoring resourcecenter.org/index.php/component/k2/item/339-mentee-training-toolkit-a-guide-for-staff.html

Zarcadoolas, C., Pleasant ,A., & Greer D. (2006). *Advancing health literacy: A framework for understanding and action.* Jossey Bass.

Zarzan, J. T., Hess, R., Schur, E., Phillips, R. S., & Rigotti, N. (2009). Making the most of mentors: A guide for mentees. *Academic Medicine*, *84*(1), 140–144.

Zeng, D., Chen, H., Lusch, R., & Li, S. (2010). *Social media analytics and intelligence.* IEEE Computer Society. https://ieeexplore.ieee.org/stamp/stamp.jsp?arnumber=5678581

Zimmerman, R. S., DiClemente, R. J., Andrus, J. K, Hosein, E. N., & SOPHE. (2016). *Introduction to Global Health Promotion.* John Wiley & Sons.

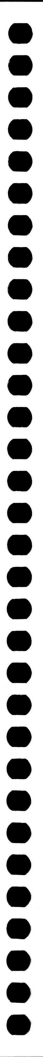

Appendix A

Appendix A
Code of Ethics for the Health Education Profession
Preamble

The Code of Ethics provides a framework of shared values within Health Education professions. The Code of Ethics is grounded in fundamental ethical principles, including value of life, promoting justice, ensuring beneficence, and avoiding harm. A Health Education Specialist's responsibility is to aspire to the highest possible standards of conduct and to encourage the ethical behavior of all those with whom they work.

Health Education professionals are dedicated to excellence in the practice of promoting individual, family, group, organizational, school, community, public, and population health. Guided by common goals to improve the human condition, Health Education Specialists are responsible for upholding the integrity and ethics of the profession as they perform their work and face the daily challenges of making ethical decisions. Health Education Specialists value equity in society and embrace a multiplicity of approaches in their work to support the worth, dignity, potential, quality of life, and uniqueness of all people.

Health Education Specialists promote and abide by these guidelines when making professional decisions, regardless of job title, professional affiliation, work setting, or populations served.

Article I: Core Ethical Expectations

1. Health Education Specialists display personal behaviors that represent the ethical conduct principles of honesty, autonomy, beneficence, respect, and justice. The Health Education Specialist should, under no circumstances, engage in derogatory language, violence, bigotry, racism, harassment, inappropriate sexual activities or communications in person or through the use of technology and other means.

2. Health Education Specialists respect and support the rights of individuals and communities to make informed decisions about their health, as long as such decisions pose no risk to the health of others.

3. Health Education Specialists are truthful about their qualifications and the qualifications of others whom they recommend. Health Education Specialists know their scope of practice and the limitations of their education, expertise, and experience in providing services consistent with their respective levels of professional competence, including certifications and licensures.

4. Health Education Specialists are ethically bound to respect the privacy, confidentiality, and dignity of individuals and organizations. They respect the rights of others to hold diverse values, attitudes, and opinions. Health Education Specialists have a responsibility to engage in supportive relationships that are free of exploitation in all professional settings (e.g., with clients, patients, community members, students, supervisees, employees, and research participants).

5. Health Education Specialists openly communicate to colleagues, employers, and professional organizations when they suspect unethical practices that violate the profession's Code of Ethics.

6. Health Education Specialists are conscious of and responsive to social, racial, faith-based, and cultural diversity when assessing needs and assets, planning, and implementing programs, conducting evaluations, and engaging in research to protect individuals, groups, society, and the environment from harm.

7. Health Education Specialists should disclose conflicts of interest in professional practice, research, evaluation, and the dissemination process.

Code of Ethics for the Health Education Profession Preamble

Article II: Ethical Practice Expectations

Section 1: Responsibility to the Public Health

Health Education Specialists are responsible for educating, promoting, maintaining, and improving the health of individuals, families, groups, and communities. When a conflict of issue arises among individuals, groups, organizations, agencies, or institutions, Health Education Specialists must consider all issues and give priority to those that promote the health and well-being of individuals and the public, while respecting both the principles of individual autonomy, human rights, and equity as long as such decisions pose no risk to the health of others.

A. Health Education Specialists advocate and encourage actions and social policies that promote maximal health benefits and the elimination or minimization of preventable risks and health inequities for all affected parties.

B. Health Education Specialists contribute to the profession by redefining existing practices, developing new practices, and by sharing the outcomes of their work.

C. Health Education Specialists actively involve individuals, groups, stakeholders, and communities in the entire educational process to maximize the understanding and personal responsibilities of those who may be affected.

Section 2: Responsibility to the Profession

Health Education Specialists are responsible for their professional behavior, the reputation of their profession, promotion of certification for those in the profession, and promotion of ethical conduct among their colleagues.

A. Health Education Specialists recognize the boundaries of their professional competence and are accountable for their professional activities and actions.

B. Health Education Specialists maintain, improve, and expand their professional competence through continued education, research, scholarship, membership, participation, leadership in professional organizations, and engagement in professional development.

C. Health Education Specialists contribute to the profession by refining existing professional health-related practices,
developing new practices, and by sharing the outcomes of their work.

D. Health Education Specialists give recognition to others for their professional contributions and achievements.

Section 3: Responsibility to Employers Health

Health Education Specialists are responsible for their professional behavior in the workplace and for promoting ethical conduct among their colleagues and employers.

A: Health Education Specialists apply current, evidence-informed standards and theories when fulfilling their professional responsibilities.

B: Health Education Specialists accurately represent and report service and program outcomes to employers.

C: Health Education Specialists maintain competence in their areas of professional practice through continuing education on a regular basis to maintain their competence.

Section 4: Responsibility in the Delivery of Health Education/Promotion

Health Education Specialists deliver evidence-informed practices with integrity. They respect the rights, dignity, confidentiality, inclusivity, and worth of all people by using strategies and methods tailored to the needs of diverse populations and communities.

A. Health Education Specialists remain informed of the latest scientific information and advances in health education theory, research, and practice.

B. Health Education Specialists support the development of professional standards grounded in theory, best-practice guidelines, and data.

C. Health Education Specialists adhere to a rigorous and ethical evaluation of health education/promotion initiatives.

D. Health Education Specialists promote healthy behaviors through informed choice and advocacy and do not use coercion or intimidation.

E. Health Education Specialists disclose potential benefits and harms of proposed services, strategies, and actions that affect individuals, organizations, and communities.

F. Health Education Specialists actively collaborate with a variety of individuals and organizations and demonstrate respect for the unique contributions provided by others. Health Education Specialists do not plagiarize.

Section 5: Responsibility in Research and Evaluation

Through research and evaluation activities, Health Education Specialists contribute to the health of populations and the profession. When planning and conducting research or evaluation, Health Education Specialists abide by federal, state, and tribal laws and regulations, organizational and institutional policies, and professional standards and ethics.

A. Health Education Specialists ensure that participation in research is voluntary and based upon the informed consent of participants. They follow research designs and protocols approved by relevant institutional review committees and/or boards.

B. Health Education Specialists respect and protect the privacy, rights, and dignity of research participants and honor commitments made to those participants.

C. Health Education Specialists treat all information obtained from participants as confidential, unless otherwise required by law and inform research participants of the disclosure requirements and procedures.

D. Health Education Specialists take credit, including authorship, only for work they have performed and give appropriate authorship, co-authorship, credit, or acknowledgment for the contributions of others.

E. Health Education Specialists report the results of their research and evaluation objectively, accurately, and in a timely manner.

F. Health Education Specialists promote and disseminate the results of their research through appropriate formats while fostering the translation of research into practice.

Section 6: Responsibility in Professional Preparation and Continuing Education

Those involved in the professional preparation and training of Health Education students and continuing education for Health Education Specialists are obligated to provide a quality education that meets professional standards and benefits the individual, the profession, and the public.

A. Health Education Specialists foster an inclusive educational environment free from all forms of discrimination, coercion, and harassment.

B. Health Education Specialists engaged in the delivery of professional preparation and continuing education demonstrate careful planning; state clear and realistic expectations; present material that is scientifically accurate, developmentally appropriate and inclusive; conduct fair assessments; and provide reasonable and prompt feedback to learners.

C. Health Education Specialists provide learners with objective and comprehensive guidance about professional development and career advancement.

D. Health Education Specialists facilitate meaningful opportunities for the professional development and advancement of learners.

Code of Ethics Taskforce Members:

Christopher Ledingham, MPH, PhD (Co-Chair)
Keely Rees, PhD, MCHES® (Co-Chair)
Andrea L. Lowe, MPH, CPH
Elisa "Beth" McNeill, Ph.D., CHES®
Fran Anthony Meyer, PhD, CHES®
Holly Turner Moses, PhD, MCHES®, FESG
Larry Olsen, MAT, MPH, Dr. P.H., MCHES®
Lori Paisley, B.S., MA.
Kerry J. Redican, MPH, PhD, CHES ®
Jody Vogelzang, PhD, RDN, CHES®, FAND
Gayle Walter, PhD, CHES®

Code of Ethics for the Health Education Profession Preamble

Suggested Citation:

Code of Ethics for the Health Education Profession®. (2020).
Coalition for National Health Education Organizations
(CNHEO). [Document].
http://www.cnheo.org/code-of-ethics.html

*The Code of Ethics for the Health Education Profession® update
by the CNHEO Task Force:*
Christopher Ledingham, MPH, PhD (Co-Chair)
Keely Rees, PhD, MCHES® (Co-Chair)
Andrea L. Lowe, MPH, CPH
Elisa "Beth" McNeill, Ph.D., CHES®
Fran Anthony Meyer, PhD, CHES®
Holly Turner Moses, PhD, MCHES®, FESG
Larry Olsen, MAT, MPH, Dr. P.H., MCHES®
Lori Paisley, BS, MA
Kerry J. Redican, MPH, PhD, CHES ®

Jody Vogelzang, PhD, RDN, CHES®, FAND
Gayle Walter, PhD, CHES®.

*The Task Force was organized by the CNHEO Committee in
2019. Significant contributions to the Code also were made by
the broader CNHEO members and full memberships. This Code
was updated from a Task Force in 2011 and adopted by the
CNHEO in February 2020.*

Appendix B
The Certified Health Education Specialist (CHES®) and
Master Certified Health Education Specialist (MCHES®) Examinations

To implement a certification program, it is necessary to develop examinations that accurately measure practice-related knowledge and skills. The National Commission for Health Education Credentialing, Inc. (NCHEC) utilizes the CHES® and the MCHES® examinations to assess the extent to which a candidate can possess, apply, and interpret knowledge relative to the Eight Areas of Responsibility, delineated from *A Competency-Based Framework for Health Education Specialists – 2020.*

Both the CHES® and MCHES® examinations are criterion-referenced examinations that consist of a total of 165 (150 scored plus 15 pilot test) multiple choice questions in a computer-based format. The passing score for each exam is determined by a modified Angoff method and represents a fixed standard of knowledge, independent of candidate performance. Essentially, this method allows subject-matter experts to establish a level of knowledge that is expected

of professionals who are minimally competent. This passing point is reviewed, and statistics are analyzed, to ensure reliability and validity of both the CHES® and MCHES® examinations. By using this method, there is no curve, and candidates do not compete against one another. There is also no penalty for guessing.

In constructing the exams, NCHEC works with a national testing organization known for expertise in developing credentialing examinations. Together, the organizations develop the examinations according to the process mentioned above. The percentage of questions in the exam pertaining to each Area of Responsibility is based on the results of the Health Education Specialist Practice Analysis 2020. The percent of questions coming from each Area of Responsibility for the current examinations are presented in the table below. When preparing for either the CHES® or MCHES® exams, it is recommended that a candidate take into account these percentages.

Areas of Responsibility	CHES® % of exam	MCHES® % of exam
I. Assessment of Needs and Capacity	17% (28)	12% (20)
II. Planning	14% (23)	10% (16)
III. Implementation	15% (24)	9% (15)
IV. Evaluation and Research	12% (20)	20% (33)
V. Advocacy	12% (20)	9% (15)
VI. Communication	12% (20)	12% (20)
VII. Leadership and Management	6% (10)	18% (30)
VIII. Ethics and Professionalism	12% (20)	10% (16)
Total	**100% (165)**	**100% (165)**

Appendix C
Certified Health Education Specialist Examination Questions

The following practice examination questions are aligned with Sub-competencies identified as entry-level as defined by the Health Education Specialist Practice Analysis II (HESPA II 2020) and outlined within this study companion. The practice questions, written by health education specialists, may assist the user in preparing for the Certified Health Education Specialist (CHES®) or Master Certified Health Education Specialist (MCHES®) examinations and/or to identify areas of concentration for professional development and training of practicing health education specialists. The questions are not on the current certification examination. Some of the questions have been altered from discarded certification examination questions. The practice questions in this publication have not been subjected to the same rigorous psychometric testing procedures as questions appearing on the CHES® or MCHES® examinations. Specifically, a passing score on the practice examination questions does not in any way predict or guarantee a passing score on the CHES®/MCHES® examinations. The practice questions should be used only to direct study efforts.

The practice questions are meant to be challenging. Initially, the user may find that more than one answer appears to be correct. In these instances, the user is encouraged to conduct careful analysis of the questions and possible answers to identify the correct responses. It might be helpful to use the practice examination questions under similar conditions in which the CHES®/MCHES® examinations are officially administered. For example, the user would be allowed no more than three hours to complete the examination. The user would not utilize or depend on resources such as the study guide, textbooks, publications, or calculators to complete the examination.

An answer key is provided at the end of the practice examination questions. In addition to providing the user with the correct answer, the user will find at least one Area of Responsibility that aligns with the question identified. A review of the number of incorrect answers from any particular Area of Responsibility may help the user to target areas of weakness where more study would be beneficial. ***It is strongly recommended that resources beyond the use of this study companion are used to adequately prepare for taking the CHES® and MCHES® examinations.***

In closing, feedback from candidates who were successful in passing previous certification examinations and previous study guide users indicates that being part of a small group that allowed participants to "work through" the practice examination questions and discuss why answers are correct or incorrect can be beneficial.

1. A health education specialist is working with a local community organization to segment the population for implementing a new health communication campaign to address rising rates of sexually transmitted infections (STIs) in the community. What characteristics will the project lead focus on to effectively segment the population?
    a. Location of health care resources (e.g., fiscal, human, and technical)
    b. Program components needed to effectively implement the campaign
    c. Behavioral, demographic, and cultural characteristics of the population
    d. Duration/timeframe for implementing communication activities

2. A health education specialist collects data in which the answers were either "yes" or "no." These data are what type?
    a. Nominal
    b. Ordinal
    c. Interval
    d. Ratio

3. When engaging priority populations in program planning, participants are defined as:
    a) individuals who will be funding the program.
    b) print and broadcast media who will be publicizing the program.
    c) community members who will receive the program intervention.
    d) researchers who will be evaluating the success of the program.

4. A Bullying Prevention community-wide intervention is being planned, with parents, of the priority population, targeted. The planning team is seeking specific information from local parents with children in grades K-12 to understand their opinions on approaches to strengthen school climate through parent teacher associations, volunteering opportunities, and school improvement events. The health education specialist should refer these local parents to what type of data collection method?
    a. Literature review
    b. Focus group
    c. Survey
    d. Nominal Group process

5. A health education specialist is assessing which valid resource to use to obtain chronic disease-related morbidity and mortality trends in a specific local community. What would be the best resource to use to access that information?
    a. US Bureau of Census data
    b. County and State health-related agencies data
    c. Literature review
    d. Centers for Disease Control and Prevention (CDC) data

6. A heath education specialist is conducting research. Which of the following is not focused on ethical principles for conducting data collection?
    a. Beneficence
    b. Justice
    c. Respect for persons
    d. Validity

7. Which of the following is <u>not</u> an adult learning principle?
   a. Actively involve adults in helping to set the curriculum, choosing training methods, or identifying training goals.
   b. Ask about adults' past experience and knowledge, and use their experiences or knowledge to avoid providing redundant content during trainings.
   c. Use a prescribed set of methods, perspectives, and content to standardize instruction and avoid confusion.
   d. Conduct assessments to identify ways to engage adults and learn about their goals or objectives for the training.

8. The health education specialist is three-quarters of the way through an agency's annual funding. It is realized there will not be sufficient funding to last through the rest of the year. This realization is an issue of program:
   a. sustainability.
   b. longevity.
   c. evaluation.
   d. planning.

9. The coalition is having a difficult time persuading a decision-maker to support an issue. The decision-maker, however, can be swayed by level of public support for the issue. The most important data collection method to use next, therefore, would be:
   a. political capital charting.
   b. communications capacity analysis.
   c. community leader surveys.
   d. voting record examination.

10. What is an effective way to identify stakeholders?
    a. Contact people in the target community to gather categories and names.
    b. Use people whom are known and have worked on other projects.
    c. Gather people in professional organizations who have worked in the general region.
    d. Work primarily with political organizations that work with segments of the community.

11. When researchers and evaluators use a combination of different methods and strategies to examine evaluation or research questions from multiple different perspectives and vantage points it is called:
    a. multi-variate analysis.
    b. comprehensive assessment.
    c. professional diligence.
    d. mixed methods methodology.

12. Using an ecological approach, the health education specialist identifies an organizational-level local business to be a member of a preventive mental health coalition. That business was selected because hiring personnel employ military veterans, many of whom suffered from Post-Traumatic Stress Disorder (PTSD). The role that local business plays on the coalition is that of a:
    a. partner.
    c. influencer.
    b. priority population.
    d. stakeholder.

13. A health education specialist is working on a new community planning initiative. The specialist wants to address community support and social network factors. Which determinant of health, therefore, will be addressed?
    a. Economic stability
    b. Social and community context
    c. Education
    d. Health and health care

14. In the informational training related to an adolescent health literacy pilot program, the attendees, all of whom are classroom teachers, state that instead of having a single facilitator come into their classroom to deliver the curriculum, they prefer to deliver it themselves. They make their case to the trainer, stating they are classroom teachers and, as such, know how to deliver curriculum. Which of the following concepts does the trainer use to explain why this health education curriculum is being implemented with a single facilitator?
    a. Fidelity
    b. Validity
    c. Reliability
    d. Evaluation

15. In media advocacy, decision-makers, as an audience for the communications strategy, are what level of priority?
    a. Secondary
    b. Tertiary
    c. Primary
    d. Emergency

16. Which of the following is not one of the three important criteria, or the three Fs, of program planning?
    a. Funding
    b. Fluidity
    c. Flexibility
    d. Functionality

17. Which of the following is true about conducting an outcome evaluation of a communication campaign? Health education specialists are assessing:
    a. if certain materials are more effective than others.
    b. if expenditures are within budget
    c. if the intended audience(s) are being reached with the communication outreach.
    d. the degree to which the communication objectives are achieved.

18. Which of the following is an example of secondary data collection?
    a. Surveys
    b. Letters
    c. Published literature
    d. Interviews

19. Type of brief provided to a decision-maker when attempting to convince that person to take a specific action on an issue covers not only policy options but also policy recommendations. This type of brief is referred to as a/an:
    a. Information.
    b. Policy.
    c. Issue.
    d. Policy impact.

The following figure is used to answer question 20 and 21.

Figure 1
NCHS Mortality Reporting System: Pneumonia, Influenza, and COVID-19 Mortality

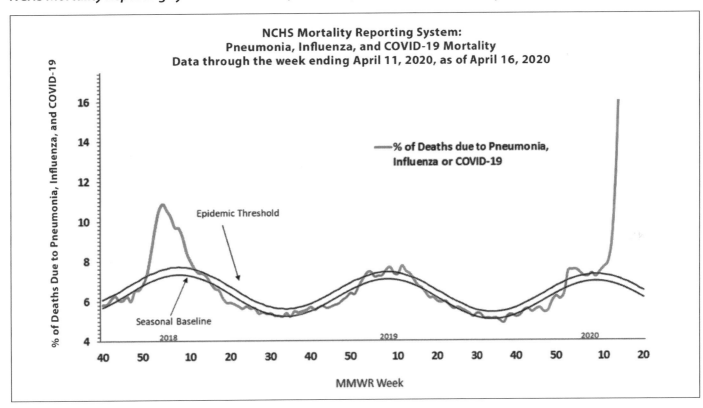

20. Which of the following statements about the data available on the graph is true?
    a. Respiratory diseases are endemic in the population as illustrated by the epidemic threshold.
    b. The increase in week 10 of 2020 was largely due to COVID-19.
    c. A particularly contagious strain of a respiratory disease hit the population around week 10 of 2020.
    d. There was an epidemic outbreak of respiratory diseases in late 2018 and early 2020.

21. The percent of deaths due to pneumonia, Influenza, and COVID-19:
    a. was higher than expected for the majority of both 2018 and 2019.
    b. in week 10 of 2020 was roughly 3X greater than expected.
    c. on average met the level of epidemic in week 20 of 2019.
    d. is highest mid-year and lowest at the end of each year.

Certified Health Education Specialist Examination Questions

22. A health education specialist is interested in gaining the support of a large number of people from a metropolitan area in which the project is being implemented. Which one of the following communication channels would be best to use?
    a. Mass media
    b. Interpersonal
    c. Intrapersonal
    d. Institutional

23. What is the main function of an Institutional Review Board (IRB)? To:
    a. make sure the study is valid and reliable.
    b. check for spelling and grammatical errors.
    c. protect human subjects involved in the research.
    d. make sure not to duplicate studies.

24. A health education specialist plans to hire a consultant to conduct an evaluation of a program. Which of the following is the first step of the process?
    a. A signed ethics agreement from the consultant or contractor
    b. Extra funds to cover the cost of unexpected expenditures
    c. An implementation plan from the consultant or contractor
    d. A written agreement outlining the work needed

25. In advocacy evaluation, measuring campaign and message reach as well as activities and tactics used is considered which type of evaluation?
    a. Process
    b. Impact
    c. Outcome
    d. Summative

26. An important indicator of capacity is "influence." What is true about influencers?
    a. One should primarily look for wealthy people to find influencers.
    b. People connected to large networks are often important influencers.
    c. Most influencers are people working in professional organizations.
    d. Influencers are rarely found in community neighborhoods.

27. A health education specialist is targeting different groups of young adults for a physical activity intervention. The specialist wants to work with those who are ready to take action to get active within the next month. In what Stage of Change are these prospective participants?
    a. Precontemplation
    b. Contemplation
    c. Preparation
    d. Action

28. Vision statements are used to describe where a program will be in the next:
    a. 1 to 2 years.
    b. 3 to 5 years.
    c. 6 to 10 years.
    d. 11 to 15 years.

29. What method of data collection is most suited to programs that are well defined and have had numerical outcomes compared with those of other groups or the general population?
    a. Interpretive
    b. Inductive
    c. Qualitative
    d. Quantitative

30. The health education specialist is working with community groups to conduct legislative advocacy for change in the community. Which theory will best assist with this strategy?
    a. Theory of Planned Behavior
    b. Community Organizing Model
    c. Transtheoretical Model
    d. Social Cognitive Theory

31. When health education specialists conduct training programs, it is important to use a variety of resources and strategies to:
    a. ensure that all the necessary material is covered.
    b. accommodate funders' expectations.
    c. reduce the costs associated with training.
    d. reach as many of the learners as possible.

32. To determine whether a proposed intervention will work as designed, the health education specialist could conduct a(n):
    a. pilot test.
    b. impact evaluation.
    c. market analysis.
    d. participant interview.

33. Health is impacted by a variety of different factors, but there are five major factors that contribute to the determinants of health for a population. Discrimination and income fall under which of the five major factors?
    a. Health behaviors
    b. Social environment or characteristics
    c. Physical environment
    d. Health services

34. Which type of objective is addressed in the following statement? "After completing the program, participants will be able to discuss three strategies to reduce the risk of falling."
    a. Process
    b. Learning
    c. Environmental
    d. Outcome

35. A health education specialist plans to conduct a food access and food desert assessment to determine how many grocery stores exist in the low-income areas of the community compared to other income level areas. When planning for the collection of secondary data, all of the following tasks should be included except to:
    a. identify existing data at the city, county, state and/or federal level.
    b. obtain resources and partners to access or collect data.
    c. create or adapt an existing instrument to collect observational data.
    d. describe how data would be systematically collected.

36. The health education specialist wants to test some new questions and use a different program evaluation survey delivery method. To do so, which of the following would be implemented first?
    a. Pilot test
    b. Pretest
    c. Posttest
    d. Poll

37. The health education specialist is creating a new program to increase cancer screening. The specialist is looking for evidence-based strategies to promote mammograms. Which is the best source of information for that data?
    a. Community assessment reports
    b. Guide to Community Preventive Services
    c. Healthy People 2030
    d. Community Toolbox

38. When health education specialists are asked to verify the credibility of media sources for health information, they should consider the element of Currency. To what does this term refer?
    a. The monetary value of the media organization.
    b. The amount of federal funding received by the media organization.
    c. How current or out-of-date the health information is for their health topic.
    d. How important the health information is for their priority population.

39. "Among program participants, smoking rates will decrease by 35% in 12 months" is an example of which type of objective?
    a. Behavioral
    b. Learning
    c. Administrative
    d. Environmental

40. A health education specialist is planning to conduct a literature review specific to the resiliency of small rural communities affected by a natural disaster to cope and rebuild. Two important search strategies should include _____ and _____ for searches.
    a. listing of bibliographies; description of priority population
    b. meta-analysis; systematic reviews
    c. identification of key words; selected source/database(s)
    d. qualitative studies; quantitative studies

41. What is an important characteristic that defines "plain language?" Language:
    a. is used in federal agencies, so it is important to health education specialists.
    b. is presented simply with a low reading level.
    c. is presented in a way that the audience can understand it quickly.
    d. follows accepted rules of grammar and composition.

42. SMART objectives are statements in which the results of the program are described in measurable terms. SMART stands for Specific, Measurable, Attainable/Achievable, Realistic/Relevant, and Time-bound. Which of the following is a correctly written SMART objective?
    a. By the end of the program, 20% of respondents will report eating more fruits and vegetables.
    b. By the end of the program, respondents will exercise more.
    c. Respondents will report drinking 30% more water.
    d. Respondents will drink less alcohol by the end of the program.

43. Which of the following is typically measured in a process evaluation?
    a. Health status and quality of life indices
    b. Fidelity, completeness, and exposure
    c. Environmental changes and skills
    d. Needs, gaps, and program goals

44. As people learn, which of the following yields the highest level of retention? What is:
    a. heard.
    b. seen.
    c. done and said.
    d. read.

45. The main drawback of pilot testing interventions is that:
    a. the results may not be entirely generalizable.
    b. it is often too expense to conduct.
    c. too many of the priority population are involved, leaving few to participate in the actual intervention.
    d. the results seldom lead to changes in materials and/or strategies for the actual intervention.

46. A health education specialist has a limited budget and is looking for baseline data. Which of the following may be a secondary data option to consider?
    a. Conducting a survey with the priority population
    b. Pilot testing an interview with family members and co-workers
    c. Randomly sampling the priority population
    d. Federal, state, city, and county open data portals

47. A health education specialist is collaborating with community stakeholders to create a health communication campaign in which mammography screenings are promoted broadly among African-American women in the southeast United States. Which messaging technique would be most appropriate?
    a. Tailoring
    b. Narratives
    c. Targeting
    d. Audience Segmentation

48. The health education specialist wishes to examine the outcome of an intervention. As such, which type of evaluation should be designed?
    a. Process
    b. Impact
    c. Formative
    d. Summative

49. Findings from an assessment revealed that the priority population's access to available community health care services is lower than another community with comparable demographics. They have identified a/an:
    a. perceived need.
    b. actual need.
    c. expressed need.
    d. elative need.

50. A health education specialist needs to find adaptive leadership training to learn how to more effectively communicate with diverse populations in the community in which the specialist serves. Which of the following training titles and modalities would be most appropriate to meet this complex professional development goal?
    a. "Risk communication for public health emergencies" (90 min webinar)
    b. "Inter-generational dynamics: Speaking the lingo of different age groups for sex education" (2 hour in-person workshop)
    c. "Listening with cultural humility before communicating your messages" (hybrid: two 2-hour in-person workshops plus 2 coaching calls)
    d. "How to write more clearly: A primer for health literacy" (3 hour online self-paced module)

51. Advocacy initiatives are created to influence policy and law, and they include many strategy areas. In which of these areas would holding a town hall meeting fall?
    a. Electioneering
    b. Media advocacy

    c. Grassroots lobbying

    d. Direct lobbying

52. A new HIV testing intervention is being planned to support efforts to increase screening rates. The intervention is planned to start in six months. Which of the following is a proven method to create a timeline and plan for the intervention?

    a. Critical path method

    b. Epidemiology curve

    c. Weekly program meetings

    d. Strategic plan

53. A health education specialist would like to use a planning tool in which the timeline for when specific tasks are to be accomplished before, during, and after a program. The health education specialist also would like to track actual accomplishment of these tasks using this same tool. Which of the following methods would be most useful?

    a. Logic model

    b. Gantt chart

    c. Activity log

    d. Progress report

54. Health education specialists are encouraged to employ health literacy universal precautions when interacting with patients and delivering health education materials to communities. According to the Agency for Healthcare Research and Quality (AHRQ), which of the following is not considered a health literacy universal precaution?

    a. Use short sentences consisting of no more than 25 words.

    b. Supplement text with relevant multimedia, including images and videos.

    c. Use numeric rates and statistics to enhance the credibility of your message.

    d. Highlight, bold, or create text-boxes to display important main points.

55. A coalition determined there was a lack of collaboration among the numerous agencies, organizations, and individuals who provide health and emergency services in a community. The coalition decided to identify community members' issues and concerns with these services and determine level of usage of the existing agencies. The coalition aims to avoid duplication of services, while designing interventions to address concerns. Which of the following represents the best strategy to obtain data?

    a. Capacity assessment

    b. Program evaluation

    c. Asset mapping

    d. Process evaluation

56. During a health education program, questions about whether the participants like the instructional materials and if instructors find them easy to use are examples of which type of evaluation?

    a. Summative

    b. Impact

    c. Outcome

    d. Process

57. A health education specialist sends cancer prevention materials to women 40 and older about breast cancer screening. This process is an example of:
    a. targeting a message.
    b. tailoring a message.
    c. weekly program meetings
    d. assessing a priority population.

58. To facilitate understanding and sensitivity for various cultures, values, and traditions, which statement is true?
    a. A high degree of depth of cultural knowledge is necessary to be effective.
    b. Cultural awareness and openness to other cultures is often sufficient.
    c. Cultural sensitivity requires setting values on differences to reduce conflict.
    d. Cultural competence includes knowledge, awareness, and sensitivity.

59. Researching information about a legislator's voting record before an initial meeting is important. Many places to gather research exist. Which would be the most helpful in understanding the voting record of a member of the United States Congress?
    a. Capwiz
    b. BALLOTPEDIA
    c. SOPHE Action Center
    d. APHA Legislative Action

60. When starting to build relationships with multiple sectors outside of public health (e.g., housing, transportation, primary care, schools), what would be the most effective first step?
    a. Communicate the needs of public health to partner with decision makers in other sectors.
    b. Ask partners about their priorities and needs.
    c. Share data and evidence about priority public health topics.
    d. Address gaps in communication, values, and understanding between sectors.

61. To determine the immediate effects of a health education program, the health education specialist should use which type of evaluation?
    a. Impact
    b. Process
    c. Formative
    d. Outcome

62. If a health education specialist were creating an intervention that included written education materials, which of the following should be checked to best facilitate learning?
    a. Cost of a two-color brochure
    b. Literacy level of all in the priority population
    c. Reading level of the written materials
    d. Health records of those exposed to the intervention

63. A community agency personnel are targeting a variety of social ecological levels to help reduce drug use in the community. Some of the levels will take substantially more time to target. Rather than wait for all aspects of the intervention to be ready, the health education specialist looks to begin with one level and then will add in other levels over time. This process is an example of:
    a. phasing in.
    b. pilot testing.
    c. total implementation.
    d. primary strategies.

64. When developing an assessment data analysis plan, which task should be considered first?
    a. Select the statistical software to use.
    b. Define variables to be used in analysis.
    c. Describe data collection instruments.
    d. Identify questions based on purpose of assessment.

65. Logic models are used to:
    a. track if activities are producing outputs which lead to outcomes.
    b. outline the lesson plan scope and sequence.
    c. identify the timing of when all of the planning should occur.
    d. outline evaluation stages for the program.

66. Which of the following is not an example of a timeline for the delivery of health education programs?
    a. Management by Objectives (MBO)
    b. Gantt chart
    c. Program Evaluation and Review Technique (PERT)
    d. Critical Path Method (CPM)

67. In developing a solid work plan to be specifically aligned to a logic model, which of the following should be included in the selected planning model?
    a. Project budgeting
    b. Intervention mapping
    c. Alternative strategies
    d. Training fidelity

68. A health education specialist who is designing a media advocacy initiative should incorporate which of the following as media strategies?
    a. Press release, exercise program, interviews, PSA
    b. An internet blog, radio interviews, social networking group site, PSA
    c. PSA, letter to the editor, behavior change intervention, TV interviews
    d. PSA, TV interviews, cooking classes, behavior change intervention

69. To increase self-efficacy to resist peer pressure to use substances, the health education specialist's curriculum should include which one of the following?
    a. Small prizes for completing all homework assignments
    b. Activities that reinforce the negative consequence of substance use
    c. Trained peer leaders elected to implement the classes
    d. Role plays and group activities that demonstrate refusal skills

70. The health education specialist is conducting a research study using an online survey in which participants' names are linked to their data. Of the following, which is the best way to protect participant confidentiality?
    a. Have only research assistants analyze the data.
    b. Store name separately from data and replace with unique identifier.
    c. Use group log-in IDs to access the data.
    d. Use untenable firewalls to protect data.

71. Services required for program implementation have been identified. A long-term program partner could provide those services at a discounted price. Which of the following is most appropriate to use for procurement?
    a. Formal contract
    b. Grant agreement
    c. Memorandum of understanding
    d. Letter of intent

72. The health education specialists wants to compare course satisfaction levels of two different groups of smoking cessation participants. Of the following, which is the best quantitative data analysis technique to use?
    a. Weighted average
    b. Range
    c. Percentage
    d. Cross tabulation

73. A health education specialist wants to ensure a fact sheet on colon cancer prevention is suitable for the chosen priority population. Which of the following assessments should be used?
    a. SMOG
    b. SAM
    c. FOG
    d. FRY

74. In conducting a smoking cessation program, which types of health education strategies most likely will encourage participants to start thinking about quitting?
    a. Identifying triggers that might encourage smoking
    b. Setting up a support group to reduce risk of relapse
    c. Increasing awareness of harmful effects of smoking
    d. Providing nicotine patches to ease the craving

75. Which of the following should be used to standardize intervention delivery by program staff?
    a. Learning motivation
    b. Motivation model
    c. Evaluation plan
    d. Training protocol

76. What percentage of the total program budget should be set aside for evaluation?
    a. 5%
    b. 10%
    c. 15%
    d. 50%

77. The route through which a message is disseminated to the priority population is referred to as the communication:
    a. means.
    b. channel.
    c. strategy.
    d. intervention.

78. Valid research designs allow valid conclusions to be drawn. Which type of validity is used to estimate the degree of cause and effect?
    a. External
    b. Primary
    c. Secondary
    d. Internal

79. A health education specialist is considering using multiple models (e.g., assessment, behavioral change, and planning) during planning of the needs assessment process. Which of the following is the most likely reason for using this strategy? It will:
    a. assist in identifying types of data needed for the assessment and the factors that may impact development of the intervention.
    b. assist in creating a systematic approach for conducting a needs assessment and developing an intervention.
    c. provide insight for developing strategies to engage the community in the assessment process.
    d. provide the components to create a logic model and to identify gaps.

80. The health education specialist can examine health determinants through a socio-ecological lens. Which socio-ecological and social determinant factor includes healthcare providers' recommendations?
    a. Individual
    b. Interpersonal
    c. Community
    d. Policy

81. When conducting a program staff training following the ARCS Motivation Model, the health education specialist wishes to improve trainee perception of relevance. Which of the following applications of the model would be best to use?
    a. Tie instruction to past experience.
    b. Build positive learning expectations.
    c. Encourage new skills.
    d. Maintain attention.

82. The health education specialist is searching for information about a health issue for an advocacy effort. The specialist is specifically looking for the facts, epidemiology, and health consequences of the issue. The most appropriate sites to search would be:
    a. JSTOR/ERIC.
    b. ACS/AHA.
    c. CDC/NIH.
    d. NLM/Community Guide.

The following figure is used to answer question 83.

Figure 2
Overdose Death Rates Involving Opoids, by Type, United States, 1999-2018

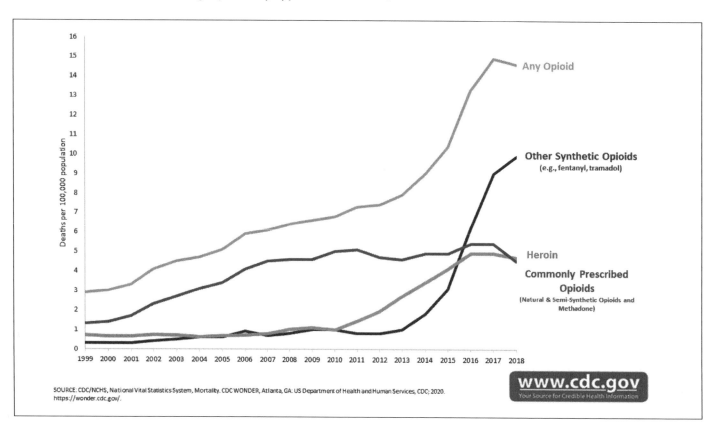

83. Which of the following statements can be inferred from the graph?
    a. Rates of deaths from prescribed opioids decreased when death rates of other synthetic opioids decreased.
    b. Opioid deaths were largely caused by commonly prescribed opioids until 2015.
    c. Heroin was the drug responsible for the majority of opioid related deaths.
    d. Deaths due to fentanyl were steady from 1999 to 2018.

84. Which of the following statements regarding overdose death rates involving opioids is true?
    a. Death rates from any opioid have increased 5 times from 1999 to 2018.
    b. Death rates from commonly prescribed opioids were roughly 5 per 100,000 in the population in 2018.
    c. Death rates from other synthetic opioids were roughly triple that of death rates from heroin and commonly prescribed opioids in 2016.
    d. Opioid overdose deaths decreased from 2013 to 2018.

85. If the health education specialist begins the program planning process by identifying desired outcomes, the most appropriate model would be:
    a. SMART.
    b. MATCH.
    c. PRECEDE-PROCEED.
    d. PATCH.

86. When allocating resources, good managers:
    a. use the organization's needs to drive use of current resources and projections for future resources.
    b. focus primarily on handling accounting to make sure resources are not overspent.
    c. delegate resource management planning to staff who they manage.
    d. pay most attention to ensuring the efficient use of resources rather than effective use.

87. The health education specialist is reading a meta-analysis of balance interventions involving frail elderly. Although this analysis can assist in guiding their senior exercise programming decisions, the health education specialist also must be aware of its limitations, including:
    a. nonspurious relationships.
    b. unique sample population.
    c. time-bound results.
    d. lack of uniformity of methodology.

88. Health education specialists are ethically obligated to ensure confidentiality and to protect the privacy of all clients. The law that protects the privacy of patient information is the:
    a. Health Information Protection Act.
    b. Health Insurance Profitability Act of Accountability.
    c. Health Information Accuracy Act.
    d. Health Insurance Portability and Accountability Act.

89. The health education specialist developed a new train-the-trainer program for a statewide positive mental health promotion inititave. Which tool would best communicate training program plans and parameters?
    a. Learning principle
    b. Training manual
    c. Fidelity framework
    d. Logistics assessment

90. An action-oriented, time-limited alliance for health issue advocacy is which of the following?
    a. Coalition
    b. Collaborative
    c. Task force
    d. Influential

91. A health education specialist choses a six-step framework in which participatory planning, multiple theories, and a systems approach are used to address intervention development for adoption and sustainability. This arrangement (or plan) refers to which of the following?
    a. PRECEDE-PROCEED
    b. Behavior Centered Design
    c. Logic Model
    d. Intervention mapping

92. A health education specialist can design health promotion programs to facilitate the learning process of all participants by:
    a. developing universal messages to reach diverse populations.
    b. adapting programs to different cultural beliefs and practices.
    c. being aware of cultural biases in developing educational programs.
    d. replicating programs that have been effective in dominant cultures.

93. An advantage of adopting an instrument for data collection is that:
    a. its reliability and validity can be used.
    b. substantial changes can be made.
    c. it's similar to developing a new instrument.
    d. permission for use is never necessary.

94. If a health education specialist wants to emphasize program implementation, the most appropriate model would be:
    a. PRECEDE-PROCEED.
    b. MATCH.
    c. SMART.
    d. PATCH.

95. The community recreation center placed speed bumps on the roadway that borders the playgrounds. This action is an example of which type of intervention strategy?
    a. Healthy policy change
    b. Communication change
    c. Environmental change
    d. Health education change

96. A computer application allows a patient to assess current cardiovascular fitness levels. Through the app, texts are sent to the patient's cellphone so that interaction throughout the day is provided for encouragement as well as to send information about the number of walking steps needed to achieve a pre-determined level. This provision of personalized support is referred to as what type of messaging?
    a. Tailored
    b. Targeted
    c. Marketing
    d. Motivational

97. The health education specialist is reviewing the evidence-informed findings of the Guide to Community Preventive Services. The health education specialist is most likely assessing resources related to:
    a. clinical preventive services.
    b. coalition development.
    c. intervention approaches.
    d. policy development.

98. When applying traditional marketing principles to health education interventions, the "product" is usually the:
    a. behavior change.
    b. tangible good.
    c. location.
    d. monetary cost.

99. Communication between a prospective human subject and an investigator from beginning of a research study to the end refers to the:
    a. protocol review.
    b. informed consent.
    c. subject compensation.
    d. Belmont Report

100. The best objective for a training workshop to build the skills of smoking cessation facilitators would be "Upon completion of the training program, the participants will be able to":
    a. summarize most of the steps of the deep breathing technique taught in the workshop.
    b. list with 100% accuracy the steps of the deep breathing technique taught in the workshop.
    c. explain 8 of the 9 steps of the deep breathing technique taught in the workshop.
    d. demonstrate with 100% accuracy the deep breathing technique taught in the workshop.

101. A health education specialist creates a draft fact sheet about diabetes. A group of six individuals are recruited to read the fact sheet and answer a series of questions. This process is an example of:
    a. pilot testing.
    b. readability testing.
    c. tailoring.
    d. cultural competency.

102. To gain organizational acceptance for strategic plans, health education specialists should:
    a. work with colleagues to develop external strategic plans that do not require emphasizing organizational culture.
    b. pay less attention to organizational culture than to effective planning.
    c. work within the organizational culture that is determined by upper management.
    d. consider organizational culture, and develop and implement strategies to change that culture if needed.

103. During program monitoring, the health education specialist determines that an educational curriculum needs modification. With modification, however, primary attention needs to be on:
    a. continuing program outputs.
    b. adapting program objectives.
    c. maintaining program fidelity.
    d. sustaining program budget.

104. A smoking ban in casinos is which type of strategy in a state-wide smoking prevention program?
    a. Health communication
    b. Health policy
    c. Health mobilization
    d. Behavior change

105. When designing audience-centered, culturally-appropriate health education materials, it is essential to:
    a. involve the target audience in developing materials.
    b. outsource the publishing to another agency.
    c. keep the production costs low.
    d. determine education level of the target audience.

106. Intervention sustainability should be planned:
    a. immediately after the first process evaluation.
    b. mid-intervention.
    c. immediately following impact evaluation.
    d. at the start of the intervention.

107. The tool used to identify advocacy campaign resources and gaps is which of the following?
    a. Network assessment
    b. Asset inventory
    c. Alliance mapping
    d. Legislative tracker

108. By 2024, volunteers will distribute informational factsheets to at least 50% of the program participants. This intent is an example of which type of objective?
    a. Process
    b. Impact
    c. Outcome
    d. Summative

109. To determine the validity of existing data, the health education specialist:
    a. looks online to verify the information on multiple sites.
    b. sends the information out to a panel of experts.
    c. uses only peer-reviewed articles contained in databases.
    d. examines the references for commonly cited sources in multiple publications.

110. When monitoring intervention financial resources, which of the following specifically provides for fiscal accountability measurement?
    a. Accounting process
    b. Acquisition assessment
    c. Internal audit
    d. Funding stability ratio

111. Which of the following survey tools would be best to use if the health education specialist has unlimited funds, wants to generate a high response rate, and wishes to keep selection bias low?
    a. Face-to-face interview
    b. Telephone survey
    c. Mail survey
    d. Online survey

112. When participants in a training program are told both the benefits and risks associated with the program, which one of the following typically occurs with the procedure?
    a. IRB submission
    b. Parental consent
    c. Beneficence consent
    d. Informed consent

113. To provide patient-centered healthcare with excellence in quality, service, and access is an example of a/an:
    a. mission statement.
    b. objective.
    c. vision statement.
    d. goal.

114. Behavioral and learning objectives also may be referred to as:
    a. impact objectives.
    b. formative objectives.
    c. process objectives.
    d. outcome objectives.

115. The health education specialist realizes that although already being connected with legislators and having collaborated with many advocacy coalitions, the specialist lacks important advocacy skills and has limited personal financial resources. The best recognized opportunity to overcome these barriers to being an advocate is to:
    a. participate in national action.
    b. enroll in a graduate degree program.
    c. conduct an environmental scan of affiliates.
    d. attend an advocacy webinar series.

116. According to the Diffusion of Innovations theory, some groups in the population are resistant to change. These groups of people are referred to as the:
    a. innovators
    b. adopters.
    c. laggards.
    d. majority.

117. In a grant-funded project budget, what are the indirect costs?
    a. Budget expenses for miscellaneous items
    b. Cost associated with marketing materials
    c. Personnel expenses such as benefits
    d. Overhead expenses such as utilities and rent

118. Which social determinant should the health education specialist consider when analyzing knowledge acquisition among youth participating in a risk reduction intervention?
    a. Circumstances
    b. Relationships
    c. Connections
    d. Environments

119. The health education specialist is planning a training workshop for research data collectors. Of the following, which training piece is most important to decrease time and effort spent to clean or correct data after collection?
    a. Data entry training at the same time
    b. Data collection pilot test
    c. Workshop held well in advance of data collection
    d. One training format used

120. The health education specialist asks an elected official to vote to increase funding for teen pregnancy prevention in the state. The specialist is engaged in:
    a. education.
    b. lobbying.
    c. advocacy.
    d. public policy.

121. A health education specialist in a hospital plans to post information throughout the facility to increase awareness of the potential dangers, spread, and prevention of the coronavirus disease 2019 (COVID-19). Which format would best accomplish this effort?
    a. A brochure containing detailed information
    b. Data printed from the CDC's website regarding coronavirus
    c. An infographic with data and short messages
    d. Graphics showing proper hand washing

122. A seminar on high blood pressure for those who already are affected with high blood pressure is being provided as a part of a worksite wellness program. Which scenario facilitates active learning of workshop participants?
    a. Distribute materials on all aspects of high blood pressure.
    b. Discuss medical scenarios from authoritative sources.
    c. Have attendees practice taking blood pressure on one another.
    d. Review strategies to make lifestyle modifications.

123. Forgetting to inform participants about the risks associated with physical activity before having the participants begin a program is an example of:
    a. commission.
    b. deregulation.
    c. ethical compliance.
    d. negligence.

124. When writing objectives for a worksite wellness program, the health education specialist wishes to measure any morbidity, mortality, and health status change that occurred as a result of the interventions. Which type of objective should be written?
    a. Outcome
    b. Process
    c. Impact
    d. Environmental

125. To increase the rate of prostate screening among men ages 50 and older is an example of what type of statement?
    a. Goal
    b. Mission
    c. Vsion
    d. Objective

126. Which of the following represents primary sources that a health education specialist could use for a community needs assessment?
    a. US census data, vital records, disease registries
    b. State health data from the health department
    c. Published scientific studies and reports
    d. Observations, surveys, and interviews

127. According to which theory or model do people assess the threat of an emerging disease by assessing their perceived susceptibility against the severity of the disease?
    a. Social Cognitive Theory
    b. Diffusion of Innovations
    c. Health Belief Model
    d. Social Marketing

128. A health department conducted a social media campaign for its new childhood immunization clinic to drive community members to the department's website for appointment scheduling. The best data to track using the website's analytics would be which of the following?
    a. Organic traffic
    b. Goal behavior
    c. Direct traffic
    d. Interest volume

129. A health education specialist works as a patient educator at a healthcare institution. Part of the job is to work with patients who have recently suffered a heart attack. This type of prevention is an example of:
    a. primary.
    b. tertiary.
    c. secondary.
    d. intermediate.

130. One of the first considerations when determining the potential appropriateness of an external organization for collaboration is an alignment of:
    a. organizational budget.
    b. staffing turnover.
    c. mission, vision, and values.
    d. organizational structure.

131. In a priority population, the infant mortality rate and overall death rate for mothers with less than a high school education is almost twice as high as mothers with 13 or more years of education. These rates are examples of health:
    a. equity.
    b. capacity.
    c. determinants.
    d. disparities.

132. When a media advocacy campaign is used to educate about proposed policy changes, decision-makers with the power to affect change are which type of audience?
    a. Primary
    b. Secondary
    c. Tertiary
    d. Quaternary

133. A health education specialist needs to determine specific alcohol, tobacco, and drug use prevention needs and immediately prioritize those needs with a few experts from the priority population. Which primary data collection technique would be the best to use in this scenario?
    a. Observations
    b. Nominal group process
    c. Delphi panel
    d. Focus group

134. To understand the three human subjects' protection guidelines of "respect for persons," "beneficence," and "justice," one would look to the:
    a. CNHEO code of ethics.
    b. Institutional Review Board.
    c. Belmont Report.
    d. Geneva Convention Treaty.

135. Conducting a capacity assessment is focused on identifying:
    a. community weaknesses.
    b. community needs.
    c. health problems.
    d. community resources.

136. Consumption, medication compliance, and self-care are considered which type of factors related to health
    a. Behavioral
    b. Beliefs
    c. Genetic
    d. Environmental

137. Which of the following is an example of a correctly written learning objective?
    a. "Individuals participating in the health education program will be able to identify three ways to protect their skin from the sun by the end of the program."
    b. "Individuals in the program will increase sun exposure prevention activities by 25% by the sixth week of the program."
    c. "Seventy-five percent of individuals participating in the program will increase their knowledge of the harmful effects of sun exposure over the following three months."
    d. "Program health education specialists will identify 10 new participants for each program period."

138. A social media campaign leading with Facebook for its new drive-through immunization clinic was conducted in a health department. The health education specialist used the platform's analytics to determine the number of unique people who viewed the initial clinic kick-off post. The health education specialist is evaluating which type of social media reach?
     a. Paid
     b. Organic
     c. Viral
     d. Likes

139. Due to financial constraints, a research team is only recruiting participants from three hospitals in the local metropolitan area. In doing so, the researchers have established:
     a. limitations.
     b. delimitations.
     c. eliminations.
     d. assumptions.

140. A health education specialist is asked to measure actual use of a biking trail in a local community. Which of the following methods is best for measuring the actual use of the trail over a period of a week?
     a. Surveys
     b. Focus groups
     c. Nominal group process
     d. Observation

141. A formal social media policy should include the use of _____ to maintain pages, post scheduled messages, and respond to follower posts.
     a. tagging
     b. apps
     c. networks
     d. moderators

142. The organization that accredits schools of public health, graduate programs in public/community health, and undergraduate programs is:
     a. SOPHE.
     b. NCHEC.
     c. CEPH.
     d. CAEP.

143. Which would be the best technique to determine whether patients have the skills necessary to prepare a healthy, low calorie, low fat meal? Have the patients:
     a. describe the steps they would follow to create the meal.
     b. create a meal through a simulation activity.
     c. take a valid test that covers the material.
     d. critique several meals created by other patients.

144. The social media campaign to change social norms related to the teen pregnancy that was developed by a health education specialist is reviewed by a group of adolescents from the priority population. Feedback from the adolescents allows the health education specialist to make changes before implementing the campaign, which refers to what type of evaluation?
    a. Formative
    b. Summative
    c. Impact
    d. Process

145. The intervention program is doing so well that it needs to be expanded; however, the sponsoring agency has limited funding for expansion. The health education specialist found another agency willing to provide the sponsor with a larger venue in exchange for access to the sponsor's educational library. This method of financing the program is called:
    a. cooperative agreements.
    b. cost-sharing
    c. third-party support.
    d. organizational sponsorship.

146. The health problems of a priority population are best identified through:
    a. a program evaluation.
    b. a contingency plan.
    c. coalition building.
    d. community assessment.

147. In a health communication campaign, stoplight (red, yellow, green) characters are used to encourage adult immunizations. The most likely behavior change theory on which the campaign was based is which of the following?
    a. Health belief model
    b. Transtheoretical model
    c. Communication-persuasion model
    d. Information-persuasion matrix

148. Which of the following is not an element of an effective advocacy plan?
    a. Market the coalition
    b. Identify goals
    c. Communication-persuasion model
    d. Strategize tactics

149. In the strategic planning process after an organization defines or refines its mission statement, the next step is to:
    a. list internal and external strengths and opportunities.
    b. list mandates and resources.
    c. identify key stakeholders.
    d. write the initial report.

150. In the ecological model, behavior has many influences. Which level best describes the role of cultural values, norms, and a built environment?
    a. Intrapersonal
    b. Interpersonal
    c. Organizational
    d. Community

151. Which of the following is not one of Frieden's Six Components for Effective Public Health Program Implementation? Use:
    a. multiple, high-priority interventions.
    b. innovation for evidence base development.
    c. partnerships and coalitions.
    d. effective program management.

152. A health education specialist is developing a new Web site as part of an intervention for people with visual disabilities. Which law should the health education specialist review and consider when developing the Web site?
    a. Plain Language Act
    b. Paperwork Reduction Act
    c. Section 508 of the Rehabilitation Act
    d. Anti-lobbying provisions

153. Which of the following is an example of a method used during a social assessment?
    a. Delphi technique
    b. Process evaluation
    c. Outcome evaluation
    d. Construct validation

154. Following the PRECEDE-PROCEDE Model, assessing if community members have adequate access to oral health care services is which type of factor in the educational and ecological assessment?
    a. Enabling
    b. Predisposing
    c. Reinforcing
    d. Motivating

155. Set of communication tools for education and persuasion using paid media is which of the following?
    a. Advocacy
    b. Promotion
    c. Publicity
    d. Advertising

156. An instrument that is used to measure what it purports to measure is said be _____, while an instrument that repeatedly produces the same results is said to be _____.
   a. reliable, valid.
   b. valid, reliable.
   c. relevant, dependable.
   d. dependable, relevant.

157. A health education specialist finds that there are more people requesting a smoking cessation program than can be accommodated. This is an example of which type of need?
   a. Expressed
   b. Normative
   c. Perceived
   d. Relative

158. In a health communications campaign for a walking program, it was emphasized that exercise can make a person feel better, other people are starting to participate in group fitness walks, and it is easy to reserve time in busy schedules for a short walk. The most likely behavior change theory on which the campaign was based is which of the following?
   a. Health belief
   b. Social cognitive
   c. Theory of planned behavior
   d. Transtheoretical

159. When planning a diabetes prevention program following the PRECEDE-PROCEDE Model, data on high sugar intake would fall into which assessment phase?
   a. Epidemiological assessment
   b. Social assessment and situational analysis
   c. Educational and ecological assessment
   d. Intervention alignment and administrative and policy assessment

160. The agency administrator wants the big picture or summary of an intervention's resources, activities, and results. Therefore, the health education specialist creates which of the following to put in the report to the administrator?
   a. Marketing mix
   b. Logic model
   c. Instructional design framework
   d. Unit of study

161. The following are benefits of involvement with coalitions, collaborative partnerships, communities of practice, and other networks EXCEPT:
   A. creating common ground and identity among interdisciplinary and multi-sector partners .
   B. persuading collaborators to view social issues from the organizer's perspective.
   C. enhancing learning by bringing together stakeholders with varied experiences.
   D. building capacity among members and organizations to address community issues.

162. The health education specialist can influence policymaking at the implementation stage by:
    a. offering comment on draft rules.
    b. recommending changes based on operational experience.
    c. defining the problem.
    d. evaluating policy solutions.

163. Which type of literature review typically is used to identify current gaps in the literature after comprehensively reviewing the literature on a topic?
    a. Systematic review
    b. Meta-analysis
    c. Pooled analysis
    d. Computerized review

164. Data analysis methods should be specified during the _____ stage.
    a. assessment
    b. planning
    c. implementation
    d. evaluation

165. In evaluating a legislative advocacy campaign, process indicators include:
    a. public attitude change.
    b. policy adoption.
    c. campaign reach.
    d. policy awareness.

Certified Health Education Specialist
Examination Questions Key

1.	c – Area 6	38.	c – Area 6	75.	d – Area 3	112.	d – Area 8	149.	a – Area 7
2.	a – Area 4	39.	a – Area 2	76.	c – Area 2	113.	a – Area 2	150.	d – Area 5
3.	c – Area 2	40.	c – Area 1	77.	b – Area 6	114.	a – Area 2	151.	a – Area 3
4.	b – Area 1	41.	c – Area 7	78.	d – Area 4	115.	d – Area 5	152.	c – Area 8
5.	b- Area 1	42.	a – Area 5	79.	a – Area 1	116.	c – Area 8	153.	a – Area 1
6.	d – Area 8	43.	b – Area 3	80.	b – Area 5	117.	d – Area 7	154.	a – Area 2
7.	c – Area 3	44.	c – Area 2	81.	a – Area 3	118.	a – Area 1	155.	d – Area 6
8.	a – Area 3	45.	a – Area 2	82.	c – Area 5	119.	b – Area 4	156.	b – Area 4
9.	c – Area 5	46.	d – Area 3	83.	b – Area 1	120.	b – Area 5	157.	a – Area 1
10.	a – Area 7	47.	c – Area 6	84.	a – Area 1	121.	c – Area 6	158.	c – Area 6
11.	d – Area 4	48.	d – Area 4	85.	c – Area 2	122.	c – Area 1	159.	a – Area 2
12.	d – Area 1	49.	b – Area 1	86.	a – Area 7	123.	d – Area 8	160.	b – Area 4
13.	b – Area 8	50.	c – Area 8	87.	d – Area 4	124.	a – Area 2	161.	b – Area 8
14.	a – Area 3	51.	c – Area 5	88.	d – Area 8	125.	a – Area 2	162.	a – Area 5
15.	c – Area 5	52.	a – Area 3	89.	b – Area 3	126.	d – Area 1	163.	a – Area 1
16.	a – Area 2	53.	b – Area 3	90.	c – Area 5	127.	c – Area 8	164.	b – Area 4
17.	d – Area 6	54.	c – Area 6	91.	d – Area 3	128.	b – Area 6	165.	c – Area 5
18.	c – Area 2	55.	d – Area 1	92.	b – Area 6	129.	b – Area 2		
19.	b- Area 5	56.	d – Area 4	93.	a – Area 4	130.	c – Area 7		
20.	d – Area 1	57.	a – Area 3	94.	b – Area 2	131.	d – Area 1		
21.	b – Area 1	58.	d – Area 7	95.	c – Area 8	132.	a – Area 5		
22.	a – Area 6	59.	b – Area 5	96.	a – Area 3	133.	b – Area 1		
23.	c – Area 4	60.	b – Area 8	97.	c – Area 1	134.	c – Area 8		
24.	d – Area 3	61.	a – Area 4	98.	a – Area 3	135.	d – Area 1		
25.	a – Area 5	62.	c – Area 6	99.	b – Area 4	136.	a – Area 1		
26.	b – Area 7	63.	a – Area 3	100.	d- Area 2	137.	a – Area 2		
27.	c – Area 8	64.	d – Area 1	101.	a – Area 6	138.	b – Area 6		
28.	b – Area 2	65.	a – Area 3	102.	d – Area 7	139.	b – Area 4		
29.	d – Area 4	66.	a – Area 2	103.	c – Area 3	140.	d – Area 1		
30.	b – Area 8	67.	b – Area 3	104.	b – Area 8	141.	d – Area 6		
31.	d – Area 6	68.	b – Area 5	105.	a – Area 6	142.	c – Area 8		
32.	a – Area 3	69.	d – Area 8	106.	d – Area 3	143.	b – Area 1		
33.	b – Area 5	70.	b – Area 4	107.	b – Area 5	144.	a – Area 2		
34.	b – Area 2	71.	c – Area 3	108.	a – Area 2	145.	a – Area 7		
35.	c – Area 1	72.	d – Area 4	109.	d – Area 1	146.	d – Area 1		
36.	a – Area 4	73.	b – Area 6	110.	d – Area 3	147.	b – Area 6		
37.	b – Area 8	74.	c – Area 8	111.	a – Area 4	148.	a – Area 5		

Appendix D
Master Certified Health Education Specialist Practice Examination Questions

The following practice examination questions are aligned with Sub-competencies identified as entry- and advanced- levels as defined by the Health Education Specialist Practice Analysis II (HESPA II 2020) and outlined within this study companion. The practice questions, written by health education specialists, may assist the user in preparing for the Certified Health Education Specialist (CHES®) or Master Certified Health Education Specialist (MCHES®) examinations and/or to identify areas of concentration for professional development and training of practicing health education specialists. These questions are not on the current certification examination. Some of the questions have been altered from discarded certification examination questions. The practice questions in this publication have not been subjected to the same rigorous psychometric testing procedures as questions appearing on the CHES® or MCHES® examinations. Specifically, a passing score on the practice examination questions does not in any way predict or guarantee a passing score on the CHES®/MCHES® examinations. The practice questions should only be used to direct study efforts.

The practice questions are meant to be challenging. Initially, the user may find that more than one answer appears to be correct. In these instances, the user is encouraged to conduct careful analysis of the questions and possible answers to identify the correct responses. It might be helpful to use the practice examination questions under similar conditions in which the CHES®/MCHES® examinations are officially administered. For example, the user would be allowed no more than three hours to complete the examination. The user would not utilize or depend on resources such as the study guide, textbooks, publications, or calculators to complete the examination.

An answer key is provided at the end of the practice examination questions. In addition to providing the user with the correct answer, the user will find at least one Area of Responsibility that aligns with the question identified. A review of the number of incorrect answers from any particular Area of Responsibility may help the user target areas of weakness where more study would be beneficial. ***It is strongly recommended that resources beyond the use of this study companion are used to adequately prepare for the certification examination.***

In closing, feedback from candidates who were successful in passing previous certification examinations and previous study guide users indicates that being part of a small group that allowed participants to "work through" the practice examination questions and discuss why answers are correct or incorrect can be beneficial.

1. The health education specialist has limited resources for program evaluation but wishes to place different variables into the intervention to see change over time as well as to eliminate any program activities that do not positively impact program objectives. The best evaluation design to use in this case is:
   a. pre- and post- single-group design.
   b. interrupted time series design with a single group.
   c. post-test only single group design
   d. pre-test only single group design.

2. A foodborne outbreak has caused the closing of three local restaurants so that epidemiologists and food safety staff can identify the outbreak source. Health education specialists and communication specialists plan to use earned media and social media to educate local community members about the outbreak. What should the health education specialists and communication specialists do first?
   a. Identify the audience.
   b. Pick a theory or model to use.
   c. Check for available funds.
   d. Find partners to help.

3. A health education specialist wants to be sure that participants in an 8-week healthy eating program have acquired the fundamental cooking skills prior to the end of the sessions. Which one of the following evaluations would the health education specialist implement to assess skills acquisition?
   a. Impact
   b. Outcome
   c. Process
   d. Formative

4. A health education specialist from the local health department has been invited to participate in a statewide cancer control consortium. The role that the health education specialist is likely to fulfil is as the:
   a. patient regulator.
   b. primary care expert.
   c. community developer.
   d. subject matter expert.

5. To design the health communication messages and select appropriate media for a health education strategy, the health education specialist must understand the priorities and influences of the audience. Therefore, the health education specialist first should conduct an audience:
   a. influence technique.
   b. analysis.
   c. ideation procedure.
   d. synthesis.

6. A health education specialist is using Social Cognitive Theory to plan a community wide program to prevent alcohol use among middle school aged youth. One aspect of the program includes a curriculum designed to help youth resist peer pressure to drink. To increase self-efficacy to resist peer pressure, the curriculum should include:
   a. activities that allow practice of skills.
   b. trained peer leaders elected by middle school youth.
   c. activities that reinforce the negative consequence of alcohol use.
   d. small prizes for completing all homework assignments.

7. In the informational training related to an adolescent health literacy pilot program, the attendees, all of whom are classroom teachers, state that instead of having a single facilitator come into their classroom to deliver the curriculum, they prefer to deliver it themselves. They make their case to the trainer, stating they are classroom teachers and, as such, know how to deliver curriculum. Which of the following concepts does the trainer use to explain why this health education curriculum is being implemented with a single facilitator?
   a. Validity
   b. Reliability
   c. Evaluation
   d. Fidelity

8. The health education specialist called the state legislator to specifically ask about that legislator's support for HR 66, a bill that permanently funds the Children's Health Insurance Program (CHIP) and related programs that are used to support the development of child health quality measures and outreach and enrollment efforts. Which of the following terms describe this activity?
   a. Direct advocacy
   b. Education advocacy
   c. Lobbying
   d. Indirect advocacy

9. A large group of tourists traveled on a cruise ship and developed an acute, flu-like illness. The suspected cause of the illness was associated with the trip on the cruise ship. Health authorities need to know the number of all passengers who became ill as well as those who traveled on the cruise ship. Which rate should the health education specialist calculate to provide information to health authorities?
   a. Prevalence rate
   b. Fatality rate
   c. Attack rate
   d. Mortality rate

10. A survey is conducted to assess community members' opinions on tobacco-free local parks. The health education specialist selects a random sample of community members from each of the four park districts. This sample plan is called:
    a. simple random.
    b. stratified random.
    c. cluster.
    d. snowball.

11. A health education specialist wants to attend a school board meeting to discuss safety issues in the school. Though multiple forms of data will be used, which of the following will cause a more emotional reaction to evidence that an intervention is necessary?
    a. Photovoice or story-telling from the students' point of view
    b. National data from the CDC compared to state data regarding safety
    c. Data presented from a survey of high school seniors
    d. GIS data of the community

12. If, in an evaluation question, a person is asked about an abstract concept, the concept seems hard to measure, and little credible data have previously been found, which of the following methods would be most helpful to use?
    a. Qualitative
    b. Quantitative
    c. Mixed
    d. Surveillance

13. When planning to work with a community to gather data for a local health program, one of the health education specialist's first steps should be to:
    a. create a coalition of partners with access to community data.
    b. assess the program's fidelity.
    c. develop a new instrument to gather community data.
    d. evaluate a similar community program.

14. In the health communications plan, the priority audiences have been identified, and, now, the influencing audiences are being analyzed. Which task will help the health education specialist determine the proportion of resources to be used on influencer advocacy?
    a. Identify health service provider networks.
    b. Ask for names of other opinion leaders.
    c. Estimate influencers' levels of influence.
    d. Consider psychographic variables.

15. An organization is undergoing restructuring because of budgetary cuts, which in turn impacts health promotion efforts. Which approach to organizational change is occurring?
    a. Revolutionary
    b. Evolutionary
    c. Regulatory
    d. Reactionary

16. Prior to a first meeting with a legislator, what is a vital first step?
    a. Develop talking points.
    b. Develop an advocacy toolkit.
    c. Conduct research on the legislator.
    d. Send a letter requesting a meeting.

17. In program evaluation, logic models link:
    a. goals, services, and measurement.
    b. plans, strategies, and maps.
    c. design, data collection, and dissemination.
    d. structure, language, and resources.

18. In strategic health behavior change communication campaigns, after identifying the issue, defining audiences, and selecting objectives, the health education specialist wishes to link the audience with positive feelings for the desired health behavior. This process is called:
    a. long-term identity.
    b. behavior positioning.
    c. product differentiation.
    d. commercial marketing.

19. Which one of the following plans includes data description, data access, data standards, and data preservation?
    a. Proprietary interest
    b. Data management
    c. Data security
    d. Project officer

20. When a health education specialist begins the process of data collection for a needs assessment, what activity should be accomplished first?
    a. Collect qualitative data that will establish need.
    b. Create a questionnaire to pilot test with a small sample.
    c. Locate relevant secondary data that will establish need.
    d. Contact key informants to identify data needed.

21. If resources are limited but audience segmentation is necessary, the most appropriate strategies the health education specialist should use for the health communications campaign should be which one of the following?
    a. Decrease the number of segments/leverage funding with other programs.
    b. Design more customized messages/segment only by stage of behavior change.
    c. Focus on behavior motivation/fundraise and ask for donations.
    d. Require a new approach/ask priority and influencing audiences for funding.

22. The health education specialist observes a problem and wants to study it using a research design that is focused on immediate solutions directly applicable to the specialist's health education practice. The type of design the health education specialist should select would be:
    a. case study.
    b. causal.
    c. experimental.
    d. action.

23. Estimating parameters and hypothesis testing are two areas of _____ statistics.
    a. descriptive
    b. inferential
    c. dispersion
    d. validation

24. The document that is passed to the creative team from the strategic communications planning team in which health issue information, audience communication needs, facts to support audience behavior change, and benefits for the audience of the change are summarized is called which one of the following?
    a. Message brief
    b. Communication plan
    c. Desired user profile
    d. Positioning statement

The following scenario is used for questions 25, 26, 27.

A health education specialist is planning a multi-level program to decrease rates of obesity in an urban community. Community gardens are planned for empty lots, and local convenience store managers have agreed to begin selling fresh fruits and vegetables. To assist families, mobile devices will be distributed and used to help deliver messages and tips and to collect data. Additionally, community leaders have pledged to focus on making the community safe for physical activity. Volunteers are mapping out walking routes to encourage families to walk together. Partnerships have formed and memorandums of understanding have been drafted.

25. In the scenario provided, which one of the following is considered an infrastructure/supply need?
    a. Partnerships
    b. Family participation
    c. Community leaders
    d. Mobile devices

26. In the scenario provided, which one of the following is considered a financial resource for the program?
    a. Partnerships
    b. Family participation
    c. Mobile devices
    d. Community gardens

27. In the scenario provided, if mobile devices were not given to the priority population, which ethical principle might have been breached, especially in terms of program delivery?
    a. Transparency
    b. Beneficence
    c. Equity
    d. Confidentiality

28. A type of predictive analysis that is used to determine the impact of independent variables on a dependent variable is:
    a. correlation.
    b. cross-tabs.
    c. regression.
    d. analysis of variance.

29. The health education specialist must analyze the meaning of the data collected during the assessment and determine health education needs. If the health education specialist aggregates the data, which cognitive process of qualitative research is the focus?
    a. Synthesizing
    b. Comprehending
    c. Theorizing
    d. Decontextualizing

30. Explaining potential positive outcomes reflects the concept of perceived _____ which is/are addressed in the Health Belief Model:
    a. barriers
    b. benefits
    c. severity
    d. susceptibility

31. Which dimension of RE-AIM is used to evaluate the extent to which health education intervention components were institutionalized within an organization's operations long term?
    a. Maintenance
    b. Adoption
    c. Implementation
    d. Reach

32. The health education specialist needs to choose the best communication tools for each channel that aligns with the chosen strategic communications plan to meet objectives. The specialist is specifically looking to create awareness of a health service during a campaign launch and have plenty of funding and staffing. Of the following, which is the most appropriate tool to use?
    a. Advertising
    b. Community participation
    c. Entertainment
    d. Event promotion

33. Which type of the following sampling procedures promotes case selection transparency and data triangulation?
    a. Probability
    b. Purposive
    c. Convenience
    d. Random

34. Which type of evaluation would a health education specialist use as an ongoing activity to monitor the reach and influence of media messages to improve and revise messages as necessary?
    a. Summative
    b. Outcome
    c. Impact
    d. Process

35. The objective of a college-student health program is to reduce binge drinking by an average of 10%. Mid-program health-risk appraisals indicate that binge drinking has increased by 50% since the program was implemented. To enhance the likelihood of program success, which one of the following actions is most appropriate?
    a. Evaluate the program using a different group of college students.
    b. Change the program objective.
    c. Modify the program interventions.
    d. Avoid any changes until the end-of-program evaluation.

36. In health communication campaign evaluation, which type of monitoring refers to quality, amount, and dissemination of campaign outputs?
    a. Process
    b. Impact
    c. Performance
    d. Outcome

37. For people with fewer than 12 years of education (high school or less), the infant mortality rate and overall death rate is almost twice as high as people with 13 or more years of education (at least one year of college). These rates are examples of health:
    a. capacity.
    b. disparities.
    c. inequities.
    d. equity.

38. In program evaluation, logic models can help create the evaluation questions. The activities and outputs sections of the model can help frame which type of evaluation questions?
    a. Context
    b. Implementation
    c. Summative
    d. Outcome

39. What theory or model is best to use for identifying facts that impact attitudes and beliefs?
    a. Theory of Planned Behavior
    b. Precaution Adoption Process Model
    c. Transtheoretical Model
    d. Stimulus Response Theory

40. Which one of the following is an example of grassroots advocacy?
    a. Donating money to a political campaign
    b. Contacting a policymaker
    c. Drafting a position paper for a professional organization
    d. Starting a door-to-door petition

The following figure is used for questions 41 and 42.

Figure 1
FIGURE Model-adjusted incidence of type 1 and type 2 diabetes among youths, overall and by race/ethnicity* — SEARCH for Diabetes in Youth Study (SEARCH., United States,† 2002–2015

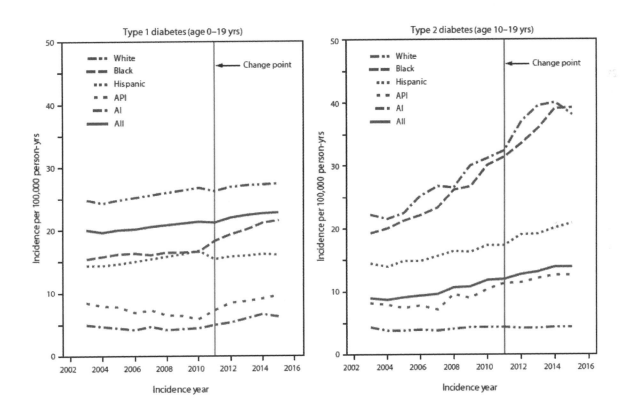

Abbreviations: AI = American Indian; API = Asian/Pacific Islander.
   * Persons who were AI were primarily from one southwestern tribe.
   † SEARCH includes data on youths (<20 years. in Colorado (all 64 counties plus selected Indian reservations in Arizona and New Mexico under the direction of Colorado., Ohio (eight counties., South Carolina (all 46 counties., Washington (five counties., and in California for Kaiser Permanente Southern California health plan enrollees in seven counties.

41. Which of the following statements regarding the graphs above is true?
    a. American Indian youth populations have the highest rates of type 1 and type 2 diabetes of all racial and ethnic groups.
    b. Rates of type 2 diabetes in youth remained relatively steady from 2002 to 2016.
    c. Rates of type 1 diabetes among Asian/Pacific Islander youth in 2016 were similar to rates of type 2 diabetes in this same population in 2010.
    d. In 2010, there was a major societal change that caused rates of type 2 diabetes to increase dramatically among Black and American Indian youth populations

42. Rates of type 2 diabetes among youth ages 10-19:
    a. increased among all races and ethnicities included in the graph.
    b. remained steady among Asian/Pacific Islanders.
    c. almost doubled among Asian/Pacific Islanders.
    d. were higher than rates of type 1 diabetes in youth for whites.

43. The least representative of non-probability sampling techniques is which one of the following?
    a. Convenience
    b. Snowball
    c. Quota
    d. Expert

44. Once a health education specialist has hired program staff, the plan for staff training should include:
    a. use of specific numerically scored performance reports.
    b. restricting activities to the most important program areas only.
    c. a six month waiting period for evaluations.
    d. ongoing mentoring and supervision.

45. In the impact assessment of a health communications campaign evaluation plan, both __ and ___ indicators should be measured.
    a. individual/social
    b. strategy/causality
    c. activities/outputs
    d. process/outcome

46. Which one of the following strategies would be most effective for developing substance abuse resistance skills?
    a. Lecture
    b. Discussion
    c. Role play
    d. Brainstorming

47. The health education specialist can examine health determinants through a socio-ecological lens. Which socio-ecological and social determinant factor includes healthcare providers' recommendations?
    a. Interpersonal
    b. Individual
    c. Community
    d. Policy

48. Health education specialists are ethically obligated to ensure confidentiality and to protect the privacy of all clients. The law that is used to protect the privacy of patient information is the:
    a. Health Information Protection Act.
    b. Health Insurance Profitability Act of Accountability.
    c. Health Information Accuracy Act.
    d. Health Insurance Portability and Accountability Act.

49. The level of measurement for communication campaign evaluation data in which process/early, impact/ middle, and outcome/late campaign results are tracked is _____ based.
    a. population
    b. program
    c. service
    d. indicator

50. Usually calculated before conducting a research study to identify the necessary sample size for appropriate analysis and to keep sample size as low as possible is what type of analysis?
    a. Power
    b. Covariate
    c. Reliability
    d. Validity

51. Which strategy is used to simplify identifying barriers to creating a nutrition program and enhancing its success on a college campus?
    a. Identify a sound evaluation tool to assess program effectiveness.
    b. Assign a committee to lead the task for program sustainability.
    c. Find out who the "gatekeepers" are for getting access to the population.
    d. Design a team to set objectives for adoption and implementation of the program.

52. In a health communication campaign, the health education specialist used stoplight (red, yellow, green) characters in marketing materials to encourage adult immunizations. The most likely behavior change theory on which the campaign was based is which one of the following?
    a. Health belief model
    b. Transtheoretical model
    c. Communication-persuasion model
    d. Information-persuasion matrix

53. The health education specialist wishes to strengthen program evaluation capacity within the organization. The specialist's evaluation capacity assessment should be focused on which factors?
    a. Individual
    b. Organizational
    c. Implementation
    d. Both individual and organizational

54. When should the health education specialist select an evaluation design?
    a. After choosing the evaluation questions and after data collection methods are identified
    b. After choosing the evaluation questions and before data collection methods are identified
    c. At the same time evaluation questions are chosen and at the same time data collection methods are identified
    d. Before choosing evaluation questions and after data collection methods are identified

The following scenario is used for questions 55, 56, and 57.

A health education specialist in the local health department has been asked to create a new program for overweight teens in which volunteers will be used to staff most of the activities. As part of this program, the health education specialist is responsible for recruiting, training, and supervising the volunteers.

55. Which one of the following factors is most important in supervising the volunteers?
    a. A clear job description for the volunteers
    b. An informal method of supervision
    c. An evaluation system that is based on incentives
    d. An appropriate evaluation tool

56. The best group from which to recruit volunteers is which one of the following?
    a. Students who have reached and maintained a lower weight
    b. Representatives from the student government
    c. College students who are overweight
    d. Members of the local recreation center

57. A critical issue in using volunteers for the program is to provide the/an:
    a. necessary needs assessment data.
    b. overview of the evaluation system.
    c. necessary training to do the work.
    d. overview of the rewards system.

58. Which one of the following statements accurately describes what is known about the principles of learning?
    a. Adults seem to accept new information at face value and do not need to validate it.
    b. Children expect what they are learning to be immediately useful.
    c. Children use the experiences of others on which to build new information.
    d. Adult learners need to see the relevance of the educational content to their personal experience.

59. When selecting volunteers who will be trained to serve as facilitators, which of the following would be most appropriate? Individuals who:
    a. have served as volunteers in the past.
    b. hold at least a college degree.
    c. are similar to the priority population.
    d. are from the priority population.

60. When conducting training of personnel, it is important to remember principles of andragogy. Which of the following is an important learning principle for andragogy?
    a. Focus on problem solving skills rather than learning content.
    b. Focus on technology and gaming to make learning fun.
    c. Use mostly traditional formats, as this format reveals to what adults are accustomed.
    d. Use examples that could be used with a variety of audiences.

61. A professional who is new to health education is seeking mentorship to help with navigating a complex role in a health department that is restructuring. All of the potential mentors, however, are extremely busy, so a more proactive responsibility for personal learning is needed. This type of mentorship is called:
    a. mentoring up.
    b. mentoring down.
    c. mentorship from multiple sources.
    d. peer mentoring.

62. How can the researcher decrease risk for Type I error in a study?
    a. Use a lower p value.
    b. Ensure statistical test chosen has enough power.
    c. Ensure large sample size.
    d. Use a higher p value.

63. In a health communications campaign for a walking program, it was emphasized that exercise can make one feel better, other people are starting to participate in group fitness walks, and it is easy to reserve time in busy schedules for a short walk. The most likely behavior change theory the campaign was based on is which one of the following?
    a. Health belief
    b. Social cognitive
    c. Theory of planned behavior
    d. Transtheoretical

64. A health education specialist is developing a new Web site as part of an intervention for people with visual disabilities. Which law or regulation should the health education specialist review and consider when developing the Web site?
    a. Section 508 of the Rehabilitation Act
    b. Plain Language Act
    c. Paperwork Reduction Act
    d. Anti-lobbying provisions

65. The objective of a worksite health promotion program is to encourage employees to stop smoking. For those employees who are not thinking about quitting, which types of health education strategies might encourage them to consider quitting?
    a. Increasing awareness of harmful effects of smoking.
    b. Identifying triggers that might encourage smoking.
    c. Setting up a support group to reduce risk of relapse.
    d. Providing nicotine patches to ease the craving.

66. Which model is used to address feelings of susceptibility and belief in the seriousness of a health problem?
    a. Stage of Change Model
    b. Precaution Adoption Process Model
    c. Health Belief Model
    d. Theory of Changed Behavior

67. In writing the research results dissemination plan, the health education specialist has defined the target audience as the healthcare consumers. Which one of the following is the most appropriate dissemination option for the results?
    a. Guideline database
    b. Journal publication
    c. Health-related organization endorsement
    d. Webinar

68. As a result of the nutrition assessment, the health education specialists realize that the diets of the community's elderly residents do not meet basic nutritional needs. Therefore, these individuals are described as which population?
    a. Priority
    b. Stakeholder
    c. Credible
    d. Service

69. The health communications campaign evaluation question: "Is the audience more engaged with the behavior change or issue? If not, how are the data used to explain why?" should be posed at which stage of the strategy?
    a. Early
    b. Middle
    c. Late
    d. Post-program

70. What is a tool used to identify advocacy campaign resources and gaps?
    a. Asset inventory
    b. Network assessment
    c. Alliance mapping
    d. Legislative tracker

71. Which one of the following is not a probability sampling method?
    a. Cluster
    b. Stratified
    c. Quota
    d. Systematic

72. A SMART objective is stated in terms of what is to be changed, the time frame for achieving the change, and the:
    a. program goals.
    b. amount of change.
    c. instructor effectiveness.
    d. specificity of content.

73. The health education specialist's role is to establish collaborative relationships with organizations to gain access to data for state-wide community needs assessment. Which of the following is the best approach to secure the data needed?
    a. Identify key individuals and stakeholders within the various organizations to build a relationship.
    b. Determine the level of relationship needed with each organization to obtain data.
    c. Establish a data sharing agreement, including the outcome, purpose, data ownership, and conditions of release.
    d. Establish a network of organizations with data needed for state-wide community needs assessment.

74. In qualitative studies, which types of questions are developed to narrow the purpose statement?
    a. Research
    b. Purpose
    c. Objective
    d. Predictive

75. Which organization or committee is responsible for protecting the rights of research participants?
    a. Conflict of Interest Committee
    b. Health and Safety Board
    c. Institutional Review Board
    d. Research Integrity Committee

76. A process that is used in organizations, similar to a needs assessment, is used to assess assumptions and values related to health education and promotion. This process is referred to as a/an:
    a. cultural audit.
    b. strategy assessment.
    c. strategic plan.
    d. asset map.

77. A health education specialist wants to present visual data regarding community assets. Which one of the following can be used to achieve a visual presentation?
    a. Prevalence rates
    b. GIS mapping
    c. Assets listed by address
    d. Visualization of public records

78. A hospital is expanding outreach services and facilities with a new unit that is focused on prevention and the treatment of chronic diseases. The health education specialist is tasked with gathering local data on these conditions. Which is the most useful rate to use?
    a. Incidence
    b. Attack
    c. Prevalence
    d. Natality

79. If a health education specialist wants to use volunteers to help implement programs, which one of the following should be most important?
    a. Make sure volunteers have appropriate training to complete assigned tasks.
    b. Make sure there is a reward system in place.
    c. Hold regular meetings to make sure volunteers stay motivated.
    d. Do not require individuals to volunteer more than once day per week.

80. The process of identifying research strengths and weaknesses at the individual, organizational, and systems levels is capacity:
    a. building.
    b. monitoring.
    c. assurance.
    d. assessment.

81. A health education specialist is managing a mobile health intervention program in which demographic and behavioral information about its participants is collected. After discovering a breach in the program's data storage system, what is the manager's most pressing ethical issue?
    a. Beneficence
    b. Confidentiality
    c. Transparency
    d. Equity

The following scenario is used for questions 82 and 83.

A health education specialist is planning a health communication campaign to distribute new mammography materials developed by the National Cancer Institute (NCI) to women 40 years and older who are at increased risk for breast cancer and are living in an urban community. Identified stakeholders include the local and state health agency leaders, cancer research organizations, local policymakers, and the medical media in the area. The promotional distribution plan involves promoting the new mammography materials to health professionals, patients, and the public through organizations, identified health professionals, and various types of media, including relevant social media outlets.

82. Which of the following is considered a characteristic of effective communication related to message delivery?
    a. Cost: The development of the message content is cost-effective.
    b. Availability: The message content is delivered in a way/place where the intended audience easily can access the message.
    c. Function: The message function (i.e., calling attention to the new mammography materials) is pilot tested.
    d. Objectives: The communication objectives of the message are clearly identified in the message content.

83. What common key performance indicator (KPI) or metric for social media is used to monitor the number of people who indicate agreement with the content posted or shared, and/or who share posted content to influence others on social media?
    a. Exposure
    b. Reach
    c. Engagement
    d. Traffic

84. The tobacco prevention and cessation program at a state health department did not have funding renewed and is scheduled to end in the next twelve months. A strategic plan, vision, and program evaluation data are available. What other sustainability domain or element should a health education specialist explore for sustaining the program?
    a. Collaborations or partnerships
    b. Creating a new vision
    c. Volunteer or intern staff
    d. Free materials and services

85. Which one of the following is the best example of a measurable behavioral objective? Program participants will:
    a. understand the importance of controlling hypertension.
    b. be able to identify controllable risk factors for hypertension.
    c. be aware of the magnitude of the problem of hypertension.
    d. know the causes of hypertension.

86. Which one of the following is not a technology tool for analysis of quantitative survey data?
    a. NVivo
    b. R (open source)
    c. SAS
    d. Stata

87. Members of an organization are planning an advocacy summit and are hoping participants will bring a list of elected officials in their individual zip codes. What online resource will be helpful for the participants?
    a. Health Action Center
    b. APHA Legislative Action
    c. Capwiz
    d. BALLOTPEDIA

88. Consumption, medication compliance, and self-care are considered which type of factors related to health?
    a. Environmental
    b. Attitudes
    c. Behavioral
    d. Genetic

89. The intervention program has been adopted, and the priority population is ready to participate in it. The implementation team members need to know their tasks and associated due dates, and the health education specialist needs a relatively simple way to track the team's projected and actual task completion progress. To meet both needs, as well as to identify and prioritize all of the tasks needed for full implementation, the health education specialist creates which type of chart?
    a. Logic
    b. TDTL
    c. CPM
    d. Gantt

90. Process and outcome evaluations pose different research questions and require different data collection methods. Process evaluations, usually aimed at program administration and organization, generally require collection of which type(s) of data?
    a. Qualitative
    b. Quantitative
    c. Both qualitative and quantitative
    d. Outcome

91. A strategy to prepare high school peer educators to implement quality health education programs is to:
    a. gain parental support for teaching controversial topics.
    b. provide service learning credits for participation.
    c. invite administrators to observe and evaluate programs.
    d. provide training and opportunities for the peer educators to practice.

92. The most important advantage of a mixed methods approach to data collection and analysis is that:
    a. weaknesses of each method is overcome.
    b. statistical generalization within margin of error is allowed.
    c. performance monitoring throughout the program is improved.
    d. textual analysis is maximized.

93. If a health education specialist wishes to use online surveys because of ease of data collection, but the priority population struggles with technology, a breach of which ethical principle in managing technology is violated?
    a. Beneficence
    b. Transparency
    c. Equity
    d. Confidentiality

94. In evaluating a legislative advocacy campaign, process indicators include which one of the following?
    a. Public attitude change
    b. Policy adoption
    c. Campaign reach
    d. Policy awareness

95. In the strategic planning process, after an organization's mission statement has been defined or refined, the next step is to:
    a. list internal and external strengths and opportunities.
    b. list mandates and resources.
    c. identify key stakeholders.
    d. write the initial report.

96. A health education specialist has finalized the marketing plan for an intervention. Feedback on print materials was received through focus group interviews. Prior to implementation, which method should be used to gather feedback on the entire intervention program?
    a. Pilot test
    b. Delphic technique
    c. Readability test
    d. Nominal group process

97. A health education specialist needs to determine specific alcohol, tobacco, and other drug use prevention needs and immediately prioritize those needs with a few experts from the priority population. Which primary data collection technique would be the best to use in this scenario?
    a. Focus group
    b. Community forum
    c. Electronic interviews
    d. Nominal group process

98. When starting to build relationships with multiple sectors outside of public health (e.g., housing, transportation, primary care, schools), what is the most effective first step?
    a. Communicate the needs of public health to partner with decision makers in other sectors.
    b. Ask partners about their priorities and needs.
    c. Share data and evidence about priority public health topics.
    d. Address gaps in communication, values, and understanding between sectors.

99. The health education specialist is preparing a grant proposal. Generally, in which one of the following categories will the specialist find costs associated with facilities and administration?
    a. Indirect
    b. Direct
    c. Fringe
    d. Salaries

100. In analyzing qualitative research data, which one of the following methods is used to analyze communication in a social context?
    a. Content
    b. Narrative
    c. Discourse
    d. Grounded Theory

101. An after-school program was developed to help overweight and obese adolescents lose weight. In developing the program, the health education specialist considered the adolescents' attitude, beliefs, and values regarding diet and physical activity. Knowing this information, the health education specialist helped to:
    a. ensure the program was culturally appropriate and relevant.
    b. institutionalize the program in the community.
    c. implement new school-based policies for youth.
    d. develop clear program goals and objectives for the program.

102. Goals, organizational considerations, constituents, allies and opponents, targets and tactics are all elements of:
    a. SMART goals and objectives.
    b. interpersonal communication channels.
    c. an advocacy plan
    d. media marketing.

103. Descriptive statistics are used to examine associations between variables, but experimental studies are used to examine _____ between variables.
    a. convergent reasoning
    b. causality
    c. frequency
    d. statistical modeling

104. Which one of the following listings represents primary sources that could be used for a community needs assessment?
    a. US census data, vital records, and disease registries
    b. State health data from the health department
    c. Published scientific studies and reports
    d. Informal interviews, observations, and surveys

The following scenario is used for questions 105 and 106.

A health education specialist is developing a program to help reduce rates of cardiovascular disease in employees at a worksite. There are multiple layers of intervention, including increasing awareness, physical activity programs, increasing the lunch hour to allow for physical activity, encouraging walking to meetings, increasing healthy foods served in the cafeteria, among others.

105. Increasing awareness of risks for cardiovascular disease occurs at which level?
    a. Institutional
    b. Organizational
    c. Intrapersonal
    d. Policy

106. Increasing the lunch hour to allow for physical activity occurs at which level?
    a. Policy
    b. Intrapersonal
    c. Interpersonal
    d. Community

107. When participants in a training program are told both the benefits and risks associated with the program, which one of the following typically occurs with the procedure?
    a. Informed consent
    b. IRB submission
    c. Parental consent
    d. Beneficence consent

108. The research or evaluation results dissemination plan should, ideally, be discussed first with:
    a. media.
    b. program participants.
    c. primary investigator.
    d. stakeholders.

109. In evaluating a legislative advocacy campaign, impact indicators include:
    a. tactic counts.
    b. policy awareness.
    c. campaign reach.
    d. policy adoption.

110. To understand the three human subjects' protection guidelines of "respect for persons," "beneficence," and "justice," one will find the answer in the:
    a. Belmont report.
    b. CNHEO code of ethics.
    c. Institutional Review Board.
    d. Geneva Convention Treaty.

111. From the following key research study finding: "Six months after completing the program, 90% of adult fitness program participants reported still exercising at least 30 minutes per day compared to 10% of non-program participants," which conclusion is most sound?
    a. The fitness intervention may have contributed to continuation of exercise behavior.
    b. Post-program, participants scored in the highest fitness zone.
    c. Participants were satisfied with the fitness program.
    d. The fitness program followed best practices for adult exercise instruction

112. Which one of the following are elements for conducting an effective employee/staff appraisal? Present the appraisal:
    a. verbally and in writing and allow opportunities for discussion.
    b. in writing without allowing opportunities for discussion.
    c. verbally and in writing without allowing opportunities for discussion.
    d. verbally and in writing when employee misconduct occurs.

113. An evaluation technique that is used to assess media coverage quality and programming content that reaches the priority audience is referred to as content:
    a. milestones.
    b. tracking.
    c. analysis.
    d. checkpoints.

114. Health is impacted by a variety of different factors, but there are five major factors that contribute to the determinants of health for a population. Discrimination and income fall under which of the five major factors?
    a. Health behaviors
    b. Social environment or characteristics
    c. Physical environment
    d. Health services

115. Health departments and worksites are implementing a new health education/promotion program to increase influenza vaccine rates for adults in a five-county area. What will the project lead focus on to assess the fidelity of implementation?
    a. Did workers read materials distributed to all work sites?
    b. Are program components being implemented in the correct order?
    c. When will the amount of vaccine run out?
    d. Are children being vaccinated at schools or the local health departments?

116. A questionnaire, a cross-sectional survey about personal eating habits, sugar consumption, and physical activity behavior, was administered to a priority population. Several from the priority population did not want to respond to the survey. Therefore, the health education specialist needs to find other evidence that the behaviors occurred or did not occur using:
    a. multi-step written surveys.
    b. proxy measures.
    c. self-assessments.
    d. telephone interviews.

117. A health education specialist works as a patient educator at a healthcare institution. Part of the job is to work with patients who have recently suffered a heart attack. This type of work is an example of what type of prevention?
    a. Tertiary
    b. Primary
    c. Secondary
    d. Intermediate

118. The audience percentage possibly reached by a paid media advertisement multiplied by the frequency that an audience possibly will view the ad is called which one of the following?
    a. Placement effect
    b. Airtime exposure rate
    c. Media buy analysis
    d. Gross rating points

119. A health education specialist is targeting different groups of young adults for a physical activity intervention. The specialist wants to work with those who are ready to take action to get active within the next month. In what Stage of Change are these prospective participants?
    a. Precontemplation
    b. Contemplation
    c. Preparation
    d. Action

120. After completing an in-service training, a health education specialist conducted an evaluation survey to:
    a. pretest new materials with participants.
    b. validate participant attendance.
    c. determine which participants get monetary incentives.
    d. elicit feedback to improve the program.

121. If study results are statistically significant and match the study hypothesis, it can be concluded that the theory is:
    a. not supported.
    b. proven.
    c. supported.
    d. disproven.

122. Which type of literature review typically is used to identify current gaps in the literature after a comprehensive review of the literature on a topic?
    a. Meta analysis
    b. Pooled analysis
    c. Systematic review
    d. Computerized review

The following scenario and table are used for questions 123, 124, 125, 126, 127.

Table 1
Health and Wellness Coaching Program

Each program manager submits a preliminary budget request to the health education specialist before the end of the fiscal year, because the health education specialist is charged with preparing an annual, short-term budget for the entire department. The health education specialist chooses a line-item budgeting system for simplicity and ease of accounting. During July, only one new wellness class was budgeted in the Health and Wellness Coaching Program Area. Two more classes, however, were added to accommodate large numbers of potential participants who were placed on a waiting list. The additional classes were problematic, because the additional expense for those two classes was not in the approved budget.

Program: Health and Wellness Coaching Program				
July 2021				
Category	**Description**	**July Actual**	**July Budget**	**July Variance**
Salaries	Health Promotion Mgr.	1000.00	1000.00	0
	Health Coaches	1500.00	500.00	(1000.00)
Operations	Office supplies	100.00	100.00	0
	Telephone	500.00	400.000	(100.00)
	Printing/copying	500.00	400.00	(100.00)
	Travel/meals	0	0	0
	Advertising	100.00	100.00	0
Equipment	-----------------	100.00	200.00	(100.00)
	Total	3800.00	2700.00	(1300.00)

123. The budget development strategy used is referred to as what type of budget?
    a. top-down
    b. functional
    c. bottom-up
    d. line-item

124. The only disadvantage of maintaining the department's budget categories at the organizational level only is that:
    a. overall analysis of department effectiveness is more difficult to determine.
    b. the cost-effectiveness of each program is difficult to determine.
    c. capital outlays are more difficult to determine.
    d. sources of funding are more difficult to determine.

125. The expenditure for hiring more part-time health coaches due to increased participation in the new wellness program is which type of expense?
    a. Semi-variable
    b. Fixed
    c. Variable
    d. Linear

126. Variations between the approved budget amounts and actual results should be examined and explained. To assure that the approved amounts are monitored and used for the specified categories, a budget efficiency ratio is calculated. The percent budget variance for the month of July in the Health Coach line-item is:
    a. 0.5.
    b. 3.0.
    c. 4.5.
    d. 2.0.

127. The written budget report for July is past the due date for submission to the health administrator. The most important information to include in this budget report is the:
    a. explanation of variance and recommended actions.
    b. detailed cash-flow projections.
    c. identification and list of expenses.
    d. creation of the working papers for each line-item.

128. Which social determinant should the health education specialist consider when analyzing knowledge acquisition among youth participating in a risk reduction intervention?
    a. Relationships
    b. Circumstances
    c. Connections
    d. Environments

129. The type of brief that covers not only policy options but also policy recommendations and is provided to a decision-maker to convince that person to take a specific action on an issue is called a/an _____ brief.
    a. information
    b. issue
    c. policy impact
    d. policy

The following table is used to answer question 130.

Table 2

HIV Prevalance by Gender and Age in Select Urban Setting

HIV Prevalence						
Characteristic	No.	%	No	%	Relative Risk	95% CI
Gender						
Female	5019	(55)	111	(2.2)	Reference	–
Male	4059	(45)	77	(1.9)	0.9	(0.6 - 1.1)
Race/Ethnicity						
Black	7014	(77)	145	(2.1)	Reference	–
Hispanic	1250	(15)	28	(2.1)	1	(0.7 - 1.5)
White	402	(4)	7	(1.7)	0.8	(0,4 - 1.8)
Other	307	(3)	8	(2.6)	1.3	(0.6 - 2.5)

Source: https://www.cdc.gov/hiv/group/poverty.html

130. Based on the data in the table, which one of the following statements is an accurate conclusion?
    a. Gender differences in the prevalence rate of HIV were not statistically significant.
    b. The percentage of HIV prevalence was higher in males than females.
    c. The prevalence rate of HIV was statistically higher in white adults compared to Hispanic adults.
    d. HIV prevalence rates vary significantly by race/ethnicity subgroups.

131. When creating the budget for a grant application, contributed income can be classified into which one of the following two categories?
    a. Earned and cash
    b. Sales and in-kind
    c. In-kind and earned
    d. Cash and in-kind

132. Given the objective, "By 2025, increase the percentage of mothers who breastfeed babies for at least 6 months from 35% to 50%, what is the appropriate intervention strategy to support achieving that objective?"
    a. Organize a small group instruction about breastfeeding for all women of childbearing age.
    b. Educate mothers and their support networks about behavior changes for breastfeeding.
    c. Sponsor a summit for key decision-makers from hospitals providing maternity care.
    d. Ensure training provides continuing education credit hours for early care education providers.

133. Performance appraisals of staff members and volunteers will normally be:
    a. performed on those who have recently joined the organization/agency.
    b. focused on strengths and areas for improvement.
    c. focused on skills and knowledge.
    d. performed on those who are having problems.

134. According to the Diffusion of Innovations theory, some groups in the population are the first to adopt to a new program. These groups of people are referred to as the:
    a. laggards.
    b. innovators.
    c. adopters.
    d. majority.

135. Answering the question: "What have the results of the study contributed to the health education field?" should be addressed in what section of a research study?
    a. Results
    b. Analysis
    c. Discussion
    d. Introduction

136. Which of the following is not an appropriate stage in development of a strategic plan?
    a. Values clarification
    b. Goals and objectives identification
    c. Standard operating procedures
    d. Evaluation

137. A formal social media policy should include the use of _____ to maintain pages, post scheduled messages, and respond to follower posts.
    a. tagging
    b. moderators
    c. apps
    d. networks

138. A health education specialist is considering the types of activities that would be included in a health education/promotion program. In a logic model, these activities would be included in:
    a. inputs.
    b. outputs.
    c. outcomes.
    d. processes.

139. Describing study results and their contributions to health education theory and practice is found in which section of a research study?
    a. Limitations
    b. Delimitations
    c. Implications
    d. Recommendations

140. The program trainer's primary responsibility is to:
    a. see that program objectives are met.
    b. establish conditions for learning.
    c. select teaching-learning methods.
    d. skillfully conduct the training.

141. Findings from an assessment revealed that the priority population's access to available community health care services is lower than another community with comparable demographics. They have identified a/an:
    a. perceived need.
    b. actual need.
    c. expressed need.
    d. relative need.

142. To best prioritize organizational allies for recruitment to the advocacy coalition, the health education specialist should:
    a. synthesize each group's strategic style.
    b. evaluate each group's counter resistance.
    c. discuss each group's facilities.
    d. analyze each group's benefit-to-cost.

143. A health education specialist has a limited budget and is looking for baseline data. Which one of the following may be a secondary data option to consider?
    a. Conducting a survey with the priority population
    b. Pilot testing an interview with family members and co-workers
    c. Federal, state, city, and county open data portals
    d. Randomly sampling the priority population

144. A non-profit organization is working with Community Health Workers, an American Indian Tribe, and the Tribal Health Organization to implement a diabetes prevention program. A two-day training is being planned for the Community Health Workers to ensure proper program delivery. What should the trainers do to create an inclusive learning environment?
    a. Build trust and respect between the learners and instructor(s).
    b. Obtain leadership approval to offer the training.
    c. Pay for food and travel to the training for all participants.
    d. Offer the training only during the working hours.

145. Creating a media activity record is the best way to evaluate which type of health communications media?
    a. Paid
    b. Social
    c. Earned
    d. Community engagement

146. Following the PRECEDE-PROCEDE Model, assessing if community members have adequate access to oral health care services is which type of factor in the educational and ecological assessment?
    a. Enabling
    b. Predisposing
    c. Reinforcing
    d. Motivating

147. Community agency personnel are targeting a variety of social ecological levels to help reduce drug use in the community. Some of the levels will take substantially more time to target. Rather than wait for all aspects of the intervention to be ready, the health education specialist decides to begin with one level and then add in other levels over time. This process is an example of:
    a. pilot testing.
    b. total implementation.
    c. primary strategies.
    d. phasing in.

148. The sections of a program evaluation report that are most likely read by the stakeholders are which one of the following?
    a. Introduction/results
    b. Executive summary/conclusion
    c. Abstract/methods
    d. Analysis/discussion

149. A health education specialist is considering using multiple models (e.g., assessment, behavioral change, and planning) during planning of the needs assessment process. Which of the following is the most likely reason for using this strategy? It will:
    a. assist in identifying types of data needed for the assessment and the factors that may impact development of the intervention.
    b. assist in creating a systematic approach for conducting a needs assessment and developing an intervention.
    c. provide insight for developing strategies to engage the community in the assessment process.
    d. provide the components to create a logic model and to identify gaps.

150. To improve nutrition knowledge acquisition for students from diverse cultures, the health education specialist should:
    a. use written examples rather than oral examples to communicate.
    b. assess diet-related enabling factors.
    c. make the learning environment more consistent with the students' culture.
    d. use the same approach used in other settings.

151. A health education specialist notices that one of the lessons is not working as it was planned. What is the proper way to proceed?
    a. Keep implementing the lesson as planned, regardless if learners are understanding it.
    b. Adapt the lesson to the learners' needs so that they are able to understand the information or skill.
    c. Stop the intervention, and rework the entire program in response to the problematic lesson.
    d. ignore the lesson and move to the next lesson in the program.

152. In media advocacy, decision-makers, as an audience for the communications strategy, are what level of priority?
    a. Secondary
    b. Tertiary
    c. Primary
    d. Emergency

153. A health education specialist at the health department conducted a social media campaign for its new childhood immunization clinic to steer community members to the department's website to schedule appointments. The best data for the health education specialist to track using the website's analytics is which one of the following?
    a. Direct traffic
    b. Organic traffic
    c. Goal behavior
    d. Interest volume

154. When creating a marketing plan for a program, which one of the following should be identified first?
    a. Audience
    b. Message
    c. Communication methods
    d. Financial resources

155. A current problem faced in organizations that rely on volunteers is the ability to retain volunteers. To increase retention of volunteers, the organization's staff might be focused on which of the following?
    a. Give recognition
    b. Supervise
    c. Train
    d. Recruit

156. In the conclusion section of a research study, results should ideally be _____ into a final, main, easily-remembered point.
    a. summarized
    b. synthesized
    c. analyzed
    d. computed

157. An action-oriented, time-limited alliance for health issue advocacy is referred to as a/an:
    a. task force.
    b. coalition.
    c. collaboration.
    d. influence.

158. The objective of a blood pressure training intervention is "After completion of the unit on health assessment techniques, participants will be able to perform according to standards." Which one of the following is the most appropriate health education strategy for achieving this objective?
    a. The health education specialist lectures on the benefits of monitoring blood pressure; then, students watch a video on how to perform blood pressure measurements.
    b. Students break into discussion groups to discuss ways to correctly perform blood pressure measurements.
    c. After viewing a skills video, the instructor demonstrates how to perform blood pressure measurements, and students practice on partners.
    d. Students complete a study guide on the correct way to perform blood pressure measurements; then, each student is paired with another student to discuss their answers.

159. When planning a diabetes prevention program following the PRECEDE-PROCEDE Model, data on high sugar intake would fall into which assessment phase?
    a. Epidemiological assessment
    b. Social assessment and situational analysis
    c. Educational and ecological assessment
    d. Intervention alignment and administrative and policy assessment

160. A health education specialist needs to find an adaptive leadership training program to learn how to more effectively communicate with diverse populations in the community in which the specialist serves. Which of the following training titles and modalities will be most appropriate to meet this complex professional development goal?
    a. "Risk communication for public health emergencies" (90 min webinar).
    b. "Inter-generational dynamics: Speaking the lingo of different age groups for sex education" (2 hour in-person workshop).
    c. "Listening with cultural humility before communicating your messages" (hybrid: two 2-hour in-person workshops plus 2 coaching calls).
    d. "How to write more clearly: A primer for health literacy" (3 hour online self-paced module).

161. When pilot testing materials for an intervention, which one of the following should be assessed before implementation of the program?
    a. Comprehension and acceptability of the intervention and materials
    b. Potential impact of the intervention on a health behavior
    c. Increases in knowledge of the priority population after the program
    d. Potential costs for development and delivery of the intervention

162. A health education specialist at the health department conducted a social media campaign leading with Facebook for its new drive-through immunization clinic. The health education specialist used the platform's analytics to determine the number of unique people who viewed the initial clinic kick-off post. The health education specialist is evaluating which type of social media reach?
    a. Paid
    b. Viral
    c. Likes
    d. Organic

163. The type of study results that are used to inform the development of new health education interventions is:
    a. evaluation.
    b. stakeholder.
    c. persuasive.
    d. research.

164. When working with consultants or contractors, it is necessary to secure:
    a. a written agreement outlining the work needed.
    b. extra funds to cover the cost of unexpected expenditures.
    c. an implementation plan from the consultant or contractor.
    d. a signed ethics agreement from the consultant or contractor.

165. The intervention program is doing so well that it needs to be expanded; however, the sponsoring agency has limited funding for expansion. The health education specialist found another agency willing to provide the sponsor with a larger venue in exchange for access to the sponsor's educational library. This method of financing the program is called:
    a. cooperative agreements.
    b. cost-sharing.
    c. third-party support.
    d. organizational sponsorship.

Master Certified Health Education Specialist
Examination Questions Key

1. b – Area 4	38. b – Area 4	75. c – Area 8	112. a – Area 7	149. a – Area 1
2. a – Area 7	39. a – Area 8	76. a – Area 7	113. c – Area 6	150. c – Area 8
3. a – Area 3	40. d – Area 5	77. b – Area 7	114. b – Area 5	151. b – Area 3
4. d – Area 8	41. c – Area 1	78. c – Area 1	115. b – Area 3	152. c – Area 5
5. b – Area 6	42. c – Area 1	79. a – Area 7	116. b – Area 1	153. c – Area 6
6. a – Area 2	43. a – Area 4	80. d – Area 4	117. a – Area 2	154. a – Area 3
7. d – Area 3	44. d – Area 7	81. b – Area 8	118. d – Area 6	155. a – Area 7
8. c – Area 5	45. a – Area 6	82. b – Area 6	119. c – Area 8	156. b – Area 4
9. c – Area 1	46. c – Area 3	83. c – Area 6	120. d – Area 7	157. a – Area 5
10. b – Area 4	47. a – Area 5	84. a – Area 3	121. c – Area 4	158. c- Area 3
11. a – Area 7	48. d – Area 8	85. b – Area 2	122. c – Area 1	159. a – Area 2
12. c – Area 4	49. a – Area 6	86. a – Area 4	123. c – Area 7	160. c – Area 8
13. a – Area 1	50. a – Area 4	87. c – Area 5	124. b – Area 7	161. a – Area 2
14. c – Area 6	51. c – Area 2	88. c – Area 1	125. a – Area 7	162. d – Area 6
15. a – Area 7	52. b – Area 6	89. d – Area 2	126. d – Area 7	163. d – Area 4
16. c – Area 5	53. d – Area 4	90. c – Area 4	127. a – Area 7	164. a – Area 3
17. a – Area 4	54. b – Area 4	91. d – Area 7	128. b – Area 1	165. a – Area 7
18. a – Area 6	55. a – Area 7	92. a – Area 4	129. d – Area 5	
19. b – Area 4	56. a – Area 7	93. a – Area 8	130. a – Area 4	
20. c – Area 1	57. c – Area 7	94. c – Area 5	131. d – Area 7	
21. a – Area 6	58. d – Area 1	95. a – Area 7	132. a – Area 2	
22. d – Area 4	59. d – Area 1	96. a – Area 2	133. b – Area 7	
23. b – Area 4	60. a – Area 3	97. d – Area 1	134. b – Area 8	
24. a – Area 6	61. a – Area 8	98. b – Area 8	135. c – Area 4	
25. d – Area 7	62. a – Area 5	99. a – Area 7	136. c – Area 7	
26. a – Area 7	63. c – Area 6	100. c – Area 4	137. b – Area 6	
27. c – Area 7	64. a – Area 3	101. a – Area 7	138. a – Area 2	
28. c – Area 4	65. a – Area 2	102. c – Area 5	139. c – Area 4	
29. a – Area 1	66. c – Area 8	103. b – Area 4	140. a – Area 7	
30. b – Area 8	67. d – Area 4	104. d – Area 1	141. b – Area 1	
31. a – Area 2	68. a – Area 1	105. c – Area 2	142. d – Area 5	
32. d – Area 6	69. b – Area 6	106. a – Area 2	143. c – Area 3	
33. b – Area 4	70. a – Area 5	107. a – Area 8	144. a – Area 3	
34. d – Area 5	71. c – Area 4	108. d – Area 4	145. c – Area 6	
35. c – Area 3	72. b – Area 2	109. b – Area 5	146. a – Area 2	
36. c – Area 6	73. c – Area 1	110. a – Area 8	147. d – Area 3	
37. b – Area 1	74. a – Area 4	111. a – Area 4	148. b – Area 4	

Appendix E
Author Background Information

Melissa Grim, PhD, MCHES®
Chair and Professor
Radford University
Radford, VA

Cam Escoffery, PhD, MPH, CHES®
Professor
Rollins School of Public Health
Atlanta, GA

C. Suzette McClellan, MPH, MCHES®
Community Systems Director
SC Department of Health & Environmental Control
Sumter, SC

Linda E. Forys, EdM, MCHES®
Retired Director of Health Education and Promotion
Harris County Public Health
Houston, TX

Angela D. Mickalide, PhD, MCHES®
Vice President of Programs and Education
American College of Preventive Medicine
Washington, DC

Anna Torrens Armstrong, PhD, MPH, MCHES®, CPH
Associate Professor
University of South Florida, College of Public Health
Tampa, FL

Phyllis K. Stoll, MPH, MCHES®
Senior Education Specialist
Centers for Disease Control and Prevention
Atlanta, GA

Cynthia A. Karlsson MS, MPH, CHES®
Rapid Health Information NetwOrk (RHINO)
Program Manager
Washington State Department of Health
Olympia, WA

Ty J. Oehrtman, MS, MCHES®
Health Educator II
Inland Empire Health Plan
Ontario, CA

Alexis Blavos, PhD, MCHES®
Associate Professor
SUNY Cortland
Cortland, NY

Carol Cox, PhD, MCHES®
Professor, Health Science
Truman State University
Kirksville, MO

Beth H. Chaney, PhD, MCHES®
Professor
The University of Alabama, Department of Health Science
Tuscaloosa, AL

Mike L. Stellefson, PhD, MCHES®
Professor
University of Alabama, Department of Health Science
Tuscaloosa, AL

Samantha R. Paige, PhD, MPH, CHES®
Postdoctoral Research Fellow
University of Florida
Gainesville, FL

William Potts-Datema, DrPH, MS, MCHES®
Adjunct Professor
Southern Connecticut State University
Atlanta, GA

Michelle L. Carvalho, MPH, MCHES®
Program Manager/Team Lead
Rollins School of Public Health, Emory University
Atlanta, GA